ECLECTIC EDUCATIONAL SERIES

KEY

TO

RAY'S™ NEW
ARITHMETICS

PRIMARY, INTELLECTUAL
AND PRACTICAL

Originally published by
Van Antwerp, Bragg & Co.

This edition published by

**MOTT
MEDIA**

ISBN 0-88062-054-4
Printed in the United States of America

PRESENT PUBLISHER'S PREFACE

We are honored and happy to bring to you the classic Arithmetics by Joseph Ray. In the 1800s these popular books sold more than any other arithmetics in America, in fact over 120,000,000 copies. Now with this reprinting, they are once again available for America's students.

Ray's Arithmetics are organized in an orderly manner around the discipline of arithmetic itself. They present principles and follow up each one with examples which include difficult problems to challenge the best students. Students who do not master a concept the first time can return to it later, work the more difficult problems, and master the concept. Thus in these compact volumes is a complete arithmetic course to study in school, to help in preparing for ACT and SAT tests, and to use for reference throughout a lifetime.

In order to capture the spirit of the original Ray's, we have refrained from revising the problems and prices. Only a few words have been changed, as we felt it wise. Thus students will have to rely on their arithmetic ability to solve the problems. Also the charm of a former era lives on in this reprinting. Flour and salt are sold by the barrel, kegs may contain tar, and postage stamps cost 3¢ each. Through this content, students learn social history of the 1800s in a unique, hands-on manner at the same time they are mastering arithmetic.

The series consists of four books ranging from Primary Arithmetic to Higher Arithmetic, as well as answer keys to accompany them. We have added a teacher's guide to help today's busy teachers and parents.

We wish to express our appreciation to the staff of the Special Collections Library at Miami University, Oxford, Ohio, for its cooperation in allowing us to use copies of their original Ray's Arithmetics.

George M. Mott, President
MOTT MEDIA, INC.

PREFACE

This Key to Ray's New Arithmetics is presented to the public in the hope that teachers may be assisted thereby in their arduous labors.

It may be supposed that every teacher is able to solve every example in the series; but it should not therefore be required that the work shall actually be done by the teacher. The examination to which every teacher in the Public Schools submits, is the only test that can be required of the possession of knowledge. In the actual work of the school-room, the teacher is clearly entitled to use all appliances that will save him from drudgery, and enable him to devote his full time and energies to the task of imparting instruction and guiding the labors of his pupils.

In most schools, the methods of instruction have so changed that twice as much labor is now expected from the teacher as was required twenty years ago. Much work is now written on slates or paper; and this must be carefully examined, criticized, and marked. This increased labor leaves the teacher little time to work out the examples, and test their correctness.

In the Key to the Intellectual Arithmetic, all the problems which might be supposed to present the least difficulty have been briefly solved. The form of solution is usually the briefest that is consistent with accuracy and clearness; no formal method is pursued.

The Key to the Practical Arithmetic is believed to be complete. It was not thought best to omit anything that might help any teacher. Here, too, the solutions are as brief as possible. Figures and signs are used wherever they serve the purpose. Lengthy explanations are avoided,—the work only being given.

With the hope that this Key will be found to be full and accurate, and so arranged as to prove helpful on all occasions, it is respectfully submitted to the teachers of Ray's Arithmetics.

Cincinnati, 1879.

ANSWERS

to

RAY'S NEW PRIMARY ARITHMETIC

LESSON VI.

(1.) 0; 1, 10; 2, 20; 3, 30; 4, 40; 5, 50; 6, 60; 7, 70; 8, 80; 9, 90.

(2.) 11; 12, 21; 13, 31; 14, 41; 15, 51; 16, 61; 17, 71; 18, 81; 19, 91.

(3.) 22; 23, 32; 24, 42; 25, 52; 26, 62; 27, 72; 28, 82; 29, 92.

(4.) 33; 34, 43; 35, 53; 36, 63; 37, 73; 38, 83; 39, 93.

(5.) 44; 45, 54; 46, 64; 47, 74; 48, 84; 49, 94.

(6.) 55; 56, 65; 57, 75; 58, 85; 59, 95.

(7.) 66; 67, 76; 68, 86; 69, 96.

(8.) 77; 78, 87; 79, 97.

(9.) 88; 89, 98.

(10.) 99; 100.

LESSON VII.

(1.) 1. (2.) 2; 1; 2. (3.) 3; 3; 3. (4.) 2; 1; 3. (5.) 4; 4; 4; 4; 4. (6.) 3; 2; 1; 4; 2. (7.) 5; 5; 5; 5. (8.) 4; 3; 2; 1; 5.

LESSON VIII.

(1.) 6; 6; 6; 6; 6; 6. (2.) 5; 4; 3; 2; 1; 6; 3; 2. (3.) 7; 7; 7; 7; 7. (4.) 6; 5; 4; 3; 2; 1; 7. (5.) 8; 8; 8; 8; 8; 8. (6.) 8; 8; 8. (7.) 7; 6; 5; 4; 3; 2; 1. (8.) 8; 4; 2.

LESSON IX.

(1.) 9; 9; 9; 9; 9; 9; 9. (2.) 9; 9. (3.) 8; 7; 6; 5; 4; 3; 2; 1. (4.) 9; 3. (5.) 10; 10; 10; 10; 10. (6.) 10; 10; 10. (7.) 10; 10; 10. (8.) 9; 8; 7; 6; 5; 4; 3; 2; 1. (9.) 10; 5; 2.

LESSON X.

2; 5; 4; 7. (1.) 7 birds; 11 birds. (2.) 7; 11. (3.) 6 birds; 12 birds. (4.) 6; 12. (5.) 6 flowers.

LESSON XI.

(1.) 3 cents. (2.) 4 raisins. (3.) 5 pears. (4.) 6 cherries. (5.) 7 cents. (6.) 8 plums. (7.) 9 oranges. (8.) 10 peaches. (9.) 11 cents.

LESSON XII.

(1.) 4 birds. (2.) 5 tops. (3.) 6 chestnuts. (4.) 7 apples. (5.) 8 chickens. (6.) 9 cakes. (7.) 10 marbles. (8.) 11 fishes. (9.) 12 cents.

LESSON XIII.

(1.) 5 cents. (2.) 6 dimes. (3.) 7 apples. (4.) 8 pears. (5.) 9 pens. (6.) 10 books. (7.) 11 rabbits. (8.) 12 cents. (9.) 13 cents.

LESSON XIV.

(1.) 6 pens. (2.) 7 pins. (3.) 8 chestnuts. (4.) 9 horses. (5.) 10 cents. (6.) 11 apples. (7.) 12 cents. (8.) 13 dollars. (9.) 14 cents.

LESSON XV.

(1.) 7 chickens. (2.) 8 square blocks. (3.) 9 cents. (4.) 10 cakes. (5.) 11 chairs. (6.) 12 boys. (7.) 13 cents. (8.) 14 letters. (9.) 15 balls.

LESSON XVI.

(1.) 8 cows. (2.) 9 marbles. (3.) 10 cents. (4.) 11 pigs. (5.) 12 plums. (6.) 13 cents. (7.) 14 horses. (8.) 15 miles. (9.) 16 days.

LESSON XVII.

(1.) 9 marbles. (2.) 10 sheep. (3.) 11 boys. (4.) 12 chairs. (5.) 13 apples. (6.) 14 cents. (7.) 13 cents. (8.) 16 roses. (9.) 17 dollars.

LESSON XVIII.

(1.) 10 nuts. (2.) 11 pins. (3.) 12 geese. (4.) 13 marbles. (5.) 14 eggs. (6.) $15. (7.) 16 yards. (8.) 17 years. (9.) 18 cents.

LESSON XIX.

(1.) 11 mice. (2.) 12 cents. (3.) 13 fish. (4.) 14 horses. (5.) 15 oranges. (6.) 16 plums. (7.) 17 buttons. (8.) 18 cents. (9.) 19 pounds.

LESSON XX.

(1.) 12 cents. (2.) $13. (3.) 14 trees. (4.) 15 cows. (5.) 16 yards. (6.) 17 girls. (7.) $18. (8.) 19 nuts. (9.) 20 cents.

LESSON XXI. (Review)

(1.) 6. (2.) 8; 11. (3.) 10, 11. (4.) 11; 10. (5.) 12; 9. (6.) 6; 8. (7.) 9; 11. (8.) 7; 13. (9.) 14; 12. (10.) 13; 12. (11.) 12; 14. (12.) 16; 16. (13.) 14; 12. (14.) 14; 17. (15.) 8; 15. (16.) 13; 19. (17.) 18; 13. (18.) 15; 4. (19.) 10; 10. (20.) 16; 18. (21.) 7; 5. (22.) 15; 17. (23.) 6. (24.) 12; 15. (25.) 16; 16. (26.) 15; 18. (27.) 17; 10. (28.) 17; 14. (29.) 17; 20. (30.) 7; 15.

LESSON XXII. (Review)

(1.) 8; 16. (2.) 13; 17. (3.) 9; 14. (4.) 10; 11. (5.) 10; 11. (6.) 12; 12. (7.) 12; 14. (8.) 13; 19. (9.) 19; 19. (10.) 15; 18. (11.) 11; 12. (12.) 20; 18. (13.) 16; 14. (14.) 13; 12. (15.) 18; 12. (16.) 15; 19. (17.) 13; 19. (18.) 20; 17. (19.) 9; 8. (20.) 20; 20. (21.) 13; 19. (22.) 14; 16. (23.) 14; 15. (24.) 18; 19. (25.) 10; 20. (26.) 14; 13. (27.) 16; 18. (28.) 19; 17. (29.) 9; 11. (30.) 18; 17. (31.) 16. (32.) 17; 14. (33.) 18; 11. (34.) 18; 16. (35.) 20; 15. (36.) 15; 13. (37.) 14; 15. (38.) 19; 15. (39.) 20; 16. (40.) 13; 16. (41.) 1, 3, 5, 7, 9, 11, 13, 15, 17, 19. (42.) 1, 4, 7, 10, 13, 16, 19. (43.) 1, 5, 9, 13, 17. (44.) 1, 6, 11, 16. (45.) 2, 4, 6, 8, 10, 12, 14, 16, 18, 20; 3, 6, 9, 12, 15, 18. (46.) 4, 8, 12, 16, 20; 5, 10, 15, 20. (47.) 2, 5, 8, 11, 14, 17, 20. (48.) 2, 6, 10, 14, 18. (49.) 2, 7, 12, 17. (50) 3, 7, 11, 15, 19.

LESSON XXIII.

(1.) 12 cents. (2.) 14 fish. (3.) 16 cents. (4.) 15 peaches. (5.) $18. (6.) 13 pins. (7.) 17 marbles. (8.) $19. (9.) $19. (10.) 20 cents. (11.) 15 apples; 17 cents. (12.) 10 pears; 15 cents.

LESSON XXIV.

(1.) 1 owl. (2.) 1. (3.) 3 bats. (4.) 3. (5.) 6 leaves. (6.) 6.

LESSON XXV.

(1.) 1 rose. (2.) 3 melons. (3.) 1 nut. (4.) 5 pigeons. (5.) 1 marble. (6.) 7 chickens. (7.) 1 cent. (8.) 1 apple. (9.) 9 plums.

LESSON XXVI.

(1.) 2 apples. (2.) 2 cents. (3.) 3 birds. (4.) 4 mice. (5.) 5 oranges. (6.) 6 marbles. (7.) 7 chickens. (8.) 2 cakes. (9.) 9 yards.

LESSON XXVII.

(1.) 1 orange. (2.) 3 ducks. (3.) 3 persons. (4.) 3 pins. (5.) 5 cents. (6.) 3 chickens. (7.) 7 lemons. (8.) 3. (9.) 9 cents.

LESSON XXVIII.

(1.) 1 apple. (2.) 4 birds. (3.) 3 ducks. (4.) 4 beans. (5.) 4 panes. (6.) 6 trees. (7.) 7 years. (8.) 4 oranges. (9.) 9 chickens.

LESSON XXIX.

(1.) 1 orange. (2.) 5 crows. (3.) 3 ships. (4.) 4 yards. (5.) 5 marbles. (6.) 5 cents. (7.) 7 cents. (8.) $8. (9.) 5 nuts.

LESSON XXX.

(1.) 6 marks. (2.) 2 cents. (3.) 3 raisins. (4.) 6 eggs. (5.) 5 cents. (6.) $6. (7.) 7 dozen. (8.) 6 oranges. (9.) 6; 8.

LESSON XXXI.

(1.) 1 cent. (2.) $7. (3.) 3 oranges. (4.) 4 cents. (5.) 7 marbles. (6.) 6 lemons. (7.) 7 years. (8.) 7 birds. (9.) 8; 7.

LESSON XXXII.

(1.) 8 pecans. (2.) 2 cents. (3.) 3 peaches. (4.) 4 cents. (5.) 8 oranges. (6.) 6 marbles. (7.) 8 pens. (8.) 8 persons. (9.) 8; 7.

LESSON XXXIII.

(1.) 1 walnut. (2.) 2 cents. (3.) $3. (4.) 9 birds. (5.) 5 horses. (6.) 9 plums. (7.) 7 marbles. (8.) 9 horses. (9.) 9 cents.

LESSON XXXIV.

(1.) 1 cent. (2.) $2. (3.) 10 pupils. (4.) 4 trees. (5.) 10 marbles. (6.) 6 cents. (7.) $10. (8.) 8 cents. (9.) 9; 10.

LESSON XXXV. (Review)

(1.) 2. (2.) 6; 4; 3. (3.) 2; 6; 7. (4.) 8; 4; 7. (5.) 8; 10; 6. (6.) 6; 10; 7. (7.) 3; 3; 5. (8.) 9; 9; 5. (9.) 9; 7; 2. (10.) 4; 5; 5. (11.) 2; 3; 6. (12.) 3; 3; 2. (13.) 5; 6; 7. (14.) 8; 9; 8. (15.) 4; 9; 8. (16.) 7; 8; 6. (17.) 4; 6; 5. (18.) 9; 7; 3. (19.) 8; 10; 5. (20.) 7; 9; 10. (21.) 3; 7; 10. (22.) 10; 2; 2. (23.) 4; 8; 3. (24.) 10; 10; 6. (25.) 4; 4; 2. (26.) 8; 9; 9. (27.) 5; 2; 5.

LESSON XXXVI.

(1.) 4. (2.) 2. (3.) 10; 7. (4.) 9; 8. (5.) 2; 3. (6.) 5; 4. (7.) 10; 8. (8.) 2; 2. (9.) 7; 9. (10.) 9; 8. (11.) 2; 5. (12.) 9; 7. (13.) 3; 7. (14.) 10; 10. (15.) 2; 5. (16.) 8; 8. (17.) 6; 9. (18.) 8; 10. (19.) 5; 4. (20.) 6; 4. (21.) 8; 6. (22.) 6; 7. (23.) 4; 7. (24.) 7; 5. (25.) 8; 3. (26.) 3; 7. (27.) 9; 2.

LESSON XXXVII.

(1.) 20, 18, 16, 14, 12, 10, 8, 6, 4, 2, 0. (2.) 18, 15, 12, 9, 6, 3, 0. (3.) 20, 16, 12, 8, 4, 0. (4.) 20, 15, 10, 5, 0. (5.) 18, 12, 6, 0. (6.) 6 cents. (7.) 3. (8.) 2 apples. (9.) 5 cents. (10.) 9 cents. (11.) 5. (12.) 18 oranges. (13.) 5 marbles. (14.) 5 apples.

LESSON XXXVIII.

(1.) 12 birds. (2.) 12. (3.) 16 eggs. (4.) 16. (5.) 16 wings. (6.) 16.

LESSON XXXIX.

(1.) 2 cents. (2.) 3 cents. (3.) 4 cents. (4.) 5 cents. (5.) $6. (6.) 7 miles. (7.) 8 cents. (8.) 9 cents. (9.) 10 cents.

LESSON XL.

(1.) 4 cents. (2.) 6 cents. (3.) 8 cents. (4.) 10 cents. (5.) 12 cents. (6.) 14 cents. (7.) 16 cents. (8.) 18 cents. (9.) 20 cents.

LESSON XLI.

(1.) 6 cents. (2.) 9 cents. (3.) 12 miles. (4.) 15 apples. (5.) 18 plums. (6.) 21 cents. (7.) 24 cents. (8.) 27 cents. (9.) 30 cents.

LESSON XLII.

(1.) 8 feet. (2.) 12 pigeons. (3.) 16 cents. (4.) 20 cents. (5.) 24 quarters. (6.) 28 cents. (7.) 32 cents. (8.) 36 cents. (9.) 40 cents.

LESSON XLIII.

(1.) 10 cents. (2.) 15 miles. (3.) 20 plums. (4.) 25 chickens. (5.) 30 eggs. (6.) 35 cents. (7.) 40 cents. (8.) 45 cents. (9.) 50 cents.

LESSON XLIV.

(1.) 12 yards. (2.) 18 chickens. (3.) 24 panes. (4.) 30 peaches. (5.) 36 cents. (6.) 42 cents. (7.) 48 ounces. (8.) 54 cents. (9.) 60 cents.

LESSON XLV.

(1.) 14 cents. (2.) 21 marbles. (3.) 28 days. (4.) 35 peaches. (5.) 42 miles. (6.) 49 boys. (7.) 56 marbles. (8.) 63 cents. (9.) 70 cents.

LESSON XLVI.

(1.) 16 cents. (2.) 24 fishes. (3.) 32 chickens. (4.) 40 windows. (5.) 48 pints. (6.) 56 cents. (7.) 64 quarts. (8.) 72 cents. (9.) 80 cents.

LESSON XLVII.

(1.) 18 cents. (2.) 27 cents. (3.) 36 panes. (4.) 45 cents. (5.) 54 cents. (6.) 63 cents. (7.) 72 miles. (8.) 81 cents. (9.) 90 cents.

LESSON XLVIII.

(1.) 20 cents. (2.) $30. (3.) 40 pecks. (4.) 50 pounds. (5.) $60. (6.) 70 marbles. (7.) 80 cents. (8.) $90. (9.) $100.

LESSON XLIX. (Review)

(1.) 10. (2.) 12; 18. (3.) 20; 9. (4.) 8; 20. (5.) 16; 4. (6.) 30; 30. (7.) 12; 24. (8.) 40; 21. (9.) 28; 25. (10.) 15; 18. (11.) 36; 24. (12.) 27; 32. (13.) 16; 45. (14.) 35; 80. (15.) 48; 70. (16.) 36; 64. (17.) 63; 54. (18.) 40; 49. (19.) 50; 60. (20.) 42; 90. (21.) 56; 81. (22.) 72; 100. (23.) 6; 14. (24.) 15; 42. (25.) 24; 54. (26.) 40; 63. (27.) 90; 72. (28.) 18. (29.) 16. (30.) 24. (31.) 20. (32.) 30. (33.) 36. (34.) 24. (35.) 42. (36.) 28. (37.) 64. (38.) 36. (39.) 48. (40.) 40. (41.) 60. (42.) 40. (43.) 32. (44.) 48. (45.) 80. (46.) 70. (47.) 90. (48.) 80. (49.) 90. (50.) 60. (51.) 54. (52.) 36. (53.) 45. (54.) 54. (55.) 100. (56.) 72. (57.) 63. (58.) 72.

LESSON L. (Review)

(1.) 9. (2.) 8. (3.) 50. (4.) 42. (5.) 49. (6.) 32. (7.) 27. (8.) 12. (9.) 28. (10.) 25. (11.) 48. (12.) 14. (13.) 64. (14.) 81. (15.) 15. (16.) 45. (17.) 20. (18.) 54. (19.) 18. (20.) 24. (21.) 16. (22.) 21. (23.) 36. (24.) 40. (25.) 56. (26.) 63. (27.) 30.

LESSON LI.

(1.) 4 cents. (2.) $20. (3.) 9 cents. (4.) $14. (5.) $9. (6.) 72 bushels. (7.) $50. (8.) 15 cents. (9.) 28 shoes. (10.) 54 cents.

LESSON LII.

(1.) 5 ducks. (2.) 4. (3.) 2 wings. (4.) 2. (5.) 2 flowers.

LESSON LIII.

(1.) 2 apples. (2.) 3 marbles. (3.) 2 lemons. (4.) 2 peaches. (5.) 6 yards. (6.) 2 oranges. (7.) 8 tops. (8.) 2 kites. (9.) 2 books.

LESSON LIV.

(1.) 2 groups. (2.) 3 yards. (3.) 3 pears. (4.) 5 yards. (5.) 6 oranges. (6.) 3 groups. (7.) 3 yards. (8.) 3 cents. (9.) 10 postage stamps.

LESSON LV.

(1.) 2 oranges. (2.) 3 gallons. (3.) 4 apples. (4.) 5 scholars. (5.) 6 copy-books. (6.) 4 tops. (7.) 8 peaches. (8.) 4 cakes. (9.) 4 books.

LESSON LVI.
(1.) 2 oranges. (2.) 5 pencils. (3.) 5 toy books. (4.) 5 pears. (5.) 5 melons. (6.) 5 weeks. (7.) 5 cakes. (8.) 9 tops. (9.) 10 slates.

LESSON LVII.
(1.) 2 quarts. (2.) 3 oranges. (3.) 4 trees. (4.) 6 pears. (5.) 6 pounds. (6.) 6 lemons. (7.) 6 pencils. (8.) 9 rings. (9.) $10.

LESSON LVIII.
(1.) 2 piles. (2.) 3 pineapples. (3.) 4 melons. (4.) 5 peaches. (5.) 7 miles. (6.) 7 cents. (7.) 7 trees. (8.) 7 yards. (9.) $10.

LESSON LIX.
(1.) 2 pecks. (2.) 3 oranges. (3.) 8 pencils. (4.) 8 cents. (5.) 6 canes. (6.) 8 tops. (7.) 8 peaches. (8.) 8 cents. (9.) 10 cents.

LESSON LX.
(1.) 2 pencils. (2.) 9 cents. (3.) 9 cents. (4.) 9 cents. (5.) 6 cents. (6.) 9 miles. (7.) 8 yards. (8.) 9 blocks. (9.) 9 books.

LESSON LXI.
(1.) 2 melons. (2.) 3 quinces. (3.) 10 pears. (4.) 5 oranges. (5.) 6 dozen. (6.) 7 coats. (7.) 10 kites. (8.) 9 balls. (9.) 10 dimes.

LESSON LXII. (Review)
Column 1: 2, 4, 2, 2, 9, 4, 7, 5, 2, 3, 6, 2, 6, 5, 7, 4.
Column 2: 3, 6, 10, 3, 2, 3, 4, 4, 3, 7, 8, 8, 5, 7, 8, 2.
Column 3: 8, 6, 3, 4, 4, 2, 10, 6, 3, 2, 3, 5, 5, 8, 5, 9.
Column 4: 7, 7, 10, 5, 5, 6, 9, 9, 6, 6, 9, 7, 10, 9, 10, 8.
Column 5: 6, 9, 8, 7, 4, 10, 5, 4, 8, 9, 8, 10, 9, 10, 7, 10.
(1.) 2. (2.) 4. (3.) 4. (4.) 7. (5.) 5. (6.) 5. (7.) 6. (8.) 6. (9.) 7. (10.) 8. (11.) 9. (12.) 9. (13.) 10. (14.) 10. (15.) 6. (16.) 3. (17.) 4. (18.) 10. (19.) 3.

LESSON LXIII.
(1.) 2 cents; 12 cents. (2.) 4 cents; 36 cents. (3.) 30 cents. (4.) 30

cents. (5.) 40 cents. (6.) 49 cents. (7.) 9 cents. (8.) 12 pears. (9.) 4 lemons. (10.) 8 cents. (11.) 3 cents.

LESSON LXIV.

(1.) 12. (2.) [reading across] 13, 14, 15, 16, 17, 18, 19, 20, 21. (3.) 13, 14, 15, 16, 17, 18, 19, 20, 21, 22. (4.) 14, 15, 16, 17, 18, 19, 20, 21, 22, 23. (5.) 15, 16, 17, 18, 19, 20, 21, 22, 23, 24. (6.) 16, 17, 18, 19, 20, 21, 22, 23, 24, 25.

LESSON LXV.

(1.) 17, 18, 19, 20, 21, 22, 23, 24, 25, 26.
(2.) 18, 19, 20, 21, 22, 23, 24, 25, 26, 27.
(3.) 19, 20, 21, 22, 23, 24, 25, 26, 27, 28.
(4.) 20, 21, 22, 23, 24, 25, 26, 27, 28, 29.
(5.) 22, 34, 46, 58, 70, 73, 85, 97, 99.
(6.) 23, 35, 47, 49, 51, 54, 66, 78, 90, 100.
(7.) 24, 36, 48, 60, 72, 75, 87, 99, 100.
(8.) 25, 37, 49, 61, 73, 76, 88, 100.
(9.) 26, 38, 50, 62, 74, 77, 89, 100.
(10.) 27, 39, 51, 63, 75, 78, 90, 100.
(11.) 28, 40, 52, 64, 76, 79, 91, 100.
(12.) 29, 41, 53, 65, 77, 80, 92, 100.
(13.) 30, 42, 54, 66, 78, 81, 93, 100.

LESSON LXVI.

(1.) 31, 43, 55, 67, 79, 82, 94, 96.
(2.) 27, 39, 51, 63, 66, 78, 90, 93.
(3.) 31, 38, 50, 62, 74, 77, 89, 94.
(4.) 32, 44, 49, 61, 73, 85, 88, 91.
(5.) 34, 42, 50, 59, 71, 83, 95, 98.
(6.) 36, 36, 43, 57, 65, 70, 82, 94.
(7.) 37, 37, 48, 56, 64, 75, 81, 93.
(8.) 26, 38, 50, 62, 65, 77, 89, 99.
(9.) 29, 36, 48, 60, 72, 83, 91, 98.
(10.) 40, 55, 64, 73, 82, 91, 98, 98.
(11.) 34, 42, 50, 66, 74, 83, 92, 99.

(12.) 32, 40, 54, 62, 76, 84, 97, 98.
(13.) 35, 47, 56, 64, 77, 83, 95, 97.
(14.) 38, 46, 57, 65, 72, 83, 91, 99.
(15.) 35, 43, 51, 64, 75, 79, 96, 87, 87, 96.

LESSON LXVII.

(1.) 20 cents. (2.) 22 cents. (3.) 25 cents. (4.) $19. (5.) 21 years.
(6.) 25 cents. (7.) 23 cents. (8.) 24 cents. (9.) 27 years. (10.) 29 pupils.
(11.) 40 chickens. (12.) 21 ducks. (13.) 51 cents. (14.) 27 oranges.
(15.) 32 cents. (16.) 50.

LESSON LXVIII.

(1.) 11 marbles. (2.) 13 cents. (3.) 13 plums. (4.) 13 peaches.
(5.) 13; 13. (6.) 14 cents. (7.) 29 needles. (8.) 29 chickens. (9.) 29
eggs. (10.) 30 cents. (11.) 49 cents. (12.) 35 quarts. (13.) 47 cents.
(14.) 33 marbles. (15.) 56.

LESSON LXIX.

(1.) 13. (2.) 17. (3.) 13. (4.) 18. (5.) 23. (6.) 19. (7.) 14. (8.) 16.
(9.) 20. (10.) 27. (11.) 24. (12.) 22. (13.) 21 (14.) 25. (15.) 30.
(16.) 29. (17.) 15. (18.) 31. (19.) 32. (20.) 26. (21.) 28. (22.) 33.
(23.) 45. (24.) 55. (25.) 65. (26.) 56. (27.) 80. (28.) 83. (29.) 89.

LESSON LXX.

(1.) 14 cents. (2.) 15 cents. (3.) 10 cents. (4.) 10 oranges were
given away; 12 oranges were left. (5.) 30 cents. (6.) 5 cents. (7.) 12
cents. (8.) 28 years. (9.) 65 cents. (10.) 4 cents. (11.) 40 cents spent;
10 cents left.

LESSON LXXI.

(1.) 7. (2.) 29; 41. (3.) 71; 11. (4.) 14; 4. (5.) 30; 16. (6.) 44; 57.
(7.) 43; 31. (8.) 39; 27. (9.) 15; 53. (10.) 22; 67. (11.) 2; 21. (12.) 7;
17. (13.) 0; 44. (14.) 68; 7. (15.) 21. (16.) 87. (17.) 57. (18.) 23.
(19.) 25. (20.) 36. (21.) 37. (22.) 33. (23.) 20. (24.) 40. (25.) 53.
(26.) 10. (27.) 10. (28.) 97.

LESSON LXXII.

(1.) 2. (2.) 3; 2. (3.) 4; 2. (4.) 3. (5.) 5; 2. (6.) 6; 4; 3; 2. (7.) 7; 2. (8.) 5; 3. (9.) 8; 4; 2. (10.) 9; 6; 3; 2. (11.) 10; 5; 4; 2. (12.) 7; 3. (13.) 8; 6; 4; 3. (14.) 5. (15.) 9; 3. (16.) 7; 4. (17.) 10; 6; 5; 3. (18.) 8; 4.

LESSON LXXIII.

(1.) 7; 5. (2.) 9; 6; 4. (3.) 10; 8; 5; 4. (4.) 7; 6. (5.) 9; 5. (6.) 8; 6. (7.) 7. (8.) 10; 5. (9.) 9; 6. (10.) 8; 7. (11.) 10; 6. (12.) 9; 7. (13.) 8. (14.) 10; 7. (15.) 9; 8. (16.) 10; 8. (17.) 9. (18.) 10; 9. (19.) 10.

LESSON LXXIV.

(1.) 16 cents. (2.) 16 oranges. (3.) Jane is 14 years old; 20 years. (4.) 3; 5; 7; 8. (5.) 5 lemons. (6.) 15 men. (7.) 10 miles; 2 hours. (8.) 37 cents. (9.) 36 days. (10.) 6 oranges; 8 oranges; 10 oranges. (11.) 44 cents. (12.) $56.

LESSON LXXV.

(1.) Charles—4 marbles; Henry—16 marbles. (2.) 3 cents. (3.) 23 cents. (4.) 10 cents. (5.) 9 cents; 3 cents. (6.) 6 cents. (7.) 7 flags; 49 cents. (8.) 45 cents. (9.) 35 cents. (10.) 50 cents. (11.) 10 cents. (12.) 48 cents. (13.) $20.

LESSON LXXVI.

(1.) 2 oranges. (2.) 12 cents; 6 coins. (3.) 4 oranges. (4.) 6 tops. (5.) 2 quarts. (6.) 6 barrels. (7.) 5 quarts. (8.) 8 barrels. (9.) 4 melons. (10.) 5 oranges. (11.) 5 pears.

LESSON LXXVII.

(1.) 3 pineapples. (2.) 8 pencils. (3.) 9 kites. (4.) 8 peaches. (5.) 5 quarts. (6.) 10 pears. (7.) 2 days. (8.) 6 yards. (9.) 4 slates. (10.) 5 bottles. (11.) 5 oranges. (12) 12 days. (13.) $60. (14.) 12 trees.

LESSON LXXVIII.

(1.) 2, 4, 6, 8, 10, 12, 14, 16, 18, 20, 22, 24, 26, 28, 30, 32, 34,

36, 38, 40, 42, 44, 46, 48, 50, 52, 54, 56, 58, 60, 62, 64, 66, 68, 70, 72, 74, 76, 78, 80, 82, 84, 86, 88, 90, 92, 94, 96, 98, 100. (2.) Same numbers as in one but in reverse order and the addition of 0. (3.) 3, 6, 9, 12, 15, 18, 21, 24, 27, 30, 33, 36, 39, 42, 45, 48, 51, 54, 57, 60, 63, 66, 69, 72, 75, 78, 81, 84, 87, 90, 93, 96, 99. (4.) See three plus 0. (5.) 4, 8, 12, 16, 20, 24, 28, 32, 36, 40, 44, 48, 52, 56, 60, 64, 68, 72, 76, 80, 84, 88, 92, 96, 100. (6.) See five plus 0. (7.) 5, 10, 15, 20, 25, 30, 35, 40, 45, 50, 55, 60, 65, 70, 75, 80, 85, 90, 95, 100. (8.) See seven plus 0. (9.) 6, 12, 18, 24, 30, 36, 42, 48, 54, 60, 66, 72, 78, 84, 90, 96. (10.) See nine plus 0. (11.) 7, 14, 21, 28, 35, 42, 49, 56, 63, 70, 77, 84, 91, 98. (12.) See eleven plus 0. (13.) 8, 16, 24, 32, 40, 48, 56, 64, 72, 80, 88, 96. (14.) See thirteen plus 0. (15.) 9, 18, 27, 26, 45, 54, 63, 72, 81, 90, 99. (16.) See fifteen plus 0. (17.) 1, 3, 5, 7, 9, 11, 13, 15, 17, 19, 21, 23, 25, 27, 29 31, 33, 35, 37, 39, 41, 43, 45, 47, 49, 51, 53, 55, 57, 59, 61, 63, 65, 67, 69, 71, 73, 75, 77, 79, 81, 83, 85, 87, 89, 91, 93, 95, 97, 99. (18.) 100, 97, 94, 91, 88, 85, 82, 79, 76, 73, 70, 67, 64, 61, 58, 55, 52, 49, 46, 43, 40, 37, 34, 31, 28, 25, 22, 19, 16, 13, 10, 7, 4, 1. (19.) See eighteen. (20.) 97, 93, 89, 85, 81, 77, 73, 69, 65, 61, 57, 53, 49, 45, 41, 37, 33, 29, 25, 21, 17, 13, 9, 5, 1. (21.) See twenty. (22.) 96, 91, 86, 81, 76, 71, 66, 61, 56, 51, 46, 41, 36, 31, 26, 21, 16, 11, 6, 1. (23.) See twenty-two. (24.) 97, 91, 85, 79, 73, 67, 61, 55, 49, 43, 37, 31, 25, 19, 13, 7, 1. (25.) See twenty-four. (26.) 100, 94, 88, 82, 76, 70, 64, 58, 52, 46, 40, 34, 28, 22, 16, 10, 4. (27.) 1, 8, 15, 22, 29, 36, 43, 50, 57, 64, 71, 78, 85, 92, 99. (28.) 100, 93, 86, 79, 72, 65, 58, 51, 44, 37, 30, 23, 16, 9, 2. (29.) 1, 9, 17, 25, 33, 41, 49, 57, 65, 73, 81, 89, 97. (30.) 100, 92, 84, 76, 68, 60, 52, 44, 36, 28, 20, 12, 4. (31.) 1, 10, 19, 28, 37, 46, 55, 64, 73, 82, 91, 100.

LESSON LXXIX.

(1.) 30 cents. (2.) 30 dimes; 70 dimes. (3.) 6 dimes. (4) $60. (5.) $4. (6.) 100 dimes; 80 dimes. (7.) 3 dimes. (8.) 4 dimes. (9.) $5. (10.) 90 cents; 9 dimes. (11.) 15 cents.

LESSON LXXX.

(1.) 12 farthings. (2.) 5 shillings. (3.) 72 pence; 96 pence; 84 pence. (4.) 40 shillings; 80 shillings; 100 shillings. (5.) 2 pounds; 3 pounds; 5 pounds. (6.) 2 pounds. (7.) 15 pence. (8.) 10 books. (9.) 8 tops. (10.) 2 shillings. (11.) 1 pound. (12.) 13 shillings.

LESSON LXXXI.

(1.) 60 ounces. (2.) 8 pounds. (3.) 60 penny-weights; 100 penny-weights. (4.) 3 ounces; 4 ounces. (5.) 48 grains. (6.) 2 grains. (7.) 60 dimes. (8.) 12 ounces. (9.) 36 pounds. (10.) 10 penny-weights. (11.) 36 ounces. (12.) 1 ounce.

LESSON LXXXII.

(1.) 32 ounces; 48 ounces. (2.) 2 pounds; 4 pounds. (3.) 64 ounces; 80 ounces. (4.) 3 pounds; 5 pounds. (5.) 4000 pounds; 6000 pounds. (6.) 2 tons; 3 tons. (7.) 2 pounds. (8.) 64 ounces. (9.) 6 tons. (10.) 5 pounds. (11.) 48 cents; 28 cents. (12.) $8. (13.) 600 pounds. (14.) 10,000 pounds (15.) 80 ounces.

LESSON LXXXIII.

(1.) 4 pints; 6 pints; 8 pints. (2.) 6 quarts; 7 quarts; 8 quarts. (3.) 8 pecks; 12 pecks, 20 pecks. (4.) 4 bushels; 6 bushels; 8 bushels. (5.) 32 pints; 48 pints. (6.) 64 quarts; 96 quarts. (7.) 28 cents. (8.) 1 cent. (9.) 3 pecks. (10.) 16 quarts. (11.) $12; $6. (12.) 2 pecks; 70 cents. (13.) 7 bushels. (14.) 9 pecks.

LESSON LXXXIV.

(1.) 16 gills; 24 gills; 32 gills. (2.) 5 pints; 7 pints; 9 pints. (3.) 12 pints; 16 pints; 20 pints. (4.) 6 quarts; 8 quarts; 9 quarts. (5.) 20 quarts; 28 quarts; 36 quarts. (6.) 4 gallons; 6 gallons; 8 gallons. (7.) 40 cents. (8.) 3 cents. (9.) 10 cents. (10.) 64 cents. (11.) 6 gallons. (12.) $8. (13.) 10 cents. (14.) 15 quarts. (15.) 40 pints.

LESSON LXXXV.

(1.) 36 inches; 60 inches; 84 inches. (2.) 2 feet; 4 feet; 8 feet. (3.) 12 feet; 24 feet; 30 feet. (4.) 3 yards; 5 yards; 9 yards.

(5.) 640 rods; 960 rods. (6.) 12 inches. (7.) 18 yards. (8.) 60 feet. (9.) 2 yards. (10.) 5 feet. (11.) 9 bricks. (12.) 8 feet. (13.) 3 miles. (14.) 360 inches.

LESSON LXXXVI.

(1.) 27 sq. ft.; 45 sq. ft. (2.) 4 sq. yds.; 8 sq. yds. (3.) 320 sq. rds.; 480 sq. rds. (4.) 2 acres; 3 acres. (5.) 27 sq. ft. (6.) 20 sq. yds. (7.) 9 sq. yds. (8.) 20 yards. (9.) 42 cents. (10.) 5 sq. ft. (11.) 36 sq. ft. (12.) 32 sq. ft. (13.) 2 sq. miles (14.) 90 sq. ft.

LESSON LXXXIX.

(1.) 50 cents; 30 cents; 70 cents. (2.) 10 pence; 8 pence. (3.) 3 eagles; 5 eagles; 7 eagles. (4.) 60 shillings; 100 shillings; 80 shillings. (5.) 80 penny-weights; 40 penny-weights. (6.) 3 pounds Troy; 5 pounds Troy. (7.) 32 ounces; 48 ounces. (8.) 2 pounds; 3 pounds. (9.) 48 quarts; 64 quarts; 80 quarts. (1.) 5 bushels; 7 bushels; 9 bushels. (11.) 28 quarts; 24 quarts; 32 quarts. (12.) 4 gallons; 5 gallons; 9 gallons. (13.) 21 feet; 30 feet; 36 feet. (14.) 5 sq. yds.; 7 sq. yds. (15.) 27 scruples; 24 scruples; 30 scruples. (16.) 54 cu. ft. (17.) 2 cu. yds. (18.) 48 hours; 72 hours. (19.) 2 days; 3 days. (20.) 28 weeks; 48 weeks. (21.) 120 minutes; 180 minutes. (22.) 80 quires; 60 quires. (23.) 144 pens. (24.) 42 feet; 30 feet; 54 feet. (25.) 5 feet. (26.) 6 chains; 7 chains; 9 chains. (27.) 1920 farthings; 9600 farthings. (28.) 4 ounces. (29.) 48 sheets; 960 sheets. (30.) 70.

ANSWERS

to

RAY'S INTELLECTUAL ARITHMETIC

LESSON I.

(1.) 2 apples. (2.) 3¢. (3.) 4 marbles. (4.) 5¢. (5.) 4 cakes.
(6.) 5 oranges. (7.) 6 apples. (8.) 6 plums. (9.) 6¢. (10.) 7 pears.
(11.) 5 fingers; 10 fingers. (12.) 8¢. (13.) 8 cakes. (14.) 9¢.
(15.) 8 oranges. (16.) 10¢. (17.) 10 boys. (18.) $9. (19.) 10 peaches.
(20.) $7. (21.) 11¢. (22.) 10 pounds. (23.) 10 oranges. (24.) 7¢.
(25.) 10. (26.) 8¢.

LESSON II.

(1.) 2; 3; 4; 5; 4; 6; 7; 7; 8; 9; 10; 9. (2.) 7; 11; 9. (3.) 7; 10;
9; 5; 8; 9. (4.) 11; 8; 9; 10; 11; 11; 12. (5.) 10; 11; 13; 11; 12; 11;
13; 12; 13. (6.) 12; 12; 12; 13; 11; 13; 12; 12; 13; 17. (7.) 10; 13;
13; 8; 12; 13; 14; 14; 6 + 4. (8.) 4; 6; 8; 10; 12; 14; 16. (9.) 1; 4;
7; 10; 13. (10.) 3 + 9; 2 + 3 + 7. (11.) 14. (12.) 14. (13.) 11. (14.)
14. (15.) 15 dozen. (16.) 10¢. (17.) 10. (18.) 13; 13. (19.) 10¢, (20.)
$11. (21.) 11¢. (22.) 16 yards. (23.) 18¢. (24.) 14; 18; 20. (25.) 21¢.

LESSON IV.

(1.) 11; 15. (2.) 8; 15; 14; 16. (3.) 14; 17; 15; 13; 16; 12; 14.
(4.) 14; 17; 15; 19; 16; 18; 16. (5.) 20; 18; 21; 19; 17. (6.) 16; 18;
20; 22; 21. (7.) 13; 15; 17; 19; 14; 22. (8.) 15; 16; 18; 20; 23; 24.
(9.) 17; 19; 18; 20; 22; 23; 21; 24; 25. (10.) 18; 20; 22; 19; 21; 24;
23; 25; 26. (11.) 20; 22; 24; 19; 23; 25; 27; 26. (12.) 20; 22; 24;
21; 23; 25; 27; 26; 28. (13.) 23; 21; 24; 22; 26; 25; 29; 28.
(14.) 28; 22; 25; 23; 26; 24; 27; 29; 30. (15.) 24; 22; 21; 26; 28;
27; 29; 25; 31; 30. (16.) 31; 51; 71; 41; 61; 81; 101. (17.) 32; 52;
62; 42; 72; 82; 92; 102. (18.) 36; 56; 46; 66; 86; 76; 96; 106. (19.)
37; 57; 47; 77; 67; 87. (20.) 28; 38; 58; 78; 68; 88; 98; 108. (21.)
31; 51; 71; 91; 101. (22.) 35; 45; 55; 75; 65; 95. (23.) 24; 34; 54;

64; 44; 74; 94; 84; 104. (24.) 37; 57; 47; 67. (25.) 21; 31; 31; 30; 30; 42; 54; 51; 63; 65; 72; 81; 92. (26.) 20; 31; 32; 41; 40; 51; 50; 60; 61; 70; 90; 100; 91. (27.) 33; 34; 43; 45; 53; 56; 63; 65; 73; 83; 81; 93; 95; 103. (28.) 27; 36; 56; 45; 65; 66; 76; 79; 86; 96; 106. (29.) 27; 38; 36; 34; 42; 46; 48; 70; 57; 59; 63; 74.

LESSON V.

(1.) 13. (2.) 16. (3.) 13. (4.) 15. (5.) 17. (6.) 17. (7.) 18. (8.) 19. (9.) 21. (10.) 32. (11.) 34. (12.) 33. (13.) 39. (14.) 39. (15.) 51. (16.) 52. (17.) 50. (18.) 56. (19.) 57. (20.) 53. (21.) 71. (22.) 82. (23.) 43. (24.) 51. (25.) 78. (26.) 15¢. (27.) $15. (28.) 23 books. (29.) $23. (30.) 26 marbles. (31.) 28¢. (32.) $23. (33.) 33¢. (34.) 41 hogs. (35.) 32¢. (36.) 34¢. (37.) 26 years. (38.) 22 marbles. (39.) 2, 4, 6, 8, 10, 12, 14, 16, 18, 20 . . . 90, 92, 94, 96, 98, 100. (40.) 3, 6, 9, 12, 15, 18, 21 . . . 78, 81, 84, 87, 90, 93, 96, 99. (41.) 4, 8, 12, 16, 20, 24, 28, 32, 36, 40, 44, 48, 52, 56, 60. 64, 68, 72, 76, 80, 84, 88, 92, 96, 100. (42.) 5, 10, 15, 20, 25, 30, 35, 40, 45, 50, 55, 60, 65, 70, 75, 80, 85, 90, 95, 100. (43.) 6, 12, 18, 24, 30, 36, 42, 48, 54, 60, 66, 72, 78, 84, 90, 96, 102. (44.) 7, 14, 21, 28, 35, 42, 49, 56, 63, 70, 77, 84, 91, 98. (45.) 8, 16, 24, 32, 40, 48, 56, 64, 72, 80, 88, 96, 104. (46.) 9, 18, 27, 36, 45, 54, 63, 72, 81, 90, 99. (47.) 1, 4, 7, 10, 13, 16, 19, 22, 25, 28, 31, 34, 37, 40, 43, 46, 49, 52, 55, 58, 61, 64, 67, 70, 73, 76, 79, 82, 85, 88, 91, 94, 97, 100. (48.) 3, 7, 11, 15, 19, 23, 27, 31, 35, 39, 43, 47, 51, 55, 59, 63, 67, 71, 75, 79, 83, 87, 91, 95, 99, 103. (49.) 2, 7, 12, 17 22, 27, 32, 37, 42, 47, 52, 57, 62, 67, 72, 77, 82, 87, 92, 97, 102. (50.) 5, 11, 17, 23, 29, 35, 41, 47, 53, 59, 65, 71, 77, 83, 89, 95, 101, 107. (51.) 6, 13, 20, 27, 34, 41, 48, 55, 62, 69, 76, 83, 90, 97, 104. (52.) 7, 15, 23, 31, 39, 47, 55, 63, 71, 79, 87, 95, 103. (53.) 8, 17, 26, 35, 44, 53, 62, 71, 80, 89, 98, 107.

LESSON VI.

(1.) 1 apple. (2.) 2 apples. (3.) 3¢. (4.) 4; 5; 6; 7; 8; 9. (5.) 2¢. (6.) 3 apples. (7.) 4; 5; 6; 7; 8; 9. (8.) 2¢. (9.) 3; 4; 5; 6; 7; 8; 9. (10.) 5 marbles. (11.) 6; 7; 8; 9; 10; 11. (12.) 5 apples. (13.) 6; 7; 8; 9; 10; 11. (14.) 5 marbles. (15.) 6; 7; 8; 9; 10; 11. (16.) 5¢.

(17.) 6; 7; 8; 9; 10; 11; 12. (18.) 5 apples. (19.) 6; 7; 8; 9; 10; 11;
12. (20.) 4 apples. (21.) 5; 6; 7; 8; 9; 10; 11. (22.) 12¢. (23.) 4 years.
(24.) $11. (25.) 8 marbles.

LESSON VIII.

(1.) 2¢. (2.) $4. (3.) 5¢. (4.) 9¢. (5.) 6¢. (6.) 4 nuts. (7.) 6 miles.
(8.) 8¢. (9.) 5 marbles. (10.) $8. (11.) $8. (12.) 9¢; 8¢. (13.) 2 apples.
(14.) 4¢. (15.) 20 marbles. (16.) 50 barrels. (17.) 13 bushels.
(18.) 24 years. (19.) 35¢. (20.) 18. (21.) 28. (22.) 10. (23.) 20.
(24.) 7. (25.) 13.

LESSON IX.

(1.) 8 marbles. (2.) 10 barrels. (3.) 11¢. (4.) $10. (5.) $9. (6.) $11.
(7.) 7¢. (8.) 11 marbles. (9.) 23 marbles; 9 marbles. (10.) 16 marbles.
(11.) 4 sheep. (12.) $7. (13.) 15¢. (14.) $9. (15.) 15.

LESSON X.

(1.) 2. (2.) 3. (3.) 5. (4.) 7. (5.) 9. (6.) 12. (7.) 2. (8.) 2. (9.) 5.
(10.) 9. (11.) 7. (12.) 6. (13.) 8. (14.) 11. (15.) 10. (16.) 6.
(17.) 5. (18.) 5. (19.) 5. (20.) 4. (21.) 5. (22.) 8. (23.) 12. (24.) 12.
(25.) 10. (26.) 1. (27.) 11.

LESSON XI.

(1.) 9¢. (2.) 8 gallons. (3.) 11. (4.) 22. (5.) $15. (6.) $17. (7.) 2.
(8.) $15. (9.) 16 (10.) $5. (11.) 10 sheep. (12.) $3. (13.) 6. (14.) 5.
(15.) 38. (16.) $20. (17.) $80. (18.) 68. (19.) $40. (20.) 8 gallons.
(21.) 8. (22.) 1.

LESSON XII.

(1.) 4¢. (2.) 6¢. (3.) 8¢. (4.) 9¢. (5.) 12¢. (6.) 15¢. (7.) 16¢.
(8.) $20. (9.) $24. (10.) 25¢. (11.) 30¢. (12.) 36¢. (13.) 14¢.
(14.) 21¢. (15.) 28¢. (16.) 35 apples. (17.) 16 apples. (18.) 24¢; 32¢.
(19.) 40 apples. (20.) 18¢; 27¢. (21.) 40¢. (22.) 33¢.

LESSON XIII.

(1) 28. (2.) 16; 35; 42. (3.) 48; 54; 63. (4.) 72; 49; 56. (5.) 24;

20; 18. (6.) 50; 44; 36. (7.) 64; 66; 18. (8.) 70; 48; 40. (9.) 6; 8;
10. (10.) 12; 14; 15. (11.) 20; 36; 22. (12.) 24; 25; 33. (13.) 60; 72;
30. (14.) 108; 36; 40. (15.) 110; 120; 96. (16.) 45; 81; 121. (17.) 132;
55; 60. (18.) 80; 84; 88. (19.) 99; 100; 132.

LESSON XIV.

(1.) 14¢. (2.) 21¢. (3.) 30¢. (4.) 56¢. (5.) $48. (6.) $27. (7.) $28.
(8.) 80¢. (9.) $42. (10.) $40. (11.) 56 miles. (12.) 64 squares.
(13.) 77 trees. (14.) $54. (15.) 72¢. (16.) 96¢. (17.) 18 miles.
(18.) 6 days. (19.) 12 days. (20.) 24 days. (21.) 32 days. (22.) $48.
(23.) 63 men. (24.) 88 persons. (25.) $56.

LESSON XV.

(1.) 15¢. (2.) 20 miles. (3.) 144 miles. (4.) $12; $3. (5.) 39¢. (6.) 4.
(7.) 56 shillings. (8.) $38. (9.) $56. (10.) 36 dimes or $3.60. (11.) 120
horses. (12.) 24. (13.) 60. (14.) 40. (15.) 20¢. (16.) $1. (17.) Albert
has 40 marbles; Edward has 60 marbles; 20. (18.) $8. (19.) $10.
(20.) 21 miles. (21.) 48 miles. (22.) nothing. (23.) 16¢. (24.) 18¢.
(25.) $1.16. (26.) 5¢. (27.) $1. (28.) $12; $32. (29.) $4. (30.) 42
books. (31.) $1.08. (32.) $52. (33.) 19¢. (34.) 63. (35.) 24. (36.)
144. (37.) $77. (38.) 64.

LESSON XVI.

(1.) 4 cakes. (2.) 2 apples. (3.) 3 boys. (4.) 4 apples (5.) 2 peaches.
(6.) 3 pears. (7.) 5 cakes. (8.) 7 balls. (9.) 3 lemons. (10.) 8 piles.
(11.) 6 plums. (12.) 4 oranges. (13.) 7 yards. (14.) 11 yards.
(15.) 4 oranges; 3 oranges. (16.) 5 trees. (17.) 9 hours. (18.) 7 sheep.
(19.) 10 marbles. (20.) 8 dimes. (21.) 7 trees. (22.) $6. (23.) 9 gallons.
(24.) 4 hours. (25.) 7¢. (26.) 5 oranges.

LESSON XVIII.

(1.) 6. (2.) 8; 12; 3; 5; 7; 9; 2; 5; 7; 9; 12. (3.) 3; 6; 9; 12; 3;
4; 6; 7; 9; 11. (4.) 2; 4; 6; 8; 9; 12; 3; 5; 7; 9; 12. (5.) 2; 3; 5; 6;
7; 9; 12; 2; 6; 9; 10. (6.) 5; 7; 9; 10; 11; 2; 4; 5; 6; 8; 9; 10; 12.
(7.) 4 peaches. (8.) 6 apples. (9.) 10¢. (10.) 7¢. (11.) 8 weeks.
(12.) 5 pears; 7 pears; 9 pears. (13.) 5 oranges; 7 oranges; 9 oranges;

11 oranges. (14.) 6 days. (15.) 8 days. (16.) 7 hours. (17.) 3 tons; 5 tons; 6 tons; 7 tons. (18.) $6. (19.) 8¢. (20.) $9. (21.) 12 trees. (22.) $12; $2. (23.) $2. (24.) $12; $4. (25.) 5 miles.

LESSON XIX.

(1.) 6. (2.) 8; 4; 3; 2. (3.) 6; 9; 12; 8. (4.) 4 oranges. (5.) 12 revolutions. (6.) 12 trees. (7.) 30 marbles. (8.) 7 barrels. (9.) 20 hours. (10.) 4 times. (11.) 6. (12.) 36. (13.) 7¢. (14.) 6 men. (15.) 5. (16.) 34 dimes. (17.) 3. (18.) 3¢. (19.) 9. (20.) 18 apples. (21.) The first number, 10. (22.) 30 apples. (23.) 63 miles. (24.) 40¢. (25.) 45 lessons. (26.) $56. (27.) 4. (28.) 6 barrels. (29.) 49. (30.) 9 yards. (31.) $21. (32.) 11 pounds. (33.) 10 hours. (34.) 6 men. (35.) 12 men.

LESSON XX.

(1.) 4; 6; 8; 10; 12; 14; 16; 18; 20. (2.) 6; 9; 12; 15; 18; 21; 24; 27; 30. (3.) 8; 12; 16; 20; 24; 28; 32; 36; 40. (4.) 10; 15; 20; 25; 30; 35; 40; 45; 50. (5.) 12; 18; 24; 30; 36; 42; 48; 54; 60. (6.) 14; 21; 28; 35; 42; 49; 56; 63; 70. (7.) 16; 24; 32; 40; 48; 56; 64; 72; 80. (8.) 18; 27; 36; 45; 54; 63; 72; 81; 90. (9.) 9; 15; 21; 27. (10.) 20; 40; 15. (11.) 66; 22; 55; 99.

LESSON XXII.

(1.) 1¢. (2.) 1¢. (3.) $4. (4.) 2 apples. (5.) 6¢. (6.) $4; $6; $8. (7.) 10¢. (8.) 6. (9.) 15. (10.) 6; 12; 20. (11.) 4; 9; 16; 25; 36. (12.) 6; 15; 28. (13.) 2; 8; 15; 28; 40. (14.) 3; 14; 27. (15.) 2; 6; 12; 20; 30; 42; 56. (16.) 10; 21; 44. (17.) 2¢. (18.) $3. (19.) 10¢. (20.) $18. (21.) 50¢. (22.) 45¢. (23.) $70.

LESSON XXIII.

(1.) $\frac{1}{2}$ apple. (2.) $\frac{1}{3}$ pear. (3.) $\frac{2}{3}$ yard. (4.) $\frac{3}{4}$ orange. (5.) $\frac{2}{5}$; $\frac{3}{5}$; $\frac{4}{5}$. (6.) $\frac{5}{6}$. (7.) $\frac{4}{7}$. (8.) $\frac{7}{10}$. (9.) $\frac{5}{8}$. (10.) $\frac{5}{7}$. (11.) $\frac{3}{8}$; $\frac{3}{10}$; $\frac{3}{11}$; $\frac{3}{20}$. (12.) $\frac{4}{9}$; $\frac{4}{11}$; $\frac{4}{15}$; $\frac{4}{25}$. (13.) $\frac{5}{8}$; $\frac{5}{9}$; $\frac{5}{12}$; $\frac{5}{16}$. (14.) $\frac{2}{15}$; $\frac{7}{15}$; $\frac{8}{15}$; $\frac{11}{15}$; $\frac{13}{15}$. (15.) $\frac{3}{20}$; $\frac{7}{20}$; $\frac{11}{20}$; $\frac{13}{20}$; $\frac{17}{20}$. (16.) $\frac{18}{23}$. (17.) $\frac{24}{35}$. (18.) $\frac{14}{19}$. (19.) $\frac{2}{3}$. (20.) $\frac{9}{20}$. (21.) $\frac{4}{9}$. (22.) $\frac{6}{25}$. (23.) $\frac{8}{21}$. (24.) $\frac{27}{35}$.

LESSON XXIV.

(1.) 2¢. (2.) 6¢. (3.) 9¢. (4.) $12. (5.) 25¢. (6.) 15¢. (7.) 42¢. (8.) 21. (9.) 27; 33. (10.) 16; 20; 28; 32; 40; 44. (11.) 25; 35; 45; 55. (12.) 36; 42; 48; 54; 66; 72. (13.) 49; 77. (14.) 64; 72; 80. (15.) 81; 99. (16.) 100. (17.) 9¢. (18.) 16 years. (19.) 25. (20.) 32. (21.) 35. (22.) 20. (23.) 55. (24.) 77. (25.) 36.

LESSON XXV.

(1.) $1\frac{1}{2}$ apples. (2.) $1\frac{1}{3}$ oranges. (3.) $2\frac{1}{2}$¢. (4.) $1\frac{2}{3}$ dollars. (5.) $1\frac{1}{4}$¢. (6.) $1\frac{1}{3}$. (7.) $3\frac{1}{2}$; $2\frac{1}{3}$; $1\frac{3}{4}$; $1\frac{2}{5}$; $1\frac{1}{6}$. (8.) $2\frac{2}{3}$; $1\frac{3}{5}$; $1\frac{1}{7}$. (9.) $4\frac{1}{2}$; $2\frac{1}{4}$; $1\frac{4}{5}$; $1\frac{2}{7}$; $1\frac{1}{8}$. (10.) $3\frac{1}{3}$; $1\frac{3}{7}$; $1\frac{1}{9}$. (11.) $5\frac{1}{2}$; $3\frac{2}{3}$; $2\frac{1}{4}$; $2\frac{1}{5}$; $1\frac{5}{6}$; $1\frac{4}{7}$; $1\frac{3}{8}$; $1\frac{2}{9}$; $1\frac{1}{10}$. (12.) $2\frac{2}{5}$; $1\frac{5}{7}$; $1\frac{1}{11}$. (13.) $2\frac{1}{2}$ apples. (14.) $2\frac{1}{3}$ yards. (15.) $3\frac{1}{4}$ yards. (16.) $3\frac{2}{5}$ pints. (17.) $3\frac{5}{6}$ barrels. (18.) $3\frac{4}{7}$ yards. (19.) $6\frac{1}{2}$. (20.) $7\frac{1}{2}$; $8\frac{1}{2}$; $9\frac{1}{2}$; $10\frac{1}{2}$; $11\frac{1}{2}$. (21.) $6\frac{2}{3}$; $8\frac{2}{3}$; $9\frac{2}{3}$; $10\frac{1}{3}$; $11\frac{2}{3}$. (22.) $6\frac{3}{4}$; $8\frac{1}{4}$; $9\frac{3}{4}$; $10\frac{1}{4}$; $11\frac{3}{4}$. (23.) $7\frac{1}{6}$; $7\frac{5}{6}$; $8\frac{1}{6}$; $9\frac{5}{6}$; $10\frac{1}{6}$. (24.) $3\frac{3}{7}$; $4\frac{4}{7}$; $5\frac{5}{7}$; $6\frac{6}{7}$; $8\frac{1}{7}$. (25.) $5\frac{5}{8}$; $6\frac{7}{8}$; $8\frac{3}{8}$; $8\frac{7}{8}$; $10\frac{1}{8}$. (26.) $3\frac{7}{9}$; $4\frac{4}{9}$; $5\frac{5}{9}$; $6\frac{8}{9}$; $7\frac{1}{9}$. (27.) $6\frac{3}{10}$; $6\frac{9}{10}$; $7\frac{7}{10}$; $8\frac{3}{10}$; $9\frac{1}{10}$. (28.) $3\frac{9}{11}$; $4\frac{2}{11}$; $4\frac{10}{11}$; $5\frac{7}{11}$; $6\frac{4}{11}$. (29.) $5\frac{2}{3}$; $6\frac{1}{12}$; $7\frac{1}{12}$; $7\frac{5}{12}$; $7\frac{11}{12}$.

LESSON XXVI.

(1.) 5. (2.) 7; 9; 11; 13. (3.) 13; 17; 19; 23. (4.) 13; 19; 21; 27. (5.) 6; 17; 32; 36. (6.) 17; 29; 31; 41. (7.) 38; 46; 54; 62. (8.) 29; 39; 41; 51. (9.) 62; 64; 74; 86. (10.) 63; 77; 89; 91. (11.) 71; 83; 95; 107. (12.) 61; 79; 89; 113.

LESSON XXVII.

(1.) $\frac{1}{2}$. (2.) $\frac{1}{3}$. (3.) $\frac{1}{2}$. (4.) $\frac{2}{3}$. (5.) $\frac{1}{2}$. (6.) $\frac{1}{2}$; $\frac{1}{3}$; $\frac{3}{4}$; $\frac{2}{5}$; $\frac{4}{5}$; $\frac{5}{6}$. (7.) $\frac{1}{2}$; $\frac{1}{3}$; $\frac{2}{3}$ $\frac{3}{4}$; $\frac{4}{5}$; $\frac{5}{6}$. (8.) $\frac{2}{3}$; $\frac{3}{4}$; $\frac{2}{5}$; $\frac{3}{5}$; $\frac{5}{6}$; $\frac{1}{7}$. (9.) $\frac{3}{8}$; $\frac{2}{7}$; $\frac{3}{4}$; $\frac{3}{5}$; $\frac{5}{6}$; $\frac{4}{7}$. (10.) $\frac{4}{9}$; $\frac{2}{3}$; $\frac{3}{4}$; $\frac{3}{5}$; $\frac{5}{6}$; $\frac{4}{7}$. (11.) $\frac{2}{5}$; $\frac{2}{3}$; $\frac{3}{4}$; $\frac{3}{5}$; $\frac{1}{2}$; $\frac{5}{8}$. (12.) $\frac{2}{3}$; $\frac{4}{5}$; $\frac{3}{4}$; $\frac{5}{8}$; $\frac{5}{9}$; $\frac{5}{6}$. (13.) $\frac{3}{4}$; $\frac{4}{5}$; $\frac{5}{6}$; $\frac{6}{7}$; $\frac{7}{9}$; $\frac{7}{8}$. (14.) $\frac{4}{5}$; $\frac{5}{6}$; $\frac{6}{7}$; $\frac{7}{9}$; $\frac{7}{8}$; $\frac{8}{9}$.

LESSON XXVIII.

(1.) $\frac{2}{4}$. (2.) $\frac{2}{6}$. (3.) $\frac{2}{8}$. (4.) $\frac{2}{10}$. (5.) $\frac{2}{12}$. (6.) $\frac{3}{9}$. (7.) $\frac{3}{12}$. (8.) $\frac{4}{6}$. (9.) $\frac{6}{9}$; $\frac{8}{12}$. (10.) $\frac{6}{8}$; $\frac{9}{12}$. (11.) $\frac{4}{10}$; $\frac{6}{15}$. (12.) $\frac{12}{20}$; $\frac{15}{25}$. (13.) $\frac{24}{30}$; $\frac{28}{35}$. (14.) $\frac{10}{12}$; $\frac{15}{18}$. (15.) $\frac{6}{14}$; $\frac{9}{21}$. (16.) $\frac{20}{28}$; $\frac{25}{35}$. (17.) $\frac{6}{16}$; $\frac{9}{24}$. (18.) $\frac{20}{32}$; $\frac{25}{40}$. (19.) $\frac{4}{18}$; $\frac{6}{27}$. (20.) $\frac{16}{36}$; $\frac{20}{45}$. (21.) $\frac{30}{54}$; $\frac{35}{63}$. (22.) $\frac{14}{20}$; $\frac{21}{30}$. (23.) $\frac{10}{24}$; $\frac{15}{36}$.

LESSON XXIX.

(1.) $\frac{8}{12}$ and $\frac{9}{12}$. (2.) $\frac{3}{6}$ and $\frac{2}{6}$; $\frac{5}{10}$ and $\frac{2}{10}$; $\frac{5}{15}$ and $\frac{3}{15}$. (3.) $\frac{4}{12}$ and $\frac{3}{12}$; $\frac{5}{15}$ and $\frac{3}{15}$; $\frac{5}{20}$ and $\frac{4}{20}$. (4.) $\frac{10}{15}$ and $\frac{6}{15}$; $\frac{10}{15}$ and $\frac{9}{15}$; $\frac{10}{15}$ and $\frac{12}{15}$. (5.) $\frac{15}{20}$ and $\frac{8}{20}$; $\frac{15}{20}$ and $\frac{12}{20}$; $\frac{15}{20}$ and $\frac{16}{20}$. (6.) $\frac{12}{30}$ and $\frac{25}{30}$; $\frac{18}{30}$ and $\frac{25}{30}$; $\frac{24}{30}$ and $\frac{25}{30}$. (7.) $\frac{35}{42}$ and $\frac{12}{42}$; $\frac{35}{42}$ and $\frac{18}{42}$; $\frac{35}{42}$ and $\frac{24}{42}$. (8.) $\frac{40}{56}$ and $\frac{21}{56}$; $\frac{48}{56}$ and $\frac{35}{56}$; $\frac{63}{72}$ and $\frac{16}{72}$. (9.) $\frac{40}{90}$ and $\frac{27}{90}$; $\frac{80}{90}$ and $\frac{63}{90}$; $\frac{70}{90}$ and $\frac{81}{90}$. (10.) $\frac{15}{30}$, $\frac{10}{30}$ and $\frac{6}{30}$; $\frac{20}{60}$, $\frac{15}{60}$ and $\frac{12}{60}$. (11.) $\frac{40}{60}$, $\frac{45}{60}$ and $\frac{24}{60}$; $\frac{18}{30}$, $\frac{25}{30}$ and $\frac{15}{30}$. (12.) $\frac{40}{60}$, $\frac{45}{60}$ and $\frac{48}{60}$; $\frac{30}{60}$. (13.) $\frac{9}{12}$ and $\frac{10}{12}$. (14.) $\frac{2}{4}$ and $\frac{1}{4}$; $\frac{3}{6}$ and $\frac{1}{6}$; $\frac{2}{6}$ and $\frac{1}{6}$. (15.) $\frac{4}{6}$ and $\frac{5}{6}$; $\frac{6}{8}$ and $\frac{3}{8}$; $\frac{5}{9}$ and $\frac{2}{9}$. (16.) $\frac{20}{24}$ and $\frac{15}{24}$; $\frac{15}{18}$ and $\frac{14}{18}$; $\frac{21}{24}$ and $\frac{10}{24}$. (17.) $\frac{6}{12}$, $\frac{4}{12}$ and $\frac{3}{12}$; $\frac{8}{24}$, $\frac{6}{24}$ and $\frac{4}{24}$. (18.) $\frac{16}{24}$, $\frac{18}{24}$ and $\frac{20}{24}$; $\frac{16}{24}$, $\frac{18}{24}$ and $\frac{15}{24}$. (19.) $\frac{18}{24}$, $\frac{20}{24}$ and $\frac{21}{24}$; $\frac{12}{18}$, $\frac{15}{18}$ and $\frac{4}{18}$. (20.) $\frac{27}{36}$, $\frac{16}{36}$ and $\frac{15}{36}$; $\frac{30}{36}$, $\frac{32}{36}$ and $\frac{21}{36}$. (21.) $\frac{6}{12}$, $\frac{4}{12}$, $\frac{3}{12}$ and $\frac{2}{12}$; $\frac{10}{30}$, $\frac{9}{30}$, $\frac{5}{30}$ and $\frac{3}{30}$. (22.) $\frac{16}{24}$, $\frac{18}{24}$, $\frac{20}{24}$ and $\frac{21}{24}$; $\frac{12}{36}$, $\frac{9}{36}$, $\frac{20}{36}$ and $\frac{21}{36}$. (23.) $\frac{18}{24}$, $\frac{20}{24}$, $\frac{21}{24}$ and $\frac{16}{24}$; $\frac{72}{180}$, $\frac{120}{180}$, $\frac{120}{180}$ and $\frac{75}{180}$. (24.) $\frac{12}{24}$, $\frac{8}{24}$, $\frac{6}{24}$, $\frac{4}{24}$ and $\frac{3}{24}$; $\frac{16}{24}$, $\frac{18}{24}$, $\frac{20}{24}$, $\frac{21}{24}$ and $\frac{22}{24}$. (25.) $\frac{30}{60}$, $\frac{40}{60}$, $\frac{45}{60}$, $\frac{48}{60}$, $\frac{50}{60}$, $\frac{54}{60}$ and $\frac{55}{60}$.

LESSON XXX.

(1.) $\frac{3}{4}$. (2.) $\$1\frac{1}{4}$. (3.) $\$1\frac{1}{6}$. (4.) $\frac{7}{8}$ orange. (5.) $\frac{7}{12}$. (6.) $\$\frac{3}{5}$. (7.) $3\frac{7}{12}$ yards. (8.) $11\frac{1}{6}$ acres. (9.) $\$1\frac{1}{4}$. (10.) $\frac{4}{5}$; $\frac{7}{8}$; $1\frac{5}{12}$. (11.) $\frac{11}{15}$; $\frac{5}{12}$; $\frac{9}{20}$. (12.) $\frac{9}{14}$; $1\frac{13}{28}$; $1\frac{3}{8}$. (13.) $1\frac{19}{30}$; $1\frac{13}{72}$; $1\frac{7}{63}$. (14.) $4\frac{1}{12}$; $1\frac{7}{60}$. (15.) $8\frac{1}{2}$. (16.) $9\frac{16}{21}$; $11\frac{1}{4}$. (17.) $9\frac{59}{72}$; $13\frac{19}{24}$.

LESSON XXXI.

(1.) $\frac{1}{6}$ orange. (2.) $\frac{1}{4}$ apple. (3.) $\frac{1}{6}$ melon. (4.) $\$\frac{7}{12}$. (5.) $\frac{1}{3}$. (6.) $\frac{7}{12}$ orange. (7.) $\frac{3}{10}$; $\frac{1}{12}$; $\frac{1}{20}$. (8.) $\frac{5}{18}$; $\frac{1}{10}$; $\frac{5}{12}$. (9.) $\frac{4}{15}$; $\frac{1}{40}$; $\frac{5}{21}$. (10.) $\frac{5}{18}$; $\frac{7}{15}$; $\frac{5}{28}$. (11.) $\frac{4}{35}$; $\frac{1}{28}$; $\frac{7}{30}$. (12.) $\frac{1}{24}$; $\frac{1}{42}$; $2\frac{1}{6}$. (13.) $2\frac{1}{2}$. (14.) $4\frac{1}{10}$; $4\frac{7}{12}$. (15.) $2\frac{8}{21}$; $2\frac{1}{18}$; $1\frac{13}{15}$.

LESSON XXXII.

(1.) $\frac{5}{12}$ quart. (2.) $\frac{1}{6}$ apple. (3.) $\frac{1}{10}$ orange. (4.) $\frac{1}{3}$ in oats. (5.) $\frac{4}{9}$; 32 miles. (6.) $\frac{1}{4}$ pound. (7.) $\frac{2}{3}$ bushel. (8.) $\frac{1}{8}$ pound. (9.) $4\frac{1}{12}$ yards. (10.) $\$\frac{3}{16}$. (11.) $\frac{1}{20}$. (12.) 9 sheep. (13.) $\frac{7}{24}$. (14.) $\frac{1}{6}$. (15.) $\frac{1}{6}$. (16.) $96.

LESSON XXXIII.

(1.) $1\frac{1}{2}$ oranges. (2.) $2\frac{1}{2}$ pecks. (3.) $1\frac{1}{3}$ oranges. (4.) $1\frac{1}{3}$ pineapples. (5.) $2\frac{2}{3}$. (6.) $1\frac{1}{2}$ apples. (7.) $1\frac{1}{2}$ pints. (8.) $2\frac{1}{4}$ oranges. (9.) $4\frac{1}{2}$; $5\frac{1}{4}$; 6. (10.) $\frac{3}{5}$; 2; $3\frac{3}{5}$. (11.) $\frac{3}{7}$; $1\frac{1}{7}$; $2\frac{6}{7}$. (12.) $\frac{5}{8}$; $\frac{3}{4}$; $3\frac{1}{2}$. (13.) $\frac{2}{9}$; $\frac{8}{9}$; $2\frac{2}{9}$. (14.) $2\frac{2}{3}$; 4; $6\frac{2}{9}$. (15.) $5\frac{5}{6}$; $4\frac{4}{5}$; $3\frac{3}{5}$. (16.) $4\frac{3}{8}$; $4\frac{2}{3}$; $3\frac{3}{7}$. (17.) $3\frac{3}{4}$; $4\frac{4}{5}$; $6\frac{6}{7}$. (18.) $11\frac{2}{3}$; 20; 12.

LESSON XXXIV.

(1.) $\$\frac{2}{3}$. (2.) $\$1\frac{1}{3}$. (3.) $\$5\frac{1}{3}$. (4.) $\$4\frac{1}{2}$. (5.) $1\frac{3}{5}$¢. (6.) $4\frac{2}{3}$¢. (7.) $14\frac{2}{5}$¢. (8.) $22\frac{1}{2}$¢. (9.) $6\frac{3}{4}$. (10.) $4\frac{4}{5}$; $5\frac{3}{5}$; $6\frac{2}{5}$; $7\frac{1}{5}$; $8\frac{4}{5}$. (11.) $4\frac{1}{6}$; $5\frac{5}{6}$; $8\frac{1}{3}$; $9\frac{1}{6}$; 10. (12.) $6\frac{6}{7}$; $7\frac{5}{7}$; $8\frac{4}{7}$, $9\frac{3}{7}$, $10\frac{2}{7}$. (13.) $4\frac{3}{8}$; $6\frac{1}{8}$; $7\frac{7}{8}$; $9\frac{5}{8}$; $10\frac{1}{2}$. (14.) $5\frac{1}{3}$; $6\frac{2}{9}$; $7\frac{1}{9}$; $8\frac{8}{9}$; $10\frac{2}{3}$. (15.) $5\frac{2}{5}$; $7\frac{1}{5}$; $8\frac{1}{10}$; $9\frac{9}{10}$, $10\frac{4}{5}$. (16.) $2\frac{8}{11}$; $4\frac{6}{11}$; $7\frac{3}{11}$; $8\frac{2}{11}$; $10\frac{10}{11}$. (17.) $6\frac{5}{12}$; $7\frac{1}{3}$; $8\frac{1}{4}$; $9\frac{1}{6}$; $10\frac{1}{12}$. (18.) $6\frac{2}{5}$ days. (19.) $14\frac{6}{11}$ days. (20.) $4\frac{3}{8}$ days. (21.) $3\frac{3}{7}$ days. (22.) $8\frac{4}{5}$ hours. (23.) $50\frac{7}{8}$¢. (24.) $11\frac{1}{3}$ minutes. (25.) $25\frac{1}{5}$ bushels. (26.) $7\frac{6}{7}$ bushels. (27.) $\$14\frac{2}{5}$. (28.) $5\frac{1}{7}$ feet in the earth; $12\frac{6}{7}$ feet in the air. (29.) A got $\$3\frac{1}{3}$; B got \$5; C got $\$6\frac{2}{3}$. (30.) 8¢. (31.) $\$7\frac{1}{5}$. (32.) \$35.

LESSON XXXV.

(1.) 3 oranges. (2.) $7\frac{1}{2}$. (3.) $\$2\frac{2}{3}$. (4.) 4; $5\frac{1}{3}$. (5.) 10; 18. (6.) $13\frac{1}{3}$; 22. (7.) $26\frac{2}{3}$; 42. (8.) $\$3\frac{3}{4}$; \$5. (9.) $6\frac{1}{4}$; $7\frac{1}{2}$. (10.) $3\frac{1}{2}$; $6\frac{3}{4}$. (11.) 13; $18\frac{3}{4}$. (12.) $19\frac{1}{2}$; 30. (13.) $15\frac{3}{4}$; $24\frac{3}{4}$. (14.) $17\frac{1}{2}$; $32\frac{1}{2}$. (15.) 45. (16.) $9\frac{3}{5}$ barrels. (17.) $13\frac{3}{5}$; 18. (18.) $13\frac{1}{5}$; $8\frac{2}{5}$. (19.) $25\frac{1}{5}$; $22\frac{4}{5}$. (20.) $30\frac{4}{5}$; $27\frac{1}{5}$. (21.) $16\frac{1}{5}$; $28\frac{4}{5}$. (22.) $13\frac{1}{2}$. (23.) 19. (24.) 22. (25.) $25\frac{1}{3}$. (26.) $32\frac{1}{2}$. (27.) 40. (28.) $47\frac{5}{6}$. (29.) $29\frac{5}{7}$. (30.) $37\frac{6}{7}$. (31.) $47\frac{1}{7}$. (32.) $33\frac{1}{2}$. (33.) $42\frac{1}{2}$. (34.) $53\frac{1}{4}$. (35.) $28\frac{2}{3}$. (36.) $48\frac{1}{3}$. (37.) $69\frac{2}{9}$. (38.) $20\frac{3}{5}$. (39.) 53. (40.) $64\frac{4}{5}$. (41.) $96\frac{3}{10}$. (42.) $98\frac{8}{9}$. (43.) $141\frac{9}{11}$. (44.) $57\frac{3}{4}$. (45.) $53\frac{1}{5}$. (46.) 54. (47.) $119\frac{1}{6}$. (48.) $128\frac{8}{9}$.

LESSON XXXVI.

(1.) 4 barrels. (2.) $5\frac{3}{5}$ boxes. (3.) $6\frac{1}{2}$ reams. (4.) $4\frac{2}{3}$. (5.) $6\frac{1}{3}$; $3\frac{4}{5}$; $3\frac{1}{6}$; $2\frac{3}{8}$; $2\frac{1}{9}$; $1\frac{9}{10}$. (6.) $10\frac{1}{4}$; $8\frac{1}{5}$; $5\frac{6}{7}$; $5\frac{1}{8}$; $4\frac{5}{9}$; $4\frac{1}{10}$. (7.) $6\frac{3}{4}$; $4\frac{1}{2}$; $3\frac{3}{8}$; 3; $2\frac{7}{10}$. (8.) 13; $10\frac{5}{6}$; $9\frac{2}{7}$; $7\frac{2}{9}$; $6\frac{1}{2}$. (9.) $8\frac{4}{5}$; $5\frac{1}{2}$; $4\frac{8}{9}$; $4\frac{2}{5}$. (10.) 9; $7\frac{5}{7}$; $6\frac{3}{4}$; 6; $5\frac{2}{5}$. (11.) $11\frac{1}{16}$; $9\frac{4}{7}$; $7\frac{4}{9}$; $6\frac{7}{10}$; $6\frac{1}{11}$. (12.) $10\frac{3}{5}$; $8\frac{5}{6}$; $6\frac{5}{8}$; $5\frac{8}{9}$; $5\frac{3}{10}$. (13.) $4\frac{5}{6}$; $4\frac{1}{7}$; $3\frac{5}{8}$; $3\frac{2}{9}$; $2\frac{9}{10}$ (14.) $11\frac{2}{5}$; $8\frac{1}{7}$; $7\frac{1}{8}$; $5\frac{7}{10}$; $5\frac{2}{11}$. (15.) $10\frac{2}{5}$; $8\frac{2}{3}$; $5\frac{7}{9}$; $5\frac{1}{5}$; $4\frac{1}{3}$. (16.) 2 hundred-weights. (17.) 2 dozen.

(18.) 2 chickens. (19.) 5 dozen. (20.) $10\frac{2}{7}$ pounds. (21.) $5\frac{1}{2}$ barrels. (22.) $6\frac{1}{3}$ pounds. (23.) 10 dozen.

LESSON XXXVII.

(1.) $\frac{1}{4}$ orange. (2.) $\frac{1}{6}$ apple. (3.) $\frac{1}{8}$. (4.) $\frac{1}{9}$. (5.) $\frac{1}{10}$. (6.) $\frac{1}{12}$. (7.) $\frac{1}{14}$. (8.) $\frac{1}{15}$; $\frac{1}{16}$; $\frac{1}{18}$; $\frac{1}{20}$; $\frac{1}{21}$. (9.) $\frac{1}{24}$; $\frac{1}{24}$; $\frac{1}{25}$; $\frac{1}{27}$; $\frac{1}{28}$; $\frac{1}{30}$. (10.) $\frac{1}{32}$; $\frac{1}{35}$; $\frac{1}{36}$; $\frac{1}{49}$; $\frac{1}{64}$; $\frac{1}{81}$. (11.) $\frac{3}{8}$. (12.) $\frac{3}{10}$. (13.) $\frac{2}{15}$. (14.) $\frac{5}{18}$; $\frac{3}{16}$; $\frac{1}{6}$; $\frac{1}{8}$. (15.) $\frac{2}{21}$; $\frac{5}{56}$; $\frac{5}{63}$; $\frac{4}{35}$. (16.) $\frac{1}{18}$; $\frac{5}{81}$; $\frac{7}{90}$; $\frac{8}{99}$. (17.) $\frac{8}{15}$. (18.) $\frac{1}{2}$. (19.) $\frac{2}{5}$; $\frac{9}{10}$; $\frac{5}{9}$; $\frac{7}{14}$. (20.) $\frac{9}{40}$; $\frac{9}{35}$; $\frac{10}{21}$; $\frac{7}{15}$. (21.) $\frac{8}{15}$; $\frac{10}{77}$; $\frac{15}{56}$; $\frac{20}{63}$. (22.) $\frac{5}{4}$ or $1\frac{1}{4}$; $\frac{9}{15}$; $\frac{21}{20}$ or $1\frac{1}{20}$; $\frac{7}{6}$ or $1\frac{1}{6}$. (23.) $\frac{63}{40}$ or $1\frac{23}{40}$; $\frac{88}{21}$ or $4\frac{4}{21}$; $\frac{55}{72}$; $\frac{72}{55}$ or $1\frac{17}{55}$. (24.) $\frac{5}{8}$. (25.) $\frac{12}{35}$. (26.) $\frac{7}{45}$. (27.) $\frac{16}{33}$. (28.) $\frac{10}{21}$.

LESSON XXXVIII.

(1.) $1\frac{1}{4}$ bushels. (2.) $\frac{5}{6}$; $\frac{5}{8}$; $\frac{7}{12}$; $\frac{11}{20}$; $\frac{13}{20}$. (3.) $\frac{7}{6}$ or $1\frac{1}{6}$; $\frac{31}{42}$; 1; $\frac{5}{4}$ or $1\frac{1}{4}$; $\frac{8}{21}$. (4.) $\frac{26}{15}$ or $1\frac{11}{15}$; $\frac{48}{35}$ or $1\frac{13}{35}$; $\frac{35}{16}$ or $2\frac{3}{16}$; $\frac{51}{64}$; $\frac{41}{21}$ or $1\frac{20}{21}$. (5.) $2. (6.) $3\frac{2}{3}$ (7.) $2\frac{1}{4}$. (8.) $3\frac{32}{49}$. (9.) $2\frac{3}{16}$. (10.) $2\frac{2}{5}$; $3\frac{1}{5}$. (11.) $\frac{1}{2}$. (12.) $\frac{7}{5}$. (13.) $6\frac{2}{9}$; $7\frac{7}{8}$. (14.) $5\frac{5}{21}$ days. (15.) 9 days.

LESSON XXXIX.

(1.) $40. (2.) 6 marbles. (3.) $25. (4.) 16 marbles. (5.) $35. (6.) $32. (7.) $35. (8.) $21. (9.) $27. (10.) $50; $30. (11.) 35¢. (12.) 42 trees. (13.) 30 feet. (14.) 30 feet. (15.) $17\frac{1}{2}$ feet. (16.) 35 feet. (17.) $6. (18.) $10. (19.) 10 barrels. (20.) $6\frac{3}{4}$ barrels. (21.) $2\frac{1}{2}$ yards. (22.) $2\frac{2}{7}$ yards. (23.) $1\frac{1}{5}$. (24.) 6 lemons. (25.) 6 oranges. (26.) 8 barrels. (27.) 2 barrels. (28.) 20 yards.

LESSON XL.

(1.) $4\frac{1}{5}$. (2.) $5\frac{1}{3}$. (3.) $6\frac{2}{9}$. (4.) $7\frac{7}{8}$. (5.) $11\frac{4}{7}$. (6.) $3\frac{3}{5}$. (7.) $6\frac{3}{7}$. (8.) 12. (9.) $8\frac{3}{4}$. (10.) $10\frac{4}{5}$. (11.) 3. (12.) $3\frac{1}{3}$ bushels. (13.) $3\frac{1}{3}$ apples. (14.) 2. (15.) $5\frac{1}{4}$. (16.) 8. (17.) $6\frac{3}{10}$. (18.) $5\frac{1}{7}$. (19.) $6\frac{7}{8}$. (20.) $3\frac{1}{3}$. (21.) $2\frac{2}{3}$. (22.) $8\frac{1}{10}$. (23.) $6\frac{2}{3}$. (24.) $4\frac{16}{21}$. (25.) $9\frac{5}{8}$. (26.) $6\frac{3}{7}$. (27.) $8\frac{3}{4}$. (28.) $9\frac{3}{5}$. (29.) $6\frac{3}{4}$. (30.) $5\frac{5}{8}$. (31.) $5\frac{2}{5}$. (32.) $5\frac{9}{11}$.

LESSON XLI.

(1.) $\frac{2}{3}$ yards. (2.) $\frac{3}{4}$ yards. (3.) $\frac{2}{5}$ yards. (4.) $\frac{3}{5}$ bushel. (5.) $1\frac{1}{8}$ yards.

(6.) $1\frac{2}{3}$ pounds. (7.) $\frac{5}{6}$ pounds. (8.) $1\frac{7}{8}$ yards; $2\frac{1}{12}$ yards; $2\frac{1}{2}$ yards. (9.) $1\frac{1}{15}$ bushels; $\frac{4}{3}$ bushels. (10.) $\frac{4}{5}$. (11.) $\frac{5}{6}$; $\frac{2}{3}$; $\frac{1}{2}$. (12.) $\frac{6}{7}$; $\frac{5}{7}$; $\frac{4}{7}$. (13.) $\frac{7}{8}$; $\frac{3}{4}$; $1\frac{1}{8}$. (14.) $1\frac{1}{5}$. (15.) $1\frac{1}{15}$. (16.) $1\frac{1}{24}$; $1\frac{1}{9}$; $1\frac{1}{4}$. (17.) $1\frac{1}{35}$; $1\frac{1}{14}$; $1\frac{1}{7}$. (18.) $1\frac{1}{48}$; $1\frac{1}{20}$; $1\frac{3}{32}$. (19.) $1\frac{1}{6}$. (20.) $1\frac{1}{63}$; $1\frac{1}{27}$; $1\frac{1}{15}$. (21.) $1\frac{1}{80}$; $1\frac{1}{35}$; $1\frac{1}{20}$. (22.) $1\frac{1}{99}$; $1\frac{1}{44}$; $1\frac{3}{77}$. (23.) $1\frac{1}{120}$; $1\frac{1}{54}$; $1\frac{1}{32}$. (24.) $1\frac{4}{5}$; $1\frac{5}{9}$; $1\frac{3}{7}$. (25.) $2\frac{2}{15}$; $1\frac{31}{32}$; $2\frac{1}{4}$. (26.) $1\frac{2}{9}$; $1\frac{8}{25}$; $1\frac{19}{77}$. (27.) $1\frac{2}{3}$; 2; $1\frac{11}{25}$. (28.) $1\frac{1}{11}$; $2\frac{7}{9}$; $4\frac{2}{5}$.

LESSON XLII.

(1.) $1\frac{5}{7}$ acres. (2.) $\frac{2}{5}$. (3.) $\frac{3}{5}$. (4.) $\frac{3}{4}$. (5.) $\frac{7}{4}$ or $1\frac{3}{4}$; $\frac{3}{4}$. (6.) $\frac{3}{7}$; $\frac{5}{7}$. (7.) 4¢. (8.) \$3. (9.) 7 miles. (10.) \$15. (11.) \$20; \$5. (12.) \$$4\frac{1}{2}$. (13.) \$$3\frac{3}{4}$. (14.) \$$1\frac{7}{8}$. (15.) $2\frac{2}{5}$. (16.) $4\frac{2}{3}$. (17.) $2\frac{1}{4}$.

LESSON XLIII.

(1.) $7\frac{2}{7}$. (2.) 3 bushels. (3.) 4 persons. (4.) 15 yards. (5.) $4\frac{1}{3}$ yards. (6.) 5 apples; 7 apples. (7.) $6\frac{1}{2}$ yards. (8.) $\frac{1}{2}$ times; $\frac{8}{15}$ times; $1\frac{5}{6}$ times. (9.) $\frac{10}{27}$ times; $\frac{20}{63}$ times; $1\frac{13}{18}$ times. (10.) $\frac{15}{128}$ times; $\frac{15}{112}$ times; $1\frac{3}{4}$ times. (11.) $10\frac{2}{3}$; $26\frac{2}{3}$. (12.) $23\frac{1}{4}$; $54\frac{1}{4}$. (13.) $15\frac{7}{15}$; $11\frac{3}{5}$. (14.) $11\frac{2}{3}$; $5\frac{3}{5}$. (15.) $4\frac{8}{9}$; $6\frac{1}{9}$. (16.) 23 times; 31 times; 28 times. (17.) 4 times; $7\frac{2}{3}$ times; $10\frac{1}{3}$ times. (18.) $7\frac{14}{15}$ times; $10\frac{8}{9}$ times; $18\frac{1}{12}$ times. (19.) $7\frac{3}{5}$ times; $8\frac{24}{25}$ times; $13\frac{5}{7}$ times. (20.) $3\frac{9}{20}$ times; $10\frac{5}{22}$ times; $14\frac{1}{8}$ times; 16 times. (21.) 6 gallons; $10\frac{1}{2}$ gallons. (22.) 6 bushels; 11 bushels.

LESSON XLIV.

(1.) \$18. (2.) \$2. (3.) \$$3\frac{1}{3}$. (4.) \$1.04. (5.) \$4; \$$\frac{1}{5}$. (6.) \$$2\frac{7}{10}$. (7.) \$$11\frac{7}{10}$; \$$\frac{3}{20}$. (8.) \$25. (9.) \$$9\frac{3}{8}$; \$$\frac{3}{16}$. (10.) \$$\frac{1}{4}$. (11.) \$$\frac{1}{15}$. (12.) \$$\frac{1}{10}$; \$3. (13.) \$$7\frac{1}{2}$. (14.) \$2. (15.) \$2. (16.) \$9. (17.) \$10. (18.) \$5. (19.) \$18. (20.) \$25. (21.) 36 pounds. (22.) 10 dozen. (23.) 12 yards. (24.) 12 yards. (25.) 400. (26.) 900; 2500; 5100. (27.) 3600; 900; 1700. (28.) 2600; 5600; 6000. (29.) 12. (30.) 12; 28; 10. (31.) $9\frac{1}{3}$; 12; 12.

LESSON XLV.

(1.) 34¢. (2.) \$43. (3.) 8¢. (4.) \$8. (5.) \$64. (6.) 35¢. (7.) \$19. (8.) \$26. (9.) 9¢. (10.) \$24. (11.) \$13. (12.) \$78. (13.) \$42; \$30.

(14.) $16; $36. (15.) $49. (16.) $56. (17.) 12¢. (18.) 9 apples.
(19.) 54¢. (20.) $49. (21.) 48¢; 64¢; 80¢. (22.) 21 miles. (23.) 18
rows. (24.) $63. (25.) 20 bushels. (26.) 7 weeks. (27.) 10 apples.
(28.) 8 horses.

LESSON XLVI.

(1.) $20; $36. (2.) 64; 81. (3.) 8 oranges. (4.) 16 times. (5.) 8
chestnuts. (6.) $6\frac{3}{4}$ times. (7.) 77; 82. (8.) $\frac{2}{5}$; $\frac{2}{7}$; $\frac{5}{6}$. (9.) $\frac{48}{144}$; $\frac{36}{144}$;
$\frac{34}{144}$. (10.) $50\frac{1}{8}$ acres. (11.) $3\frac{17}{24}$. (12.) $\frac{5}{12}$; 35 miles. (13.) $3\frac{1}{2}$.
(14.) $7\frac{5}{11}$. (15.) $26\frac{1}{4}$. (16.) 54. (17.) $3\frac{33}{49}$. (18.) 14 quarts.
(19.) $2\frac{1}{2}$. (20.) $1\frac{19}{20}$. (21.) $72. (22.) 10 barrels. (23.) 8 times.
(24.) 9. (25.) 64. (26.) 4. (27.) $4. (28.) 24 apples. (29.) $10\frac{11}{15}$.
(30.) $6\frac{3}{10}$. (31.) $3\frac{3}{4}$. (32.) $23\frac{1}{4}$ yards. (33.) $1\frac{1}{2}$. (34.) $\frac{2}{3}$.
(35.) 20 lemons. (36.) 2 yards. (37.) father—50 years; son—5 years.
(38.) 45 bushels. (39.) $3\frac{1}{3}$. (40.) $8\frac{4}{5}$. (41.) 24. (42.) 12. (43.) 2.
(44.) 18. (45.) 40. (46.) 10. (47.) 12¢. (48.) 6¢. (49.) 1 pear.
(50.) $4. (51.) 10 peaches. (52.) 10 chestnuts. (53.) $6. (54.) $3\frac{1}{3}$
quarts. (55.) 3¢. (56.) $12; $4. (57.) $\frac{1}{4}$. (58.) $\frac{1}{9}$. (59.) $\frac{5}{16}$. (60.) $\frac{1}{3}$.
(61.) $20. (62.) 32 yards. (63.) 12 days. (64.) $48. (65.) 14 days.
(66.) 20 days. (67.) $7\frac{1}{2}$ days. (68.) 4 apples. (69.) 26. (70.) 5. (71.)
5. (72.) $10\frac{1}{6}$. (73.) 6. (74.) 4¢. (75.) 15 marbles to Thomas; 6
marbles. (76.) $5. (77.) $54. (78.) $28. (79.) $1. (80.) 8 days.
(81.) 30 seconds; hound—300 ft.; hare—210 ft. (82.) 20 rods.
(83.) 5 hours; 25 miles. (84.) 8 hours. (85.) 12 hours. (86.) $32.
(87.) 10¢. (88.) $3\frac{3}{4}$. (89.) $\frac{2}{3}$. (90.) $1\frac{1}{11}$ days. (91.) $15; $\frac{3}{7}$.
(92.) 8 bushels. (93.) 24 hours.

LESSON XLVII.

(1.) 20 mills. (2.) 30 mills; 40 mills; 50 mills; 60 mills; 70 mills;
80 mills; 90 mills. (3.) 20 cents; 30 cents; 40 cents; 50 cents; 60
cents; 70 cents; 80 cents; 90 cents. (4.) 20 dimes; 30 dimes; 40 dimes;
50 dimes; 60 dimes; 70 dimes; 80 dimes; 90 dimes. (5.) $20; $30;
$40; $50; $60; $70; $80; $90. (6.) 200 ¢. (7.) 300¢; 400¢; 500¢; 600¢;
700¢; 800¢; 900¢. (8.) 2 dimes. (9.) 3 dimes; 4 dimes; 5 dimes; 6
dimes; 7 dimes; 8 dimes; 9 dimes. (10.) $2; $3; $4; $5; $6; $7; $8;
$9. (11.) $2. (12.) $3; $4; $5; $6; $7; $8; $9.

LESSON XLVIII.

(1.) 4 pints; 6 pints; 8 pints; 10 pints; 12 pints; 14 pints. (2.) 16 quarts; 24 quarts. (3.) 8 pecks; 12 pecks; 16 pecks; 20 pecks; 24 pecks; 28 pecks; 32 pecks; 36 pecks; 40 pecks; 44 pecks; 48 pecks. (4.) 2 quarts; 3 quarts; 4 quarts; 5 quarts; 6 quarts; 7 quarts. (5.) 2 pecks; 3 pecks. (6.) 2 bushels; 3 bushels; 4 bushels; 5 bushels; 6 bushels; 7 bushels. (7.) 7 pints. (8.) 29 quarts. (9.) 14 pecks. (10.) 39 pints. (11.) 95 quarts. (12.) 101 pints. (13.) 3 quarts 1 pint. (14.) 4 qt. 1 pt.; 5 qt. 1 pt.; 6 qt. 1 pt.; 7 qt. 1 pt. (15.) 1 pk. 2 qt.; 1 pk. 3 qt.; 1 pk. 4 qt.; 1 pk. 5 qt.; 2 pk. 1 qt.; 2 pk. 3 qt.; 2 pk. 7 qt.; 3 pk. 3 qt. (16.) 1 bu. 3 pk.; 2 bu. 2 pk.; 3 bu. 1 pk.; 3 bu. 3 pk.; 4 bu. 1 pk.; 5 bu. 3 pk. (17.) 1 pk. 5 qt. 1 pt. (18.) 2 pk. 1 qt. 1 pt.; 2 pk. 3 qt. 1 pt.; 2 pk. 5 qt. 1 pt.; 2 pk. 6 qt. 1 pt. (19.) 1 bu. 2 pk. 5 qt.; 1 bu. 2 pk. 7 qt.; 1 bu. 3 pk. 1 qt.; 1 bu. 3 pk. 3 qt. (20.) 2 bu. 2 pk. 3 qt.; 2 bu. 2 pk. 6 qt.; 2 bu. 3 pk. 1 qt.; 2 bu. 3 pk. 4 qt. (21.) 3 bu. 1 pk. 7 qt. 1 pt.; 3 bu. 2 pk.; 3 bu. 2 pk. 1 qt.; 3 bu. 2 pk. 2 qt. (22.) 5 bu. 1 pk. 4 qt. 1 pt.; 5 bu. 1 pk. 5 qt.; 5 bu. 1 pk. 5 qt. 1 pt.; 5 bu. 1 pk. 6 qt. (23.) 194 quarts. (24.) 129 pints. (25.) 288 pints. (26.) 207 pints. (27.) 369 pints. (28.) 510 pints.

LESSON XLIX.

(1.) 4 pints; 6 pints. (2.) 8 qt.; 12 qt.; 16 qt.; 20 qt.; 24 qt.; 28 qt.; 32 qt.; 36 qt.; 40 qt.; 44 qt.; 48 qt. (3.) 1 pt. 1 gi.; 1 pt. 2 gi.; 1 pt. 3 gi. (4.) 1 qt. 1 pt.; 2 qt.; 2 qt, 1 pt.; 3 qt.; 3 qt. 1 pt. (5.) 1 gal. 1 qt.; 1 gal. 2 qt.; 1 gal. 3 qt.; 2 gal.; 2 gal. 1 qt.; 2 gal. 2 qt.; 2 gal. 3 qt.; 3 gal. (6.) 8 gi.; 16 gi.; 24 gi. (7.) 8 pt.; 16 pt.; 24 pt.; 32 pt.; 40 pt. (8.) 32 gi.; 64 gi.; 96 gi.; 128 gi.; 160 gi. (9.) 7 gi. (10.) 7 pt. (11.) 22 qt. (12.) 21 gi. (13.) 39 pt. (14.) 47 gi. (15.) 1 qt. 1 pt. 1 gi. (16.) 2 gal. 3 qt. 1 pt. (17.) 2 gal. 1 qt. 1 pt. 3 gi. (18.) 3 gal. 1 gi.; 3 gal. 2 gi.; 3 gal. 1 pt.; 3 gal. 1 pt. 2 gi. (19.) 5 gal. 3 qt. 3 gi.; 5 gal. 3 qt. 1 pt.; 5 gal. 3 qt. 1 pt. 2 gi.; 5 gal. 4 qt. (20.) 200 gi. (21.) 259 gi. (22.) 440 gi.

LESSON L.

(1.) 32 dr.; 48 dr.; 64 dr.; 80 dr.; 96 dr. (2.) 32 oz.; 48 oz.; 64 oz.;

80 oz.; 96 oz.; 160 oz. (3.) 200 lb.; 300 lb.; 400 lb.; 500 lb.; 600 lb.; 700 lb.; 800 lb.; 900 lb. (4.) 40 cwt.; 60 cwt.; 80 cwt.; 100 cwt.; 120 cwt. (5.) 1 oz. 4 dr.; 1 oz. 11 dr.; 2 oz. 3 dr. (6.) 2 lb. 10 oz.; 3 lb. 5 oz.; 4 lb. 11 oz.; 5 lb. 10 oz. (7.) 3 cwt.; 4 cwt. 50 lb.; 5 cwt. 75 lb.; 12 cwt. (8.) 2 T.; 2 T. 10 cwt.; 3 T. 15 cwt.; 4 T.; 4 T. 16 cwt. (9.) 8 oz. (10.) 4 oz.; 12 oz. (11.) 50 lb.; 25 lb.; 75 lb.; 20 lb.; 40 lb.; 60 lb.; 80 lb. (12.) 75 dr. (13.) 2731 dr. (14.) 1545 lb. (15.) 9075 lb. (16.) $\frac{3}{4}$ lb. (17.) $\frac{1}{2}$ lb.; $\frac{5}{8}$ lb.; $\frac{7}{8}$ lb. (18.) $\frac{1}{10}$; $\frac{1}{5}$; $\frac{1}{4}$; $\frac{2}{5}$; $\frac{1}{2}$; $\frac{3}{5}$; $\frac{3}{4}$; $\frac{4}{5}$. (19.) $\frac{1}{5}$; $\frac{1}{4}$; $\frac{3}{10}$; $\frac{2}{5}$; $\frac{1}{2}$; $\frac{3}{5}$; $\frac{3}{4}$; $\frac{4}{5}$; $\frac{9}{10}$.

LESSON LI.

(1.) 24 in. (2.) 6 ft.; 9 ft.; 12 ft.; 15 ft. (3.) 11 yd.; 22 yd.; $27\frac{1}{2}$ yd.; 38 $\frac{1}{2}$ yd.; 55 yd. (4.) 120 rods; 160 rods; 200 rods; 240 rods; 280 rods; 360 rods. (5.) 72 fur. (6.) 3 ft.; 4 ft. (7.) 5 yd.; 7 yd. (8.) 4 rods; 6 rods. (9.) 2 mi. (10.) 2 ft. 6 in. (11.) 8 in.; 9 in. (12.) 2 ft.; 2 ft. 3 in. (13.) 3 yd.; 2 yd. 2 ft. 3 in.; 3 yd. 2 ft.; 2 yd. $7\frac{1}{5}$ in. (14.) 2 fur.; 2 fur. 26 rd. 3 yd. 2 ft.; 5 fur. 13 rd. 1 yd. 2 ft. 6 in.; 6 fur.; 3 fur. 8 rd. (15.) $\frac{1}{20}$ mi. (16.) $\frac{3}{40}$ mi. (17.) $\frac{6}{11}$ rd. (18.) $\frac{2}{3}$ yd.; $\frac{4}{33}$ rd. (19.) $\frac{1}{2}$ ft.; $\frac{1}{6}$ yd.; $\frac{1}{33}$ rd.

LESSON LII.

(1.) 30 sec.; 20 sec.; 40 sec.; 45 sec. (2.) 12 min.; 24 min.; 36 min .; 48 min.; 10 min.; 50 min.; 8 min. $34\frac{2}{7}$ sec. (3.) 12 hr.; 16 hr.; 20 hr.; 6 hr. 51 min. $25\frac{5}{7}$ sec.; 9 hr.; 16 hr. 48 min. (4.) 3 da.; 5 da. (5.) 2 wk.; 3 wk.; 1 wk. 1 da.; 3 wk. 3 day.; 2 wk. 4 da; 3 wk. 5 da. (6.) $\frac{1}{3}$ min. (7.) $\frac{5}{6}$ hr. (8.) $\frac{1}{2}$ da.; $\frac{1}{14}$ wk. (9.) $\frac{5}{7}$ wk. (10.) $\frac{2}{3}$ yr. (11.) $\frac{7}{48}$ da. (12.) $\frac{1}{2}$ wk. (13.) $\frac{5}{14}$ mon. (14.) $\frac{8}{21}$ mon. (15.) 61 da. (16.) 92 da. (17.) 91 da. (18.) 16 da. (19.) 59 da. (20.) 186 da. (21.) 183 da.

LESSON LIII.

(1.) \$3.45. (2.) \$1.85. (3.) $77\frac{1}{2}$¢. (4.) \$66. (5.) 85 mi. (6.) 2 gal. 3 qt. 1 pt. ($2\frac{7}{8}$ gal.) (7.) 16 lb. $10\frac{2}{3}$ oz. ($16\frac{2}{3}$ lb.) (8.) $7\frac{3}{5}$ hr. (9.) $7\frac{3}{4}$ ft. (2 yd. $1\frac{3}{4}$ ft.) (10.) $\frac{3}{4}$ pk. (11.) 95¢. (12.) 23 yd. 1 ft. (4 rd. 1 yd. 1 ft.) (13.) \$$2\frac{1}{4}$ (\$2.25) (14.) 25 mph. (15.) 3 rev. (16.) 13 wk. (17.) 5 lb. 14 oz. (18.) \$18. (19.) 60¢. (20.) \$22.50; 15¢. (21.) \$$90\frac{10}{11}$.

LESSON LIV.

(1.) 165 gal. (2.) $50. (3.) $185. (4.) $19. (5.) $35. (6.) 3¢ (7.) $2. (8.) $12.50. (9.) 140 miles. (10.)$2.82. (11.) 66¢. (12.) 600 yd. (13.) 28 mi. (14.) 40 lb. (15.) $11. (16.) $22\frac{1}{5}$ lb. (17.) 100 bu.

LESSON LV.

(1.) $$1\frac{1}{2}$ ($1.50) (2.) $$5\frac{5}{8}$. (3.) $5. (4.) 15¢. (5.) $$13\frac{1}{2}$ ($13.50) (6.) 35 trees. (7.) $25. (8.) $$8\frac{3}{4}$. (9.) 51¢. (10.) 58 mi. (11.) $$1\frac{3}{8}$. (12.) $$12\frac{2}{5}$. (13.) $$5\frac{1}{3}$. (14.) $9\frac{1}{3}$. (15.) $3\frac{3}{4}$. (16.) $$3\frac{3}{5}$. (17.) $$\frac{3}{4}$. (18.) $2\frac{4}{5}$. (19.) $3\frac{3}{8}$. (20.) $5\frac{1}{2}$. (21.) $5\frac{5}{9}$. (22.) $1\frac{3}{5}$. (23.) $\frac{7}{12}$. (24.) $2\frac{2}{15}$. (25.) 11 marbles. (26.) 24 plums. (27.) 8 mi. (28.) $25. (29.) $30. (30.) 14 plums. (31.) 20¢. (32.) A had $28; B had $16. (33.) 32 apples; 24 pears; 8 plums; 32 cherries. (34.) 35 apples; 10 pears.

LESSON LVI.

(1.) 7. (2.) 8. (3.) 4 and 12. (4.) 6 and 42. (5.) 4, 8 and 12. (6.) 5, 15 and 25. (7.) 30. (8.) 5. (9.) 3 and 9. (10.) 12. (11.) 4. (12.) 13. (13.) 6 and 10. (14.) 10 and 15. (15.) 12 and 19. (16.) A has 6¢, B has 9¢. (17.) Thomas has $12, James has $7. (18.) 12¢. (19.) Thomas had 11, William had 9. (20.) Mary had 17, Sarah had 7. (21.) 15. (22.) 28. (23.) 35. (24.) Henry is 10; Oliver is 13; James is 14. (25.) Jane has 10¢; Sarah has 15¢; Mary has 18¢. (26.) Frank is 15; Mary is 27. (27.) chain—$15; ring—$20; watch—$27. (28.) 126¢. (29.) James had $7; John had $17; Frank had $31. (30.) Thomas has $4; Joseph has $10; Paul has $8. (31.) Harness cost $25; horse cost $75; buggy cost $125.

LESSON LVII.

(1.) 6 and 9. (2.) Thomas owes $42; John owes $18. (3.) First day—$32; second day—$24. (4.) 37 and 63. (5.) 20, 10, 15. (6.) A has 20¢; B has $12; C has $8. (7.) 30, 25, 15. (8.) Hat cost $8; coat cost $20; vest cost $6. (9.) A's share was 18¢; B's share was 20¢. (10.) 20 cows; 35 sheep. (11.) 24 and 36. (12.) Sarah is 6; Mary is 8. (13.) 24 and 27. (14.) 30 apple trees; 35 peach trees. (15.) 6 miles. (16.) 36 apple trees; 12 plum trees; 21 cherry trees. (17.) Sarah is 24; Jane is 21. (18.) 9. (19.) Charles has $60; John has $36.

(20.) 48 hogs; 32 sheep; 24 cows. (21.) 4 o'clock. (22.) 4:30. (23.) 2 o'clock. (24.) 3 o'clock. (25.) 4 o'clock. (26.) 1:20.

LESSON LVIII.

(1.) 10. (2.) 12. (3.) 15. (4.) 20. (5.) 28. (6.) 20 (7.) 12. (8.) 24. (9.) 50¢. (10.) 30. (11.) The son is 15; the father is 55. (12.) 15. (13.) 36 yd. (14.) A to B is 15 mi.; C to D is 30 mi. (15.) 30.

LESSON LIX.

(1.) $\frac{1}{2}$. (2.) $\frac{1}{10}$. (3.) 2 times. (4.) $2\frac{2}{3}$ lots. (5.) $\frac{2}{5}$. (6.) $\frac{2}{7}$. (7.) $\frac{3}{5}$. (8.) $\frac{3}{4}$. (9.) $\frac{19}{20}$. (10.) $1\frac{1}{5}$ da. (11.) 4 da. (12.) $2\frac{11}{12}$ da. (13.) 1 da. (14.) 6 da. (15.) 20 da. (16.) 24 da. (17.) $1\frac{1}{5}$ da. (18.) $1\frac{3}{7}$. (19.) 2 da.

LESSON LX.

(1.) $\frac{1}{4}$; $\frac{1}{2}$; $\frac{1}{8}$. (2.) 5; $\frac{1}{5}$. (3.) 6 to 1. (4.) 2; 2 to 1. (5.) 3 to 1; 5 to 1; 6 to 1; 4 to 1; 1 to 2; 3 to 4. (6.) 1 to 2; 1 to 2; 1 to 2; 4 to 5; 5 to 6; 3 to 2. (7.) 30. (8.) 12. (9.) 2. (10.) 2. (11.) $2\frac{1}{2}$. (12.) John gets 10¢; George gets 15¢. (13.) 20. (14.) A gets 8; B gets 12. (15.) John get 12¢; James get 16¢. (16.) 60 apple trees; 36 peach trees. (17.) 14 boys; 21 girls. (18.) 12. (19.) 5 and 20. (20.) 12 and 16. (21.) A pays $20; B pays $25. (22.) First gets 5 doz.; second gets $2\frac{1}{2}$ doz. (23.) A gets $35; B gets $21. (24.) C lost $18; D lost $12.

LESSON LXI.

(1.) 10 and 12. (2.) Henry gets 6 apples; Oliver gets 10 apples. (3.) A gets 6¢; B gets 8¢. (4.) James has 21 marbles; John has 12 marbles. (5.) First got $10; second got $18. (6.) William is 20; Frank is 12. (7.) 21 sound apples; 9 apples which are not sound. (8.) One built 12 feet; the other built 15 feet. (9.) 15, 20 and 25. (10.) 7, 14, 21 and 28. (11.) 18, 12 and 9. (12.) William got 9 peaches; Thomas got 12 peaches; John got 15 peaches. (13.) A lost $45.50; B lost $91; C lost $227.50. (14.) A has $24; B has $12; Charles has $6. (15.) A gets 20¢; B gets 15¢; C gets 10¢. (16.) 6 horses; 18 cows; 36 sheep. (17.) A gets 7 plums; B gets 14 plums; C gets 21 plums. (18.) Emma gets 5 cherries; Agnes gets 10 cherries, Sarah gets 20 cherries.

LESSON LXII.

(1.) 10 men. (2.) 10 men. (3.) 8 da. (4.) 4 1/2 hr. (5.) $48. (6.) $12. (7.) $48. (8.) 4. (9.) 10. (10.) 15; 12. (11.) 6 oz.; 4 4/5 oz. (12.) 12 oz. (13.) 8 oz. (14.) 50 men. (15.) 4 1/6 da. (16.) 5 1/2 da. (17.) $56. (18.) $45. (19.) 7 1/2 rd. (20.) 27 bu. (21.) 10 da. (22.) $880. (23.) 126 sheep.

LESSON LXIII.

(1.) A should pay $15, and B $10. (2.) A should pay $35, and B $25. (3.) A should pay $24, and B $48. (4.) A should pay $14, and B $21. (5.) C should get $18, and D $27. (6.) A should get $36, and B $45. (7.) A should get $25, and B $30. (8.) E should pay $9, and F $18. (9.) M should get $60, and N $90. (10.) C should get $150, and D $100. (11.) E's share $210 and F's $560. (12.) A invested $1300, and B $1100. (13.) C invested $420 and D $560. (14.) A invested $700, and B $1000. (15.) E gained $300, and F $540.

LESSON LXIV.

(1.) 1/50. (2.) 1/25; 1/20; 3/50; 2/25. (3.) 1/10; 3/25; 3/20. (4.) 4/25; 1/5; 6/25. (5.) 1/4; 7/25; 3/10. (6.) 8/25; 7/20; 9/25. (7.) 2/5; 9/20; 12/25. (8.) 1/2; 3/5; 7/10. (9.) 3/4; 4/5; 9/10. (10.) 1/40. (11.) 7/200; 1/16. (12.) 1/15; 3/40. (13.) 1/12; 1/8. (14.) 2/15; 1/6. (15.) 7/40; 3/16. (16.) 7/30; 5/16. (17.) 3/8; 7/16. (18.) 9/16; 5/8. (19.) 2/3. (20.) 7/8.

LESSON LXV.

(1.) 2. (2.) 3; 6. (3.) 2; 3. (4.) 3; 6. (5.) $8; $20. (6.) 17 bu. (7.) 7 horses. (8.) $2. (9.) $1. (10.) 38 sheep. (11.) 55 sheep. (12.) $3.80. (13.) 33¢. (14.) 9¢; 18¢. (15.) 6 1/2¢; 19 1/2¢. (16.) 15¢; 20¢; 25¢; 43 3/4¢.

LESSON LXVI.

(1.) 50%. (2.) 33 1/3%; 66 2/3%; 25%. (3.) 75%; 20%; 40%. (4.) 60%; 80%; 16 2/3%. (5.) 12 1/2%; 37 1/2%; 62 1/2%. (6.) 10%; 30%; 70%. (7.) 90%; 8 1/3%; 41 2/3%. (8.) 6 2/3%; 6 1/4%; 18 3/4%. (9.) 31 1/4%; 5%; 15%. (10.) 35%; 45%; 55%. (11.) 4%; 8%; 12%. (12.) 16%; 24%; 28%. (13.) 32%; 36%; 44%. (14.) 23 1/3%; 5 5/7%; 22 1/2%. (15.) 27 1/2%; 13 1/3%; 10 5/12%. (16.) 2%; 6%; 14%. (17.) 18%; 1 2/3%; 1 1/3%.

(18.) 62½%; 75%; 87½%. (19.) 56¼%; 68¾%; 81¼%. (20.) 16⅔%; 50%; 83⅓%. (21.) 41⅔%; 58⅓%; 68¾%. (22.) 91⅔%; 93¾%; 15%.

LESSON LXVII.

(1.) 40%. (2.) 60%; 25%. (3.) 50%; 12½%. (4.) 25%; 16⅔%. (5.) 5%. (6.) 25%. (7.) 33⅓%. (8.) 66⅔%. (9.) 20%. (10.) 40% (11.) 25%. (12.) 20%. (13.) 50%. (14.) 60%. (15.) 30%. (16.) 60%. (17.) 60%. (18.) 16⅔%; 25%. (19.) 55⅑%.

LESSON LXVIII.

(1.) $10. (2.) $20. (3.) 10¢. (4.) $72. (5.) $70. (6.) $12. (7.) 3¢. (8.) $8; $4 (or 50%). (9.) 25%. (10.) 50%. (11.) $1.50. (12.) $2. (13.) $4. (14.) 60%. (15.) 16⅔%. (16.) 20%. (17.) 140. (18.) 12. (19.) 3¹¹⁄₂₀. (20.) 8.

LESSON LXIX.

(1.) $2⅖. (2.) $100. (3.) $700. (4.) $380. (5.) $950. (6.) $6. (7.) $1080. (8.) $175. (9.) $480. (10.) $55.10.

LESSON LXX.

(1.) $100. (2.) $28. (3.) $12.50. (4.) $75; $1425. (5.) $980. (6.) $2000. (7.) $600. (8.) 19 shares.

LESSON LXXI.

(1.) $10. (2.) $30. (3.) $17.50. (4.) $30. (5.) $17. (6.) $37.50.

LESSON LXXII.

(1.) 30¢. (2.) 60¢. (3.) $2. (4.) $4.80. (5.) $6. (6.) $8. (7.) $9. (8.) $8.40. (9.) $9. (10.) $36.

LESSON LXXIII.

(1.) $1.50. (2.) $1. (3.) $2.80. (4.) $2.40. (5.) $4.50. (6.) $3.90. (7.) $6.20. (8.) $3.53. (9.) $4.80. (10.) $19.20. (11.) $8.45. (12.) $4.24. (13.) $3.20. (14.) $6.75. (15.) $3.80. (16.) $28. (17.) $44. (18.) $68.20. (19.) $32.80. (20.) $56.80. (21.) $99.12.

LESSON LXXIV.

(1.) $25. (2.) $50. (3.) $60. (4.) $75. (5.) $140. (6.) $240. (7.) $350. (8.) $4000.

LESSON LXXV.

(1.) $50. (2.) $200. (3.) $500. (4.) $250. (5.) $300. (6.) $25. (7.) $125.

LESSON LXXVI.

(1.) 3 yr. 4 mo. (2.) 4 yr. (3.) 2 yr. 6 mo. (4.) 2 yr. 8 mo. (5.) 3 yr. 5 mo. 4$\frac{2}{7}$ da. (6.) 6 yr. 8 mo. (7.) 25 yr. (8.) 50 yr.; 33$\frac{1}{3}$ yr.; 20 yr.; 16$\frac{2}{3}$ yr.; 14$\frac{2}{7}$ yr.; 12$\frac{1}{2}$ yr.; 10 yr.; 8$\frac{1}{3}$ yr. (9.) 40 yr. (10.) 25 yr.; 20 yr.

LESSON LXXVII.

(1.) 6%. (2.) 8%. (3.) 5%. (4.) 7%. (5.) 8%. (6.) 7%. (7.) 5%. (8.) 6%. (9.) 5%. (10.) 8$\frac{1}{3}$%; 10%; 12$\frac{1}{2}$%; 20%; 25%; 50%.

LESSON LXXVIII.

(1.) Present worth is $60; discount is $12. (2.) Present worth is $400; discount is $120. (3.) Present worth is $25; discount is $5. (4.) Present worth is $500; discount is $250. (5.) The discount is $45. (6.) The discount is $96. (7.) The discount is $4. (8.) The present worth is $50. (9.) The present worth is $44. (10.) The present worth is $55. (11.) The discount is $196.79. (12.) The discount is $162.30.

LESSON LXXIX.

(1.) $\frac{1}{4}$. (2.) $\frac{1}{5}$. (3.) 10%. (4.) 10%. (5.) 6 yr. (6.) 25%. (7.) 40%. (8.) 6%. (9.) $16. (10.) $15.30. (11.) 8 yr. (12.) A has $160; B has $80. (13.) A has $300; B has $200. (14.) A has $177.78 (or 177\frac{7}{9}$; B has $133.33 (or 133\frac{1}{3}$).

LESSON LXXX.

(1.) 105 plums. (2.) Mary gets 13 peaches; James gets 8 peaches; Lucy gets 11 peaches. (3.) 8. (4.) A has $3; B has $6; C has $18.

(5.) James has $16; Thomas has $18. (6.) 72 sheep. (7.) 2½ da.
(8.) 4¢. (9.) A should pay $16; B should pay $36; C should pay
$40. (10.) 8 children. (11.) 10. (12.) 3 children. (13.) 60 leaps.
(14.) 140 steps. (15.) $60. (16.) A had 14¢; B had 10¢. (17.) A is
5; B is 10; C is 30. (18.) A has $90; B has $75. (19.) 10 hrs.
(20.) 25%. (21.) 7 playmates. (22.) 105 steps. (23.) The watch cost
$35; the chain $10. (24.) 6 da. (25.) 80. (26.) 9%. (27.) 10 yd.
(28.) A has $40; B has $11. (29.) $25. (30.) 60 leaps. (31.) Thomas
is 15; James is 5. (32.) John traveled 56 mi.; George traveled 30
mi. (33.) I would make an additional 11¢ per yard (instead of
making 4¢ per yard I would make 15¢ per yard). (34.) 7⅗¢ per
dozen. (35.) A is 20; B is 10. (36.) 73 mi. (37.) A can do the job
in 12 da.; B in 24 da.; C in 8 da. (38.) 30 ducks; 60 chickens.
(39.) 50¢. (40.) 11¼ mi. (41.) $25. (42.) A received $480; B received
$560; C received $640. (43.) The man would consume the meal in
24 da; his wife in 40 da. (44.) 20 lb. (45.) A is 50; B is 10; C is
5. (46.) Mary is 9; Ella is 15. (47.) A can do the job in 24 days;
B in 48 days. (48.) 12¢. (49.) 5 da. (50.) 22 da. (51.) 16 yd.
(52.) 100 steps. (53.) 14 men (assuming a full 7 day week).
(54.) First field contains 10 sheep; second field contains 40 sheep;
third field contains 120 sheep. (55.) 20 da. (56.) A get $12; B gets
$18; C get $24. (57.) 48¢. (58.) $200. (59.) 17 lb. (60.) 9 steps.
(61.) John should get 6¢; James 3¢.

SOLUTIONS

OF THE

MORE DIFFICULT EXAMPLES

IN

RAY'S NEW INTELLECTUAL ARITHMETIC.

LESSON I.

18. All together have the sum of 5 dollars, 3 dollars, and 1 dollar, which is 9 dollars.

25. As many as the sum of 4, 4, and 2, which is 10.

LESSON II.

25. I have the sum of 10 cents, 5 cents, 3 cents, and 3 cents, which is 21 cents.

LESSON V.

37. William's age is the sum of 8 years and 5 years, which is 13 years; and the sum of all their ages is 13 years, plus 5 years, plus 8 years, which is 26 years.

LESSON VI.

24. I received in money as many dollars as the difference between 17 dollars and 6 dollars, which is 11 dollars.

LESSON VIII.

19. I spent the sum of 20 cents and 10 cents, which is 30 cents; I had left the difference between 65 cents and 30 cents, which is 35 cents.

LESSON IX.

8. Both had the sum of 18 marbles and 18 marbles, which is 36 marbles; if when they quit one had 25 marbles, the other had the difference between 36 marbles and 25 marbles, which is 11 marbles.

14. He is worth the sum of 20 dollars and 10 dollars, which is 30 dollars. He owes the sum of 5 dollars, 6 dollars, and 10 dollars, which is 21 dollars. Should he pay his debts, he would be worth the difference between 30 dollars and 21 dollars, which is 9 dollars.

LESSON XI.

4. The sum of 19 and 10 is 29; the difference between 17 and 10 is 7; if I take 7, the difference, from 29, the sum, 22 will be left.

21. There are as many peach-trees in the orchard as the sum of 15 peach-trees, 9 peach-trees, and 10 peach-trees, which is 34 peach-trees. There are as many apple-trees as the sum of 5 apple-trees, 11 apple-trees, and 10 apple-trees, which is 26 apple-trees. Then there are as many more peach-trees than apple-trees as the difference between 34 trees and 26 trees, which is 8 trees.

LESSON XII.

22. If 1 yard of muslin cost 11 cents, 3 yards will cost 3 times 11 cents, which is 33 cents.

LESSON XIV.

11. If a man travel 7 miles in 1 hour, in 8 hours he will travel 8 times 7 miles, which is 56 miles.

17. In one hour they would be as far apart as the sum of 2 miles and 4 miles, which is 6 miles; in 3 hours they would be 3 times 6 miles apart, which is 18 miles.

LESSON XVI.

22. Each one would receive one sixth of 36 dollars, which is 6 dollars.

23. Since there are 4 quarts in 1 gallon, in 36 quarts there are as many gallons as 4 quarts are contained times in 36 quarts, which are 9.

LESSON XVIII.

24. One man will earn in 3 days one ninth of $108, which is $12. In one day he would earn one third of $12, which is $4..

25. In 1 day the former travels one third of 15 miles, which is 5 miles. In 1 day the latter travels one half of 20 miles, which is 10 miles; and if the latter travels 10 miles in 1 day, and the former, 5 miles, the latter travels as much farther in 1 day than the former as the difference between 10 miles and 5 miles, which is 5 miles.

LESSON XIX.

7. The sum of 1, 2, and 3 is 6, and 6 is contained in 60 ten times. If I have as many marbles as 3 times the number of times 6 is contained in 60, I have 3 times 10 marbles, which is 30 marbles.

8. Six hats will cost 6 times $5, which is $30 ; 4 yards of cloth will cost 4 times $3, which is $12. Both will cost the sum of $30 and $12, which is $42; and if he gave in exchange flour at $6 a barrel, it took as many barrels as $6 are contained times in $42, which are 7.

9. If a man gain 6 miles in 5 hours, it will take as many times 5 hours to gain 24 miles as 6 miles are contained times in 24 miles, which are 4; and 4 times 5 hours are 20 hours.

34. It will take 1 man 3 times 10 days, which is 30 days. It will take as many men to do it in 5 days as 5 days are contained times in 30 days, which are 6.

LESSON XXII.

2. One third of an apple is worth $\frac{1}{3}$ of three cents, which is 1 cent.

5. One fourth of a melon is worth $\frac{1}{4}$ of 8 cents, which is 2 cents; and if $\frac{1}{4}$ of a melon is worth 2 cents, $\frac{3}{4}$ of a melon are worth 3 times 2 cents, which is 6 cents.

23. One calf cost $\frac{1}{12}$ of $120, which is $10; and if 1 calf cost $10, he sold the 7 calves for 7 times $10, which is $70.

LESSON XXIII.

9. For $1 you can buy $\frac{1}{8}$ of a bushel, and for $5 you can buy 5 times $\frac{1}{8}$ of a bushel, which is $\frac{5}{8}$ of a bushel.

16. One fifth of 30 is 6; then $\frac{3}{5}$ of 30 are 3 times 6, which is 18; and 18 is $\frac{18}{23}$ of 23.

LESSON XXIV.

7. One sixth of a gallon will cost $\frac{1}{6}$ of 35 cents, which is 7 cents; and if $\frac{1}{6}$ of a gallon cost 7 cents, $\frac{6}{6}$, or 1 gallon, will cost 6 times 7 cents, which is 42 cents.

17. One fourth of 8 cents is 2 cents, and $\frac{3}{4}$ are 3 times 2 cents, which is 6 cents; and if 6 cents are $\frac{2}{3}$ of mine, $\frac{1}{3}$ of mine is $\frac{1}{2}$ of 6 cents, which is 3 cents; and if 3 cents are $\frac{1}{3}$, then $\frac{3}{3}$ will be 3 times 3 cents, which is 9 cents.

LESSON XXV.

4. One yard will cost $\frac{1}{3}$ of 5 dollars, which is $1\frac{2}{3}$ dollars.

LESSON XXVI.

4. Since there are $\frac{4}{4}$ in 1, in 3 there are 3 times $\frac{4}{4}$, which is $\frac{12}{4}$; and $\frac{12}{4} + \frac{1}{4} = \frac{13}{4}$. Other answers, $\frac{19}{4}$, $\frac{21}{4}$, $\frac{27}{4}$.

LESSON XXVII.

13. To reduce a fraction to its lowest terms, divide both terms by their greatest common divisor. Of 27 and 36, the G. C. D. is 9; 9 in 27 is contained 3 times, and 9 in 36 is contained 4 times.

Therefore, $\frac{27}{36}$ changed to its lowest terms $= \frac{3}{4}$.

LESSON XXVIII.

10. Since there are $\frac{8}{8}$ in 1, in $\frac{1}{4}$ there is $\frac{1}{4}$ of $\frac{8}{8}$, which is $\frac{2}{8}$; and if $\frac{2}{8} = \frac{1}{4}$, then $\frac{3}{4}$ will be 3 times $\frac{2}{8}$, which is $\frac{6}{8}$.

LESSON XXIX.

4. The common denominator is 15. $1 = \frac{15}{15}$; $\frac{1}{3} = \frac{5}{15}$, and $\frac{2}{3} = \frac{10}{15}$; $\frac{1}{5} = \frac{3}{15}$, and $\frac{2}{5} = \frac{6}{15}$.

LESSON XXX.

2. Three fourths $= \frac{6}{8}$, and $\frac{1}{2} = \frac{4}{8}$. He gave for both $\$\frac{6}{8} + \$\frac{4}{8} = \$\frac{10}{8} = \$1\frac{1}{4}$.

LESSON XXXI.

3. One half of the first $= \frac{3}{6}$ of a melon; $\frac{2}{3}$ of the second $= \frac{4}{6}$ of a melon. $\frac{4}{6} - \frac{3}{6} = \frac{1}{6}$.

LESSON XXXII.

14. Find how much is in both air and water: as much as the sum of $\frac{1}{2}$ and $\frac{1}{3}$. $\frac{1}{2} = \frac{3}{6}$, and $\frac{1}{3} = \frac{2}{6}$; their sum is $\frac{5}{6}$. Since there are $\frac{6}{6}$ in the pole, there would be as much in the earth as the difference between $\frac{6}{6}$ and $\frac{5}{6}$, which is $\frac{1}{6}$.

LESSON XXXIII.

2. To 5 horses he would give 5 times $\frac{1}{2}$ peck, which is $\frac{5}{2}$ pecks; and $\frac{5}{2}$ pecks $= 2\frac{1}{2}$ pecks.

LESSON XXXIV.

8. One pound of cheese will sell for $\frac{1}{4}$ of 30 cents, which is $7\frac{1}{2}$ cents. Then 3 pounds will sell for 3 times $7\frac{1}{2}$ cents, which is $22\frac{1}{2}$ cents.

28. One seventh of 18 is $2\frac{4}{7}$; then $\frac{2}{7} = 2$ times $2\frac{4}{7}$ feet, which is $5\frac{1}{7}$ feet; and $\frac{5}{7} = 5$ times $2\frac{4}{7}$ feet, which is $12\frac{6}{7}$ feet.

29. One ninth of \$15 is \$1$\frac{2}{3}$; then $\frac{2}{9} = 2$ times \$1$\frac{2}{3}$, which is \$3$\frac{1}{3}$; $\frac{1}{3}$ of \$15 is \$5; \$5 + \$3$\frac{1}{3}$ = \$8$\frac{1}{3}$, \$15 - \$8$\frac{1}{3}$ = \$6$\frac{2}{3}$.

31. $\frac{5}{5} - \frac{2}{5} = \frac{3}{5}$. \$18 $= \frac{3}{5}$ of the number, then $\frac{1}{5}$ would be $\frac{1}{3}$ of \$18, which is \$6; and $\frac{2}{5}$ would be 2 times \$6, which is \$12.

32. \$45 $= \frac{7}{7} + \frac{2}{7}$, which is $\frac{9}{7}$ of the cost. $\frac{1}{7}$ is $\frac{1}{9}$ of \$45 $=$ \$5; and $\frac{7}{7}$ would be 7 times \$5 $=$ \$35.

LESSON XXXVI.

22. Five and three sevenths pounds of sugar cost $5\frac{3}{7}$ times 7 cents, which is 38 cents. It would take as many pounds of raisins to pay for it as 6 cents are contained times in 38 cents, which are $6\frac{1}{3}$.

LESSON XXXVIII.

9. One pound will cost $\frac{1}{4}$ of $\$\frac{5}{4} = \$\frac{5}{16}$; then 7 pounds will cost 7 times $\$\frac{5}{16} = \$\frac{35}{16} = \$2\frac{3}{16}$.

LESSON XXXIX.

16. The sum of $\frac{1}{5}$ and $\frac{2}{5} = \frac{3}{5}$; $\frac{5}{5} - \frac{3}{5} = \frac{2}{5}$; then 14 ft. $= \frac{2}{5}$ of the pole; $\frac{1}{5} = 7$ ft.; $\frac{5}{5} = 35$ ft.

23. $\$12 = \frac{4}{3}$ of the cost; $\frac{1}{3}$ of the cost is $\frac{1}{4}$ of $\$12 = \$3$; $\frac{3}{3} = \$9$. One yard cost $\frac{1}{5}$ of $\$9 = \$1\frac{4}{5}$.

28. One eighth of the cost was $\frac{1}{5}$ of $\$50$, which is $\$10$; then $\frac{8}{8}$ are 8 times $\$10$, which is $\$80$. It would take as many yards as $\$4$ are contained times in $\$80$, which are 20.

LESSON XL.

11. One third of the number is $\frac{1}{8}$ of 56, which is 7; then $\frac{3}{3}$ are 3 times 7, which is 21; 21 is 3 times 7.

LESSON XLI.

9. One fourth of a bu. of wheat is worth $\frac{1}{3}$ of a bu. of rye; then $\frac{4}{4}$ of a bu. of wheat are worth $\frac{4}{3}$ of a bu. of rye; and $\frac{1}{5}$ of a bu. of wheat is worth $\frac{1}{5}$ of $\frac{4}{3}$ of a bu. of rye, which is $\frac{4}{15}$ of a bu. of rye; and $\frac{4}{5}$ of a bu. of wheat are worth 4 times $\frac{4}{15}$ of a bu. of rye, which is $\frac{16}{15}$, or $1\frac{1}{15}$ bu. of rye.

LESSON XLIII

22. As many bu. of rye as $\frac{3}{4}$ are contained times in $4\frac{1}{2}$. $4\frac{1}{2} = \frac{18}{4}$; $\frac{18}{4} \div \frac{3}{4} = 6$.

LESSON XLIV.

11. $\$3\frac{1}{10} = \$\frac{31}{10}$; $7\frac{3}{4} = \frac{31}{4}$; $\frac{1}{4}$ of a doz. cost $\frac{1}{31}$ of $\$\frac{31}{10}$, which is $\$\frac{1}{10}$; then 1 pair cost $\frac{1}{3}$ of $\$\frac{1}{10}$, or $\$\frac{1}{30}$. He gained the difference between $\$\frac{1}{10}$ and $\$\frac{1}{30}$, which is $\$\frac{1}{15}$.

12. $2\frac{1}{2} = \frac{5}{2}$. $\frac{1}{2}$ doz. cost $\frac{1}{5}$ of \$15, which is \$3; then each one cost $\frac{1}{6}$ of \$3, which is $\$\frac{1}{2}$. He gained on each one the difference between $\$\frac{2}{5}$ and $\$\frac{1}{2}$, which is $\$\frac{1}{10}$.

On $\frac{1}{2}$ doz. he gained $\$\frac{6}{10}$; and on $\frac{5}{2}$ doz. $\$\frac{30}{10}$, or \$3.

LESSON XLV.

22. A walks 5 miles 7 times in walking 35 miles; B walks 3 miles 7 times in the same time. Therefore, B walks 7 times 3 miles, which is 21 miles.

25. One horse will eat $\frac{1}{6}$ of 12 bu. in a week, which is 2 bu. a week; then 10 horses will eat 10 times 2 bu. in a week, which is 20 bushels.

26. Five horses will eat in 1 week $\frac{1}{2}$ of 16 bu., which is 8 bu; to eat 56 bu., it will take them as many weeks as 8 is contained times in 56, which are 7.

28. It will take 6 times 12 horses, which is 72 horses, to eat it in 1 day; and to eat it in 9 days it will take $\frac{1}{9}$ of 72 horses, which is 8 horses.

LESSON XLVI.

6. Nine times $9 = 81$. $81 \div 12 = 6\frac{9}{12}$, or $6\frac{3}{4}$.

8. $\frac{48}{120} = \frac{2}{5}$. $\frac{54}{189} = \frac{2}{7}$. $\frac{240}{288} = \frac{5}{6}$.

9. One ninth $= \frac{16}{144}$, $\frac{3}{9} = \frac{48}{144}$; $\frac{1}{16} = \frac{9}{144}$, $\frac{4}{16} = \frac{36}{144}$; $\frac{1}{72} = \frac{2}{144}$, $\frac{17}{72} = \frac{34}{144}$.

12. If he traveled $\frac{1}{4}$, or $\frac{3}{12}$, the first day, and $\frac{1}{3}$, or $\frac{4}{12}$, the second day, then the third day he must have traveled $\frac{12}{12}$ less $\frac{7}{12}$, which is $\frac{5}{12}$; $\frac{5}{12}$ of 84 miles $= 35$ miles.

21. $\$99 = \frac{8}{8} + \frac{3}{8}$, or $\frac{11}{8}$, of the cost; then $\frac{1}{8} = \$9$, and $\frac{8}{8}$, the cost, $= \$72$.

22. One eighth of $\$96 = \$12$, or $\frac{1}{5}$ of the cost; then the cost was 5 times $\$12 = \$60$. It took as many barrels of flour to pay for the horse as $\$6$ are contained times in $\$60$, which are 10.

23. Eighty-four is $\frac{7}{6}$ of 72, and 72 is 8 times 9.

25. Eight ninths of $81 = 72$, and $72 = \frac{9}{8}$ of 64.

26. Four sevenths of 35 are 20, and 20 is $\frac{5}{6}$ of 24. Three eighths of 16 are 6, and 24 is 4 times 6.

27. $17½ = $$\frac{3.5}{2}$. 4$\frac{3}{8}$ yd. = $\frac{35}{8}$ yd. $\frac{1}{8}$ of a yd. would cost $\frac{1}{35}$ of $$\frac{3.5}{2}$, which is $½; then $\frac{8}{8}$ of a yd. would cost $$\frac{8}{2}$, or $4.

33. In one week he would earn $\frac{1}{8}$ of $72, which is $9; in one day he would earn $\frac{1}{6}$ of $9, which is $1½.

37. One half of 20 years = 10 years, or $\frac{1}{5}$ of the father's age; then 5 times 10 years = 50 years, the father's age. $\frac{1}{10}$ of 50 years = 5 years, or the age of the youngest son.

38. $21 = $\frac{7}{5}$ of the cost. $\frac{1}{5} = \frac{1}{7}$ of $21, which is $3. $\frac{5}{5}$ = $15, or the cost. At $1 a bushel, it would take 15 bushels of corn to pay for it; at $$\frac{1}{3}$, it would take 3 times 15 bushels, which is 45 bushels.

39. Three yards = $\frac{1.5}{5}$ yards. $\frac{1.5}{5}$ are 5 times $\frac{3}{5}$, and will cost 5 times $$\frac{2}{3}$, which is 3\frac{1}{3}$.

41. One half of 12 = 6. 6 + 2 = 8. 8 is $\frac{1}{3}$ of 24.

44. Three fourths of 24 = 18. 18 — 6 = 12. 12 is $\frac{2}{3}$ of 18. 18 is 6 more than $\frac{2}{3}$ of itself.

50. Two fifths of 30 yards = 12 yards. He sold one yard for $\frac{1}{12}$ of $48, which is $4.

60. Three fifths of $20 are $12. Fourteen is $\frac{7}{9}$ of 18, and 2 times 18 are 36. Twelve is $\frac{1}{3}$ of 36.

79. Two fifths of 10 yards are 4 yards, and they cost $\frac{2}{5}$ of $90, which is $36. $40 $36 = $4, the gain on 4 yards, and on 1 yard the gain is $1.

80. B gains in one day 23 miles less 18 miles, which are 5 miles. It will take as many days to gain 40 miles as 5 miles are contained times in 40 miles, which are 8.

81. The hound gains in one second 10 feet less 7 feet = 3 ft., or 1 yd.; then to gain 90 yards it will take 90 seconds, or $1\frac{1}{2}$ min. The hound runs 90 times 10 feet, which are 900 ft. = 300 yd. The hare runs 90 times 7 ft. = 630 feet, or 210 yd.

85. In one hour the cistern would lose 9 gallons less 6 gallons, which are 3 gallons; and it would take as many hours to empty the cistern as 3 gallons are contained times in 36 gallons, which are 12.

89. Such part of the journey as $2\frac{1}{4}$ days are of $3\frac{3}{8}$ days. $3\frac{3}{8} = \frac{27}{8}$. $2\frac{1}{4} = \frac{18}{8}$. $\frac{18}{8} = \frac{18}{27}$, or $\frac{2}{3}$, of $\frac{27}{8}$. He can therefore perform $\frac{2}{3}$ of the journey in $2\frac{1}{4}$ days.

90. In one day A can do $\frac{1}{2}$, B $\frac{1}{4}$, and C $\frac{1}{6}$; then all do the sum of $\frac{1}{2}$, $\frac{1}{4}$, and $\frac{1}{6}$, which is $\frac{11}{12}$, in one day. To do $\frac{12}{12}$, it will take as many days as $\frac{11}{12}$ are contained times in $\frac{12}{12}$, which are $1\frac{1}{11}$.

91. Twenty yards at $4 per yard = $80. 15 yards at $3 per yard = $45. $80 + $45 = $125, or what I paid for 35 yards. I received for $\frac{6}{7}$, or 30 yards, $3 per yard = $90, and for $\frac{1}{7}$, or 5 yards, $4 per yard = $20. For all I received $90 + $20 = $110. My loss on 35 yards was $125 — $110 = $15, or $\frac{15}{35}$ = $\frac{3}{7}$ per yard.

93. Three fourths of 6 miles are $4\frac{1}{2}$ miles. 6 miles less $4\frac{1}{2}$ miles = $1\frac{1}{2}$ miles, the distance B gains in one hour. To gain 36 miles, it will take as many hours as $1\frac{1}{2}$ miles are contained times in 36 miles, which are 24.

LESSON LIII.

1. Five bu. will cost 5 times 60 cents, which is $3; 3 pk. will cost $\frac{3}{4}$ of 60 cents, which is 45 cents; then 5 bu. and 3 pk. will cost $3.45.

2. Four gal. 2 qt. 1 pt. $= 37$ pt.; at 5 cents a pint, the milk will cost 37 times 5 cents, which is $1.85.

4. One rod contains 198 in.; 2 yd. 2 ft. 3 in. $= 99$ in., or $\frac{1}{2}$ a rod; then $5\frac{1}{2}$ rods will cost $5\frac{1}{2}$ times $12, which is $66.

5. Twenty-six min. and 40 sec. $= \frac{4}{9}$ of an hour; 9 hours $+ \frac{4}{9}$ hours $= 9\frac{4}{9}$ hours. If it traveled 9 miles an hour, the distance is $9\frac{4}{9}$ times 9 miles $= 85$ miles.

8. Three tenths da. $= \frac{3}{10}$ of 24 hr., which is $7\frac{1}{5}$ hr.; $7\frac{1}{5}$ hr. $+ \frac{2}{5}$ hr. $= 7\frac{3}{5}$ hours.

9. One third rd. $= 5\frac{1}{2}$ ft., or $5\frac{2}{4}$ ft.; $\frac{1}{2}$ yd. $= 1\frac{1}{2}$ ft., or $1\frac{2}{4}$; then $5\frac{2}{4}$ ft. $+ 1\frac{2}{4} + \frac{3}{4}$ ft. $= 7\frac{3}{4}$ ft.

11. One bu. 3 pk. $= 7$ pk; 1 pk. is worth $\frac{1}{7}$ of 70 cents, which is 10 cents; 2 bu. 1 pk. $= 9$ pk.; and 4 qt. $= \frac{1}{2}$ pk.; then $9\frac{1}{2}$ pk. are worth $9\frac{1}{2}$ times 10 cents, which is 95 cents.

13. One third of a T. cost $\frac{1}{2}$ of $8, which is $4; 1 T. cost $12; 1 cwt. cost $\frac{1}{20}$ of $12, which is 60 ct.; 3 cwt. 75 lb. $= 3\frac{3}{4}$ cwt.; then $3\frac{3}{4}$ cwt. cost $3\frac{3}{4}$ times 60 ct., which is $2.25.

14. In 2 hr. 24 min. there are 144 min.; the rate per min. is $\frac{1}{144}$ of 60 miles $= \frac{60}{144}$ mi., or $\frac{5}{12}$ mi.; the rate per hr. is 60 times $\frac{5}{12}$ mi., which is $\frac{300}{12}$ mi. $= 25$ mi.

15. In 3 yd. 1 ft. 6 in. there are $3\frac{1}{2}$ yd.; in 1 rd. 5 yd. there are $10\frac{1}{2}$ yd.; the wheel would make as many revolutions in going $10\frac{1}{2}$ yd. as $3\frac{1}{2}$ yd. are contained times in $10\frac{1}{2}$ yd., which are 3.

17. I bought as many pounds as 40 ct. are contained times in 235 ct., which are $5\frac{7}{8}$; $\frac{7}{8}$ lb. $= 14$ oz. I bought 5 lb. 14 oz.

20. In 150 bu. are 6 T.; 6 T. will cost 6 times \$3.75, which is \$22.50; 1 bu. will cost $\frac{1}{25}$ of \$3.75, which is 15 ct.

21. The distance around the lot is 50 ft. $+ 100$ ft. $\times 2$ $= 300$ ft.; 300 ft. $= 100$ yd.; 100 yd. $= 18\frac{2}{11}$ rd. If 1 rd. cost \$5, then $18\frac{2}{11}$ rd. cost $18\frac{2}{11}$ times \$5, which is $\$90\frac{10}{11}$.

LESSON LIV.

15. The entire cost was \$90 plus $\$3 \times 6 = \$108$; the sum received for him was $\$42 + \$99 = \$141$; all gained $\$141 - \$108 = \$33$; each man received $\frac{1}{3}$ of \$33, which is \$11.

LESSON LV.

12. In 6 da. of 8 hr. each there are 48 hr.; in 7 da. of 9 hr. each there are 63 hr.; $\$9\frac{3}{5} = \$\frac{48}{5}$. In 1 hr. he would earn $\frac{1}{48}$ of $\$\frac{48}{5}$, which is $\$\frac{1}{5}$; in 63 hr., $\$\frac{63}{5} = \$12\frac{3}{5}$.

15. In $3\frac{1}{2}$ are $\frac{7}{2}$; $2\frac{1}{3} = \frac{7}{3}$. $\frac{1}{3}$ of the number is $\frac{1}{7}$ of $\frac{7}{2} = \frac{1}{2}$; then $\frac{3}{3} = \frac{3}{2}$, or $1\frac{1}{2}$. $1\frac{1}{2} \times 2\frac{1}{3} = \frac{3}{2} \times \frac{5}{2} = \frac{15}{4} = 3\frac{3}{4}$.

18. Two thirds of $\frac{6}{5} = \frac{4}{5}$. If $\frac{4}{5}$ are $\frac{2}{7}$, then $\frac{1}{7}$ is $\frac{1}{2}$ of $\frac{4}{5}$, which is $\frac{2}{5}$; and $\frac{7}{7}$ would be 7 times $\frac{2}{5}$, which is $\frac{14}{5} = 2\frac{4}{5}$.

22. Two thirds of $1\frac{2}{5}$ are $\frac{8}{5}$. If $\frac{8}{5}$ are $\frac{1}{2}$, then $\frac{2}{2}$ are $\frac{16}{5}$; and 2 is contained in $\frac{16}{5}$, $\frac{8}{5}$ or $1\frac{3}{5}$ times.

25. Four fifths of 10 marbles are 8 marbles. If 8 is $\frac{8}{11}$, then $\frac{1}{11}$ is 1, and $\frac{11}{11}$ are 11.

26. Three fifths of 60 plums are 36 plums; $\frac{3}{4}$ of 36 are 27; $\frac{4}{9}$ of 27 are 12, or what she gave away. She had left $36 - 12 = 24$.

27. Five sevenths of the distance is 35 mi.; then $\frac{1}{7}$ is 7 mi., and $\frac{2}{7}$ are 14 mi.; $\frac{3}{7}$ of 14 mi. $= 6$ mi.; 14 mi. $- 6$ mi. $= 8$ mi.

30. Seven sevenths less $\frac{2}{7} = \frac{5}{7}$; $\frac{2}{5}$ of $\frac{5}{7} = \frac{2}{7}$; $\frac{5}{7} - \frac{2}{7} = \frac{3}{7}$, the part she had left. $\frac{3}{7} = 6$, $\frac{1}{7} = 2$, $\frac{7}{7} = 14$.

31. Two thirds of 12 ct. are 8 ct. If 8 is $\frac{1}{2}$, then $\frac{2}{2}$ are 16; if 16 ct. are $\frac{4}{5}$ of William's money, then William has 20 ct.

32. If $\frac{1}{2}$ of B's money equals $\frac{2}{7}$ of A's, then all of B's money $= \frac{4}{7}$ of A's; $\frac{7}{7} - \frac{4}{7} = \frac{3}{7}$, the difference between A's and B's money; $\frac{3}{7} = 12$ ct., $\frac{1}{7} = 4$ ct., $\frac{7}{7} = 28$ ct., A's money; 28 ct. $- 12$ ct. $= 16$ ct., B's.

33. One third $= \frac{4}{12}$, $\frac{1}{4} = \frac{3}{12}$; $\frac{4}{12} + \frac{3}{12} + \frac{1}{12} = \frac{8}{12} = \frac{2}{3}$; then $32 = \frac{1}{3}$; $\frac{3}{3} = 96$, the number of trees in the orchard. $\frac{1}{3}$ of $96 = 32$; $\frac{1}{4}$ of $96 = 24$; $\frac{1}{12}$ of $96 = 8$.

34. If $\frac{2}{9}$ are pear-trees, $\frac{7}{9}$ must be apple-trees. The excess of apple-trees is therefore $\frac{5}{9}$ of the whole; 25 is then $\frac{5}{9}$ of the whole; $\frac{2}{9}$, or the pear-trees, $= 10$, and $\frac{7}{9}$, or the apple-trees, $= 35$.

LESSON LVI.

3. If the second is three times the first, then the whole number is four times the first. Therefore, the first is $\frac{1}{4}$ of $16 = 4$, and the second $4 \times 3 = 12$.

5. The whole number will be six times the first part; then the first part $= \frac{1}{6}$, the second $\frac{2}{6}$, the third $\frac{3}{6}$, or 4, 8, and 12, respectively.

10. The difference of the two numbers is $6 + 2 = 8$; the sum of 8, the difference, and 4, one of the numbers, $= 12$, the other number.

11. The sum of 19 and 6 is 25; $25 - 10 = 15$, the difference between the numbers; then $19 - 15 = 4$, the smaller number.

12. The sum of the numbers is $10 + 8 = 18$; $18 - 5 = 13$, the other number.

18. They had at first 32 ct. $- 8$ ct. $= 24$ ct.; each had $\frac{1}{2}$ of 24 ct. $= 12$ ct. If Thomas found 8 more, he had 12 ct. $+ 8$ ct. $= 20$ ct.

19. They bought 4 peaches $+ 6$ peaches $+ 20$ peaches $= 30$ peaches; each one bought $\frac{1}{2}$ of 30 peaches, which is 15 peaches. Thomas had left $15 - 4 = 11$; William had left $15 - 6 = 9$.

20. Both bought 24 cherries $+ 7$ cherries $+ 5$ cherries $= 36$ cherries. Since Mary bought twice as many as Sarah, both bought three times as many as Sarah; there-

fore Sarah bought $\frac{1}{3}$ of 36 cherries $= 12$ cherries, and
Mary bought 2 times 12 cherries $= 24$ cherries; $24 - 7 =$
17, the number of cherries Mary had left; $12 - 5 = 7$,
the number Sarah had left.

21. Three times the number is $50 - 5 = 45$; $\frac{1}{3}$ of 45 is
15, the number.

22. Three fourths of the number would be $31 - 10 =$
21; $\frac{1}{4}$ would be $\frac{1}{3}$ of $21 = 7$; $\frac{4}{4}$, or the number, would
be 28.

23. Four fifths of the number would be $21 + 7 = 28$;
then $\frac{1}{5}$ is $\frac{1}{4}$ of $28 = 7$, and $\frac{5}{5} = 35$.

25. Since Sarah has 3 cents less than Mary, she has
only 5 cents more than Jane.   Three times Jane's money
is 43 ct. $- 8$ ct. $- 5$ ct. $= 30$ ct.; then Jane's money is $\frac{1}{3}$
of 30 ct. $= 10$ ct.; Mary's is 10 ct. $+ 8$ ct. $= 18$ ct.;
Sarah's is 10 ct. $+ 5$ ct. $= 15$ ct.

26. Three times Frank's age $= 42$ yr. $+ 3$ yr., which is
45 yr.; then Frank's age is $\frac{1}{3}$ of 45 yr. $= 15$ yr.   Mary's
age is 2 times 15 yr. less 3 yr. $= 27$ yr.

27. The ring cost \$5 and the watch \$12 more than the
chain; then \$62 $-$ \$12 $-$ \$5 $=$ \$45, which is 3 times the
cost of the chain; $\frac{1}{3}$ of \$45 $=$ \$15, the cost of the chain;
\$15 $+$ \$5 $=$ \$20, cost of the ring; and \$15 $+$ \$12 $=$ \$27,
cost of the watch.

28. One half of $\frac{4}{7}$ is $\frac{2}{7}$.   If $30 + 6$, or 36, is $\frac{2}{7}$, then $\frac{1}{7}$
is 18, and $\frac{7}{7}$ are 7 times $18 = 126$.

29. James has one part; John has two parts + $3; Frank has three parts + $3 + $7; $55 — $3 — $3 — $7 = $42, which is 6 times James's money. $\frac{1}{6}$ of $42 is $7, James's money; 2 times $7, + $3 = $17, John's money; and 3 times $7, + $3, + $7 = $31, Frank's.

30. Thomas has 1 part; Joseph has 3 parts less $2; Paul has 8 parts less $4 less $20; then $20 + $4 + $2 + $22 equal $48, which is 12 times Thomas's money. $\frac{1}{12}$ of $48 is $4, Thomas's money; 3 times $4, — $2 = $10; Joseph's money; 8 times $4, — $24 = $8, Paul's money.

31. The harness cost 1 part; the horse, 1 part + $50; the buggy, 2 parts + $50 + $25; then $225 — $50 — $50 — $25 = $100, which is 4 times the cost of the harness. $\frac{1}{4}$ of $100 is $25, cost of harness; $25 + $50 = $75, cost of horse; 2 times $25 + $75 = $125, cost of buggy.

LESSON LVII.

2. Both have to pay $\frac{3}{7} + \frac{7}{7} = \frac{10}{7}$; $\frac{1}{7}$ is $\frac{1}{10}$ of $60 = $6. John pays 3 times $6 = $18; Thomas pays 7 times $6 = $42.

3. Four fourths + $\frac{3}{4} = \frac{7}{4}$; $\frac{1}{4}$ is $\frac{1}{7}$ of 56 mi. = 8 mi.; $\frac{4}{4}$ are 32 mi., and $\frac{3}{4}$ are 24 mi., the distance traveled each day, respectively.

4. Since the first, plus $\frac{5}{7}$ of the first, less 8 (that is $\frac{12}{7}$ of the first less 8), = 100, then $\frac{12}{7}$ of the first = 108; $\frac{1}{7}$ is $\frac{1}{12}$ of 108 = 9; $\frac{7}{7} = 63$, the first; $\frac{5}{7} = 45$, and 45 less 8 = 37, the second.

5. Four fourths $+ \frac{2}{4} + \frac{3}{4} = \frac{9}{4}$, or 45; $\frac{1}{4}$ is $\frac{1}{9}$ of $45 = 5$. $\frac{4}{4} = 20$, the first part; $\frac{2}{4} = 10$, the second part; $\frac{3}{4} = 15$, the third part.

10. If $\frac{1}{2}$ of the cows $= \frac{2}{7}$ of the sheep, then all of the cows $= \frac{4}{7}$ of the sheep, and $1 + \frac{4}{7} = \frac{11}{7}$ of the sheep; $\frac{1}{7}$ of the sheep is $\frac{1}{11}$ of $55 = 5$; $\frac{7}{7} = 35$, the number of sheep; $\frac{4}{7} = 20$, the number of cows.

11. If $\frac{1}{3}$ of the less $= \frac{2}{9}$ of the greater, $\frac{3}{3}$, or the whole of the less, $= 3$ times $\frac{2}{9}$, which is $\frac{6}{9} = \frac{2}{3}$; then $\frac{3}{3} + \frac{2}{3} = 60$; $\frac{1}{3}$ is $\frac{1}{5}$ of $60 = 12$; $\frac{3}{3} = 36$, the greater number; $\frac{2}{3} = 24$, the smaller number.

12. If $\frac{1}{4}$ of Mary's age $= \frac{1}{3}$ of Sarah's, $\frac{4}{4}$ of Mary's age $= \frac{4}{3}$ of Sarah's; $\frac{4}{3} + \frac{3}{3} = \frac{7}{3}$; $\frac{1}{3}$ of Sarah's age is $\frac{1}{7}$ of $14 = 2$; $\frac{3}{3} = 6$, Sarah's age; $\frac{4}{3} = 8$, Mary's age.

13. If $\frac{2}{3}$ of the first $= \frac{3}{4}$ of the second, $\frac{1}{3}$ is $\frac{1}{2}$ of $\frac{3}{4} = \frac{3}{8}$, and $\frac{3}{3}$, or the whole of the first, $= \frac{9}{8}$ of the second. If the first is $\frac{9}{8}$ of the second, and the second $\frac{8}{8}$, both $= \frac{17}{8}$ of the second. $\frac{1}{8}$ is $\frac{1}{17}$ of $51 = 3$; $\frac{9}{8} = 27$, the first part; $\frac{8}{8} = 24$, the second.

14. If $\frac{2}{3}$ of the apple-trees $= \frac{4}{7}$ of the peach-trees, $\frac{1}{3} = \frac{2}{7}$, and $\frac{3}{3} = \frac{6}{7}$; $\frac{3}{3} = \frac{7}{7}$; then $\frac{7}{7}$ of the peach-trees $+ \frac{6}{7}$ of the peach-trees $= \frac{13}{7}$ of the peach-trees, and $\frac{1}{7}$ is $\frac{1}{13}$ of 65 trees $= 5$ trees. $\frac{7}{7} = 35$, the number of peach-trees; $\frac{6}{7} = 30$, the number of apple-trees.

15. If $\frac{2}{3}$ of A's distance $= \frac{5}{9}$ of B's, then $\frac{1}{3} = \frac{5}{18}$, and $\frac{3}{3} = \frac{15}{18}$, or $\frac{5}{6}$; then A travels $\frac{5}{6}$ as far as B, and both traveled $\frac{5}{6} + \frac{6}{6} = \frac{11}{6}$, or 66 miles. $\frac{1}{6}$ is $\frac{1}{11}$ of 66 mi. $= 6$ mi.; $\frac{6}{6} = 36$ mi., B's distance; $\frac{5}{6} = 30$ mi., A's distance; and 36 mi. $- 30$ mi. $= 6$ mi., the number of miles B traveled more than A.

16. Let $\frac{12}{12}$ = the apple-trees; $\frac{4}{12}$ = the plum-trees; $\frac{1}{2}$ of $\frac{12}{12} + \frac{1}{4}$ of $\frac{4}{12} = \frac{7}{12}$, the cherry-trees; then $\frac{12}{12} + \frac{4}{12} + \frac{7}{12} = \frac{23}{12}$, or 69 trees. $\frac{1}{12}$ is $\frac{1}{23}$ of $69 = 3$; $\frac{12}{12} = 36$, the number of apple-trees; $\frac{4}{12} = 12$, the plum-trees; and $\frac{7}{12} = 21$, the cherry-trees.

17. Five thirds of 12 yr. are 20 yr. If 20 yr. are $\frac{4}{9}$ of both Jane's and Sarah's age, $\frac{1}{9}$ is 5 yr., and $\frac{9}{9}$ are 45 yr. If Jane's age is $\frac{7}{8}$ of Sarah's, then $\frac{8}{8} + \frac{7}{8} = \frac{15}{8}$, and $\frac{15}{8} = 45$ yr.; $\frac{1}{8} = 3$ yr., and $\frac{8}{8} = 24$ yr., Sarah's age; $\frac{7}{8} = 21$ yr., Jane's age.

18. Three elevenths of 44 are 12; $\frac{4}{5}$ of 30 is 24; 24 is $\frac{4}{9}$ of 54; twice 54 are 108; 12 is contained in 108 nine times.

19. John's money is $\frac{3}{5}$, and Charles's $\frac{5}{5}$, or $\frac{20}{20}$; $\frac{3}{4}$ of $\frac{3}{5}$ $= \frac{9}{20}$, and $\frac{9}{20} + \$33 = \frac{20}{20}$, Charles's money; then $\frac{11}{20} =$ \$33. $\frac{1}{20} = \$3$, and $\frac{20}{20} = \$60$, Charles's money; $\frac{3}{5}$ of \$60 $= \$36$, John's money.

20. Let $\frac{12}{12}$ = the hogs; then $\frac{8}{12}$ = the sheep, and $\frac{6}{12}$ the cows; $\frac{12}{12} + \frac{8}{12} + \frac{6}{12} = \frac{26}{12}$, and $\frac{26}{12} = 104$; $\frac{1}{12} = 4$, $\frac{12}{12} = 48$, the hogs; $\frac{8}{12} = 32$, the sheep; and $\frac{6}{12} = 24$, the cows.

22. From noon to midnight is 12 hr. If the time elapsed since noon is $\frac{3}{5}$ of the time to midnight, then it is still $\frac{5}{5}$ to midnight; $\frac{3}{5} + \frac{5}{5} = \frac{8}{5}$, and $\frac{8}{5} = 12$ hr; $\frac{1}{5}$ is $\frac{1}{8}$ of 12 hr. $= 1\frac{1}{2}$ hr.; $\frac{3}{5} = 4\frac{1}{2}$ hr. Therefore it is half-past four o'clock, P. M.

23. Since once the time past noon $+ 3$ hr. is $\frac{1}{2}$ the time to midnight, twice the time past noon $+ 6$ hr. $=$ the whole time to midnight; but the time past noon $+$

the time to midnight is 12 hr.; hence the time **past** noon, with twice the time past noon + 6 hr. = 12 hr.; hence 3 times the time past noon is 6 hr., and the time past noon is $\frac{1}{3}$ of 6 hr. = 2 hr.

24. Let $\frac{5}{5}$ = the whole time; the time past noon is $\frac{1}{5}$; from midnight to noon is $\frac{4}{5}$; then $\frac{4}{5}$ = 12 hr; $\frac{1}{5}$ = 3 hr. It is 3 o'clock in the afternoon.

25. Let $\frac{4}{4}$ = the whole time; from midnight to noon is $\frac{3}{4}$; the time past noon = $\frac{1}{4}$; $\frac{3}{4}$ = 12 hr.; $\frac{1}{4}$ = 4 hr. It is 4 o'clock in the afternoon.

26. If $\frac{1}{2}$ the time past noon = $\frac{1}{20}$ of the time past midnight, the whole time past noon = $\frac{1}{10}$ the time past midnight; $\frac{10}{10}$ = the whole time; $\frac{1}{10}$ = the time past noon; $\frac{9}{10}$ = the time from midnight to noon, or 12 hr.; $\frac{1}{10}$ = $1\frac{1}{3}$ hr. It is 20 min. past one o'clock P. M.

LESSON LVIII.

2. One + $\frac{2}{3}$ = $\frac{5}{3}$; $\frac{1}{3}$ is $\frac{1}{5}$ of 20 = 4; $\frac{3}{3}$ = 12, the number.

4. Twice the number is $\frac{10}{5}$, and $\frac{10}{5}$ + $\frac{3}{5}$ = $\frac{13}{5}$. If $\frac{13}{5}$ = 52, then $\frac{1}{5}$ is $\frac{1}{13}$ of 52 = 4, and $\frac{5}{5}$ = 20, the number.

5. Twice the number is $\frac{14}{7}$, and $\frac{14}{7}$ less $\frac{4}{7}$ = $\frac{10}{7}$. If $\frac{10}{7}$ = 40, then $\frac{1}{7}$ is $\frac{1}{10}$ of 40, which is 4, and $\frac{7}{7}$ = 28.

6. Let $\frac{5}{5}$ = the number; 3 times $\frac{5}{5}$ less $\frac{3}{5}$ = $\frac{12}{5}$. If $\frac{12}{5}$ = 48, then $\frac{1}{5}$ is $\frac{1}{12}$ of 48 = 4, and $\frac{5}{5}$ = 20.

7. Let $\frac{6}{6}$ = his age; then $\frac{6}{6}$ + $\frac{3}{6}$ + $\frac{4}{6}$ = $\frac{13}{6}$. If 26 = $\frac{13}{6}$, then $\frac{1}{6}$ = 2, and $\frac{6}{6}$ = 12.

8. Her age $= \frac{12}{12}$, and $\frac{12}{12} + \frac{4}{12} + \frac{3}{12} = \frac{19}{12}$; twice her age is $\frac{24}{12}$, and $\frac{24}{12} - \frac{19}{12} = \frac{5}{12}$; ten years $= \frac{5}{12}$, and $\frac{1}{12} = 2$ years; then $\frac{12}{12}$, her age, is 24 years.

9. Five fifths less $\frac{2}{5} = \frac{3}{5}$; $\frac{3}{5}$ are 30 cents, then $\frac{5}{5}$ are 50 cents.

10. Let $\frac{10}{10} =$ the number; $\frac{10}{10} + \frac{5}{10} + \frac{6}{10} = \frac{21}{10}$; three times the number is $\frac{30}{10}$; $\frac{30}{10} - \frac{21}{10} = \frac{9}{10}$; $27 = \frac{9}{10}$; $\frac{1}{10} = 3$; $\frac{10}{10} = 30$.

11. Let $\frac{11}{11} =$ the father's age; $\frac{11}{11} - \frac{3}{11} = \frac{8}{11}$; $\frac{8}{11} = 40$ yr.; $\frac{1}{11} = 5$ yr.; $\frac{11}{11} = 55$ yr.

12. Let $\frac{5}{5} =$ her age; $\frac{5}{5} + \frac{4}{5} = \frac{9}{5}$; three times her age is $\frac{15}{5}$; $\frac{15}{5} - \frac{9}{5} = \frac{6}{5}$; 18 yr. $= \frac{6}{5}$; $\frac{1}{5} = 3$ yr.; $\frac{5}{5} = 15$ yr.

13. Let $\frac{9}{9} =$ the whole length; then $\frac{9}{9} - \frac{2}{9} = \frac{7}{9}$; $\frac{7}{9} = 28$ yd.; $\frac{1}{9} = 4$ yd.; $\frac{9}{9} = 36$ yd.

14. Let $\frac{6}{6} =$ the distance from A to B, and $\frac{6}{6}$ the distance from C to D; $\frac{2}{3}$ of $\frac{3}{6}$ are $\frac{6}{18} = \frac{2}{6}$. $\frac{2}{6} + 20 = \frac{6}{6}$; then $20 = \frac{4}{6}$; $\frac{1}{6} = 5$; $\frac{6}{6} = 30$, the distance from C to D; $\frac{3}{6} = 15$, the distance from A to B.

15. Let $\frac{15}{15} =$ my age; $\frac{15}{15} + \frac{5}{15} + \frac{3}{15} = \frac{23}{15}$; $\frac{2}{3}$ of 69 years $= 46$ years; $\frac{23}{15} = 46$ years; $\frac{1}{15} = 2$ years; $\frac{15}{15} = 30$ years.

LESSON LIX.

4. As many lots as $\frac{3}{8}$ are contained times in $\frac{8}{8}$, which are $2\frac{2}{8}$.

5. In $2\frac{1}{2}$ days are $\frac{5}{2}$ days; in $\frac{1}{2}$ day he would do $\frac{1}{5}$ of the work; in 1 day he would do $\frac{2}{5}$ of the work.

7. In $3\frac{1}{3}$ days are $\frac{10}{3}$ days. In $\frac{1}{3}$ of a day he would walk $\frac{1}{10}$; in 1 day, $\frac{3}{10}$; in 2 days, $\frac{6}{10} = \frac{3}{5}$.

8. Both do $\frac{1}{2} + \frac{1}{4}$, which are $\frac{3}{4}$.

9. All do the sum of $\frac{1}{2}$, $\frac{1}{4}$ and $\frac{1}{5}$, which is $\frac{19}{20}$.

11. A digs $\frac{1}{6}$ in 1 day; B digs $\frac{1}{12}$ in 1 day; both dig $\frac{3}{12} = \frac{1}{4}$ in 1 day. If they dig $\frac{1}{4}$ in 1 day, it will take 4 days to dig the whole trench.

12. C does $\frac{1}{5}$ in 1 day; B does $\frac{1}{7}$ in 1 day; both do $\frac{12}{35}$ in 1 day. It will take as many days to do it all as $\frac{12}{35}$ are contained times in $\frac{35}{35}$, which are $2\frac{11}{12}$

13. A can do $\frac{1}{2}$ in 1 day, B $\frac{1}{3}$, and C $\frac{1}{6}$; all do in 1 day the sum of $\frac{1}{2}$, $\frac{1}{3}$, and $\frac{1}{6}$, which is $\frac{6}{6}$. Therefore, all three do it in 1 day.

15. Both drink $\frac{1}{12}$ in 1 day; the woman drinks $\frac{1}{30}$ in 1 day; the man drinks $\frac{1}{12} - \frac{1}{30} = \frac{1}{20}$ in 1 day. If he drink $\frac{1}{20}$ in 1 day, he would drink it all in 20 days.

16. All do $\frac{1}{4}$ in 1 day; A and B do $\frac{1}{8} + \frac{1}{12} = \frac{5}{24}$ in 1 day; C does in 1 day $\frac{1}{4} - \frac{5}{24} = \frac{1}{24}$. Therefore, C can reap it all in 24 days.

17. Both do in 1 day $\frac{1}{2} + \frac{1}{3} = \frac{5}{6}$. If they do $\frac{5}{6}$ in 1 day, they would do it all in $1\frac{1}{5}$ days.

18. A digs $\frac{2}{5}$ in 1 day, and B digs $\frac{3}{10}$ in 1 day; both dig $\frac{2}{5} + \frac{3}{10} = \frac{7}{10}$ in 1 day. Therefore, if they dig $\frac{7}{10}$ in 1 day, they would dig it all in $1\frac{3}{7}$ days.

19. C reaps $\frac{1}{5}$ in 1 day; D reaps $\frac{3}{10}$ in 1 day; both reap in 1 day $\frac{1}{5} + \frac{3}{10} = \frac{5}{10} = \frac{1}{2}$. If they reap $\frac{1}{2}$ in 1 day, they would reap the whole in 2 days.

LESSON LX.

8. The ratio of 21 to 7 is 3; $36 \div 3 = 12$, the number.

9. The ratio of 20 to 2 is 10; $10 - 5 = 5$, 5 is $\frac{1}{4}$ of 20, and 20 is the ratio of 40 to 2.

10. The ratio of 18 to 2 is $9, + 3 = 12, + 7 = 19$; and 19 is the ratio of 38 to 2.

11. The ratio of 27 to 9 is $3, + 5 = 8$; and 8 is the ratio of 20 to $2\frac{1}{2}$.

13. Five $+ 7 = 12$; $\frac{5}{12}$ of $48 = 20$, the first part; $\frac{7}{12}$ of $48 = 28$, the second part.

18. Once the number $+ 3$ times the number $= 4$ times the number, or 48; and $\frac{1}{4}$ of 48 is 12, the number.

19. One $+ 4 = 5$; the first is $\frac{1}{5}$ of 25 yd. $= 5$ yd.; the second is $\frac{4}{5} = 20$ yd.

22. The first has $\frac{2}{3}$ of $7\frac{1}{2}$ doz. $= 5$ doz.; the second has $\frac{1}{3}$ of $7\frac{1}{2}$ doz. $= 2\frac{1}{2}$ doz.

23. A paid $\frac{25}{40} = \frac{5}{8}$ of the cost, and B paid $\frac{15}{40} = \frac{3}{8}$ of the cost. A should receive $\frac{5}{8}$ of $56 = 35$, and B should receive $\frac{3}{8}$ of $56 = 21$.

24. Three $+ 2 = 5$. C's loss was $\frac{3}{5}$ of $30 = 18$; D's loss was $\frac{2}{5}$ of $30 = 12$.

LESSON LXI.

3. Three thirds $+ \frac{4}{3} = \frac{7}{3}$. A has $\frac{3}{7}$ of **14 ct.** $= $ **6 ct.;**
B has $\frac{4}{7}$ of 14 ct. $= 8$ ct.

5. In $2\frac{1}{2}$ are $\frac{5}{2}$, and $4\frac{1}{2} = \frac{9}{2}$; $\frac{5}{2} + \frac{9}{2} = \frac{14}{2}$. The first
would receive $\frac{5}{14}$ of $28 = \$10$; the second would receive
$\frac{9}{14}$ of $28 = \$18$.

6. Three thirds $+ \frac{5}{3} = \frac{8}{3}$. William's age is $\frac{5}{8}$ of 32 yr.
$= 20$ yr.; Frank's age is $\frac{3}{8}$ of 32 yr. $= 12$ yr.

7. Three thirds $+ \frac{7}{3} = \frac{10}{3}$. $\frac{7}{10}$ of 30 apples $= 21$ apples,
the number of sound ones; $\frac{3}{10}$ of 30 apples $= 9$ apples,
the number not sound.

8. Four fifths $+ \frac{5}{5} = \frac{9}{5}$. One built $\frac{4}{9}$ of 27 ft. $= 12$ ft.;
the other, $\frac{5}{9} = 15$ ft.

10. One $+ 2 + 3 + 4 = 10$. The first part is $\frac{1}{10}$ of **70**
$= \textbf{7}$; the second, $\frac{2}{10}$ of $70 = 14$; the third, $\frac{3}{10}$ of $70 = 21$;
the fourth, $\frac{4}{10}$ of $70 = 28$.

11. One half $= \frac{6}{12}$; $\frac{1}{3} = \frac{4}{12}$; $\frac{1}{4} = \frac{3}{12}$; and $\frac{6}{12} + \frac{4}{12} + \frac{3}{12} = \frac{13}{12}$. The first is $\frac{6}{13}$ of $39 = 18$; the second, $\frac{4}{13} = 12$; the third is $\frac{3}{13} = 9$.

12. All had 3 ct. $+ 4$ ct. $+ 5$ ct. $= 12$ ct. William's
share, $\frac{3}{12}$ of 36, $= 9$; Thomas's, $\frac{4}{12}$ of 36, $= 12$; John's,
$\frac{5}{12}$ of 36, $= 15$.

13. The whole loss was $\$864 - \$500 = \$364$; $\frac{1}{8}$ of $364
is $\$45\frac{1}{2}$, A's loss; $\frac{1}{4}$ of $364 is $91, B's loss; $\frac{5}{8}$ of $364 are
$\$227\frac{1}{2}$, C's loss.

14. A has $\frac{4}{4}$, B $\frac{2}{4}$, and C $\frac{1}{4}$; all have $\frac{4}{4} + \frac{2}{4} + \frac{1}{4} = \frac{7}{4}$. A has $\frac{4}{7}$ of \$42 = \$24; B has $\frac{2}{4}$ of \$24 = \$12; and C has $\frac{1}{4}$ of \$24 = \$6.

15. Four $+ 3 + 2 = 9$. A has $\frac{4}{9}$, B $\frac{3}{9}$, and C $\frac{2}{9}$, or 20, 15, and 10, respectively.

16. One $+ 3 + 6 = 10$. $\frac{1}{10}$ of 60 = 6, the horses; $\frac{3}{10}$ of 60 = 18, the cows; $\frac{6}{10}$ of 60 = 36, the sheep.

17. One $+ 2 + 3 = 6$. A has $\frac{1}{6}$ of 42 = 7; B, $\frac{2}{6} = 14$; C, $\frac{3}{6} = 21$.

18. One $+ 2 + 4 = 7$. Emma has $\frac{1}{7}$ of 35 = 5; Agnes has $\frac{2}{7}$ of 35 = 10; Sarah has $\frac{4}{7}, = 20$.

LESSON LXII.

2. It will take 15 times 8 men = 120 men to do the work in 1 day; to do it in 12 days it will take $\frac{1}{12}$ of 120 men = 10 men.

4. One will fill it in 9 times $2\frac{1}{2}$ hr. = $22\frac{1}{2}$ hr.; then 5 pipes will fill it in $\frac{1}{5}$ of $22\frac{1}{2}$ hr. = $4\frac{1}{2}$ hr

6. Fifteen ct. = $\$\frac{3}{20}$; 80 times $\$\frac{3}{20} = \$\frac{240}{20} = \$12$.

7. Sixty ct. = $\$\frac{3}{5}$; 80 times $\$\frac{3}{5} = \$\frac{240}{5} = \$48$.

10. It will make 3 times 20 = 60 one cent loaves. $\frac{1}{4}$ of 60 = 15 four cent loaves; $\frac{1}{5}$ of 60 = 12 five cent loaves.

11. A loaf will weigh 3 times 8 oz. = 24 oz., when flour is \$1 a barrel; it will weigh $\frac{1}{4}$ of 24 oz. = 6 oz., when flour is \$4 a barrel.

12. Six times 10 oz. $= 60$ oz.; $\frac{1}{5}$ of 60 oz. $= 12$ oz.

13. In $\$5\frac{1}{3}$ are $\$\frac{16}{3}$; $\frac{16}{3}$ times 7 oz. $= \frac{112}{3}$ oz.; $\$4\frac{2}{3} = \$\frac{14}{3}$. When flour is worth $\$4\frac{2}{3}$ a barrel, a loaf will weigh as many oz. as $\frac{14}{3}$ are contained times in $\frac{112}{3} = 8$.

14. It will take 5 times 5 men $= 25$ men to do the same work in $\frac{1}{5}$ of the time; to do twice as much will take 2 times 25 men $= 50$ men.

15. Six men will do $\frac{1}{2}$ of it in $\frac{1}{2}$ of 5 days $= 2\frac{1}{2}$ days; one man will do the other $\frac{1}{2}$ in 6 times $2\frac{1}{2}$ days $= 15$ days. $6 + 3 = 9$; 9 men will do it in $\frac{1}{9}$ of 15 days $= 1\frac{2}{3}$ days. Therefore, the whole time is $2\frac{1}{2}$ days $+ 1\frac{2}{3}$ days $= 4\frac{1}{6}$ days.

16. Seven men will do $\frac{1}{2}$ of the work in 2 days; one man will do the other half in 7 times 2 days $= 14$ days. $7 - 3 = 4$; 4 men will do it in $\frac{1}{4}$ of 14 days $= 3\frac{1}{2}$ days. Therefore, it will take 2 days $+ 3\frac{1}{2}$ days $= 5\frac{1}{2}$ days to do the whole work.

18. One man would spend $\frac{1}{6}$ of $\$36 = \$6$ in 8 days; in 1 day he would spend $\frac{1}{8}$ of $\$6 = \$\frac{6}{8}$. 5 persons would spend 5 times $\$\frac{6}{8} = \$\frac{30}{8}$ in 1 day; in 12 days, 12 times $\$\frac{30}{8} = \$\frac{360}{8} = \$45$.

19. One third of 12 rd. is 4 rd.; $\frac{1}{8}$ of 4 rd. is $\frac{4}{8}$ rd. $= \frac{1}{2}$ rd; 5 times $\frac{1}{2}$ rd. $= \frac{5}{2}$ rd.; 3 times $\frac{5}{2}$ rd. $= \frac{15}{2}$ rd. $= 7\frac{1}{2}$ **rd.**

20. One sixth of 36 bu. $= 6$ bu.; $\frac{1}{10}$ of 6 bu. $= \frac{3}{5}$ bu.; 5 times $\frac{3}{5}$ bu. $= \frac{15}{5}$ bu.; 9 times $\frac{15}{5}$ bu. $= \frac{135}{5}$ bu. $= 27$ bu.

21. One man will eat 2 B. in 5 times 6 days = 30 days; one man will eat 8 B. in 4 times 30 days = 120 days; 12 men will eat 8 B. in $\frac{1}{12}$ of 120 days = 10 days.

22. One person would spend $\frac{1}{8}$ of $400 = $50 in 5 months; in 1 month he would spend $\frac{1}{5}$ of $50 = $10; in 8 mo. 1 person would spend 8 times $10 = $80, and 11 persons would spend 11 times $80 = $880.

23. One ox can be kept on $\frac{1}{10}$ of 5 T. = $\frac{1}{2}$ T. for 3 mo.; one ox can be kept 1 mo. on $\frac{1}{3}$ of $\frac{1}{2}$ T. = $\frac{1}{6}$ T.; for 5 mo. on 5 times $\frac{1}{6}$ T. = $\frac{5}{6}$ T. 15 T. = $\frac{90}{6}$ T., and $\frac{90}{6}$ T. will keep as many oxen as $\frac{5}{6}$ are contained times in $\frac{90}{6}$ = 18. If 7 sheep eat as much as an ox, it will keep 18 times 7 sheep = 126 sheep.

LESSON LXIII.

2. One horse eats as much as $1\frac{1}{2}$ cows, and 14 horses eat as much as 21 cows; 15 cows + 21 cows = 36 cows. A pays $\frac{21}{36} = \frac{7}{12}$ of $60 = $35; B pays $\frac{15}{36} = \frac{5}{12}$ of $60 = $25.

3. B's 120 sheep = 6 horses; his 15 oxen = 10 horses; then B has the same as 6 horses + 10 horses = 16 horses. Both have 16 horses + 8 horses = 24 horses. A pays $\frac{8}{24}$, or $\frac{1}{3}$, of $72 = $24; B pays $\frac{2}{3}$ of $72 = $48.

5. C's $50 for 4 mo. = $200 for 1 mo.; D's $60 for 5 mo. = $300 for 1 mo.; $200 + $300 = $500. C has $\frac{2}{5}$ of $45 = $18; D has $\frac{3}{5}$ of $45 = $27.

6. Three men for 4 days = 12 men 1 day; 5 men 3 days = 15 men 1 day; 12 men + 15 men = 27 men. A receives $\frac{4}{9}$ of $81 = $36; B receives $\frac{5}{9}$ of $81 = $45.

7. A's $2 for 5 mo. = $10 for 1 mo.; B's $3 for 4 mo. = $12 for 1 mo.; $10 + $12 = $22. A receives $\frac{5}{11}$ of $55 = $25; B, $\frac{6}{11}$ = $30.

8. E's 4 horses = 6 cows; 6 cows for 5 mo. = 30 cows 1 mo.; F's 10 cows for 6 mo. = 60 cows 1 mo.; 30 cows + 60 cows = 90 cows. E pays $\frac{1}{3}$ of $27 = $9; F pays $\frac{2}{3}$ of $27 = $18.

9. The net gain is $300 − $150 = $150; $600 + $900 = $1500. M has $\frac{2}{5}$ of $150 = $60; N has $\frac{3}{5}$ of $150 = $90.

10. C's capital = $600 for 12 mo., or $7200 for 1 mo.; D's = $600 for 8 mo., or $4800 for 1 mo.; $7200 + $4800 = $12000. C has $\frac{72}{120}$ = $\frac{3}{5}$ of $250 = $150; D has $\frac{48}{120}$ = $\frac{2}{5}$ of $250 = $100.

11. E had $1000 for 12 mo. = $12000 for 1 mo.; F had $3000 for 12 mo. = $36000 for 1 mo., less $1000 for 4 mo. = $4000 for 1 mo., and $36000 − $4000 = $32000; $32000 + $12000 = $44000. E has $\frac{3}{11}$ of $770 = $210; F has $\frac{8}{11}$ of $770 = $560.

12. $240 − $20 = $220; B's share is $\frac{1}{2}$ of $220 = $110; A's share is $110 + $20 = $130. B has $\frac{110}{240}$ = $\frac{11}{24}$ of the gain, and also $\frac{11}{24}$ of the capital, $2400, = $1100; A has $\frac{13}{24}$ of the gain, and also $\frac{13}{24}$ of $2400, = $1300.

13. Since D's time was only $\frac{3}{4}$ of C's, he must have had $\frac{1}{4}$ more capital than C; then $\frac{4}{4}$ = D's capital, and $\frac{3}{4}$ = C's capital; $\frac{4}{4} + \frac{3}{4} = \frac{7}{4}$, and $\frac{7}{4}$ = $980. $\frac{1}{4}$ = $\frac{1}{7}$ of $980 = $140; $\frac{4}{4}$ = $560, D's capital; $\frac{3}{4}$ = $420, C's capital.

14. A's gain per mo. was $\frac{1}{10}$ of $70 = \$7$; B's gain per mo. was $\frac{1}{8}$ of $80 = \$10$. Both gained $\$7 + \$10 = \$17$ per mo. If A has $\frac{7}{17}$ of the gain, his capital is $\frac{7}{17}$ of $1700 = \$700$; B's capital is $\frac{10}{17}$ of $1700 = \$1000$.

15. The ratio of their stock was as 2 to 3, and of the time as 10 to 12; $2 \times 10 = 20$; $3 \times 12 = 36$; $20 + 36 = 56$. E's gain was $\frac{5}{14}$ of $840 = \$300$; F's gain was $\frac{9}{14}$ of $840 = \$540$.

LESSON LXVII.

8. $\frac{30}{45} = \frac{2}{3} = 66\frac{2}{3}$ per cent.

9. He gains $\frac{5}{25} = \frac{1}{5}$, and $\frac{1}{5} = 20$ per cent.

14. He gains $\$24 - \$15 = \$9$; $\$9 = \frac{3}{5}$ of the cost, or 60 per cent.

15. In 5 gal. are 20 qt. He lost $\frac{6}{20} = \frac{3}{10} = 30$ per cent.

16. Six cents $= \frac{6}{5}$ of the cost; $\frac{5}{5} = 5$ cents, the cost; 8 ct. $- 5$ ct. $= 3$ ct.; $\frac{3}{5} = 60$ per cent.

17. He paid $\frac{1}{6}$ of $3 = 50$ cents for 1 yd.; he sold 1 yd. for $\frac{1}{5}$ of $4 = 80$ ct.; 80 ct. $- 50$ ct. $= 30$ ct.; $\frac{30}{50} = \frac{3}{5} = 60$ per cent.

18. Eight ct. $= \frac{4}{5}$ of the cost; $\frac{5}{5} = 10$ ct., the cost. $\frac{1}{3}$ of 25 ct. $= 8\frac{1}{3}$ ct.; $10 - 8\frac{1}{3} = 1\frac{2}{3} = \frac{1\frac{2}{3}}{10} = \frac{5}{30} = \frac{1}{6} = 16\frac{2}{3}$ per cent loss. $\frac{1}{2}$ of 25 ct. $= 12\frac{1}{2} - 10 = 2\frac{1}{2}$; $\frac{2\frac{1}{2}}{10} = \frac{5}{20} = \frac{1}{4}$; $\frac{1}{4} = 25$ per cent gain.

19. One lemon cost $\frac{1}{2}$ of 3 ct. $= 1\frac{1}{2}$ ct. He sold 1 lemon for $\frac{1}{3}$ of 2 ct. $= \frac{2}{3}$ ct. $1\frac{1}{2} = \frac{9}{6}$; $\frac{2}{3} = \frac{4}{6}$; $\frac{9}{6} - \frac{4}{6} = \frac{5}{6}$; $\frac{5}{6}$ are $\frac{5}{9}$ of $\frac{9}{6}$, and $\frac{5}{9} = 55\frac{5}{9}$ per cent.

LESSON LXVIII.

2. $26 = 130$ per cent of the cost, or $\frac{13}{10}$; $\frac{1}{10} = \frac{1}{13}$ of $26 = \$2$; $\frac{10}{10} = \$20$, the cost.

3. Fourteen cents $= \frac{14}{10}$ of the cost; $\frac{1}{10}$ is $\frac{1}{14}$ of 14 ct. $= 1$ ct.; $\frac{10}{10} = 10$ ct., the cost.

4. $81 = \frac{9}{8}$ of the cost; $\frac{1}{8} = \$9$; $\frac{8}{8} = \$72$.

5. $63 = \frac{9}{10}$ of the cost; $\frac{1}{10} = \$7$; $\frac{10}{10} = \$70$.

6. $21 = \frac{7}{4}$ of the cost; $\frac{1}{4} = \$3$; $\frac{4}{4} = \$12$.

7. Forty ct. $= \frac{4}{3}$ of the cost; $\frac{1}{3} = 10$ ct.; $\frac{3}{3} = 30$ ct. Each orange cost $\frac{1}{10}$ of 30 ct. $= 3$ ct.

8. $10 = \frac{5}{4}$ of the cost; $\frac{1}{4} = \$2$; $\frac{4}{4} = \$8$, the cost; $12 - \$8 = \$4$. He would gain $\frac{4}{8} = 50$ per cent.

9. Seven ct. $= \frac{7}{8}$ of the cost; $\frac{1}{8} = 1$ ct.; $\frac{8}{8} = 8$ ct., the cost. 8 ct. $- 6$ ct. $= 2$ ct.; and 2 ct. are $\frac{1}{4}$ of the cost $= 25$ per cent loss.

10. $35 = \frac{5}{6}$ of the cost; $\frac{1}{6} = \$7$; $\frac{6}{6} = \$42$, the cost. $63 - \$42 = 21$; $21 is $\frac{1}{2}$ of the cost $= 50$ per cent gain.

11. $18 = \frac{6}{5}$ of its value; $\frac{5}{5} = \$15$, its value; 10 per cent of $15 is $\frac{1}{10}$ of $15 = \$1.50$; $18 - \$15 = \$3$. He lost $3 + \$1\frac{1}{2} = \$4\frac{1}{2}$.

12. $60 = \frac{6}{5}$ of the cost; $\frac{5}{5} = \$50$, the cost. A gained $60 - \$50 = \$10$; B lost 20 per cent, or $\frac{1}{5}$ of $60 = \$12$. B lost $12 - \$10 = \$2$ more than A gained.

13. $30 = $\frac{5}{4}$ of the cost of the first; $\frac{4}{4}$ = $24, the cost. The gain was $30 — $24 = $6. $30 = $\frac{3}{4}$ of the cost of the second; $\frac{4}{4}$ = $40, the cost. The loss on the watch was $40 — $30 = $10; loss by sale $10 — $6 = $4.

14. One apple sold for $\frac{1}{4}$ of 3 ct. = $\frac{3}{4}$ ct.; $\frac{3}{4}$ ct. = 150%, or $\frac{3}{2}$% of the cost. $\frac{1}{2} = \frac{1}{4}$ ct.; $\frac{2}{2} = \frac{2}{4}$ ct. = $\frac{1}{2}$ ct., the cost. 5 apples for 4 ct. = $\frac{4}{5}$ ct. for 1 apple. Gain $\frac{4}{5} - \frac{1}{2} = \frac{3}{10}$ and $\frac{3}{10} = \frac{3}{5}$ of $\frac{5}{10}$, or 60 per cent.

15. One lemon sold for $\frac{4}{5}$ ct.; $\frac{4}{5}$ ct. = $\frac{4}{5}$ per cent of the cost; 1 ct. = the cost; 6 for 5 ct. = $\frac{5}{6}$ ct. for 1; 1 ct. — $\frac{5}{6}$ ct. = $\frac{1}{6}$ ct.; $\frac{1}{6}$ of 1 ct. = 16$\frac{2}{3}$ per cent.

16. Ten per cent of 60 = 6; $\frac{2}{3}$ of 6 = 4; 4 is $\frac{1}{2}$ of 8; 8 = $\frac{1}{5}$, or 20 per cent, of 40.

17. Fifty per cent of 120 = 60; $\frac{3}{5}$ of 60 = 36; $\frac{1}{2}$ of 36 = 18; 18 is 10 less than 28, and 28 is 20 per cent, or $\frac{1}{5}$, of 140.

18. Sixty per cent of 10 is 6; $\frac{2}{3}$ of 6 = 4; $\frac{1}{4}$ of 4 = 1. 1 is 5 less than 6, and 6 is 50 per cent, or $\frac{1}{2}$, of 12.

19. Seventy-five per cent of 15 = $\frac{45}{4}$; $\frac{2}{5}$ of $\frac{45}{4} = \frac{18}{4}$; $\frac{3}{4}$ of $\frac{18}{4} = \frac{27}{8}$; $\frac{27}{8}$ are 1$\frac{3}{5}$ more than $\frac{71}{40}$, and $\frac{71}{40}$ are 50 per cent, or $\frac{1}{2}$, of $\frac{142}{40} = 3\frac{11}{20}$.

20. Twenty-five per cent of 4 is 1; $\frac{2}{3}$ of 1 = $\frac{2}{3}$; $\frac{3}{2}$ times $\frac{2}{3} = \frac{3}{3} = 1$; 1 is 25 per cent, or $\frac{1}{4}$, of 4; and 4 is $\frac{1}{2}$ of 8.

LESSON LXIX.

1. One fifth of $3 is 60 ct.; $3 — 60 ct. = $2.40.

2. One fifth of $125 = $25; $125 — $25 = $100.

3. One sixth of $840 = $140; $840 — $140 = $700.

4. Twenty $\% = \frac{1}{5}$; $\frac{1}{5}$ of $500 = $100; $500 — $100 = $400. 5$\% = \frac{1}{20}$; $\frac{1}{20}$ of $400 = $20; $400 — $20 = $380.

5. One sixth of $1200 = $200; $1200 — $200 = $1000. 5$\% = \frac{1}{20}$; $\frac{1}{20}$ of $1000 = $50; $1000 — $50 = $950.

6. $4.80 = $\frac{4}{5}$ of the retail price; $\frac{1}{5} = $1.20; $\frac{5}{5} = $6.

7. $720 = $\frac{2}{3}$ of the retail price; $\frac{1}{3} = $360; $\frac{3}{3} = $1080.

8. One hundred per cent less 5 per cent $= 95\%$, or $\frac{19}{20}$; $\frac{19}{20} = $133; $\frac{1}{20} = $7; $\frac{20}{20} = $140. $140 is $\frac{4}{5}$ of the list price; $\frac{1}{5} = $35; $\frac{5}{5} = $175.

9. $399 = $\frac{19}{20}$ of the remainder after $\frac{1}{8}$ per cent discount; $\frac{1}{20} = $21; $\frac{20}{20} = $420. $420 = $\frac{7}{8}$ of the list price; $\frac{1}{8} = $60; $\frac{8}{8} = $480.

10. $50 less $\frac{1}{5} = $40; $40 less $\frac{1}{20} = $38; $20 less $\frac{1}{10} = $13; $18 less $\frac{1}{20} = $17.10; $38 + $17.10 = $55.10.

LESSON LXX.

1. His commission was $2\frac{1}{2}$ per cent, or $\frac{1}{40}$, of $4000, = $100.

2. One twentieth of $560 = $28.

3. The corn cost 1000 times 50 ct. $= $500; $\frac{1}{40}$ of $500 = $12.50.

4. Five times $300 = $1500; $\frac{1}{20}$ of $1500 = $75. The owner receives $1500 — $75 = $1425

5. The wheat sells for 800 times $1.25 = $1000; $\frac{1}{50}$ of $1000 = $20, the commission; $1000 — $20 = $980.

6. $100 = $\frac{1}{20}$ of $2000.

7. $60 = $\frac{1}{10}$; $\frac{10}{10}$ = $600.

8. The commission was $\frac{1}{20}$ of $1000 = $50; $1000 — $50 = $950. He bought as many shares as $50 are contained times in $950 = 19.

LESSON LXXI.

1. One per cent of $2000 = $20; $\frac{1}{2}\%$ = $\frac{1}{2}$ of $20 = $10

2. One half of $3000 = $1500; $\frac{1}{50}$ of $1500 = $30.

3. Two thirds of $2400 = $1600; 1% of $1600 is $16, and $16 + $1.50 = $17.50.

4. $2500 + $1500 = $4000; 1% of $4000 is $40; $\frac{3}{4}\%$ is $\frac{3}{4}$ of $40 = $30.

5. Two thirds of $1800 are $1200; $\frac{1}{100}$ of $1200 is $12; $\frac{2}{3}$ of $1200 are $800; 1% of $800 is $\frac{1}{100}$ of $800 = $8; $\frac{1}{2}\%$ is $\frac{1}{2}$ of $8 = $4; and $12 + $4 + $1 = $17.

6. One half of $2600 = $1300; $\frac{1}{50}$ of $1300 = $26; $\frac{2}{3}$ of $1500 are $1000; $\frac{1}{100}$ of $1000 is $10; and $26 + $10 + $1 50 = $37.50.

LESSON LXXII.

4. The interest on $1 for 1 year is 8 ct.; for 3 yr. 3 times 8 ct. = 24 ct.; for $20 it is 20 times 24 ct. = $4.80.

5. The interest on $1 for 6 yr. at 4% is 24 ct.; and for $25 it is 25 times 24 ct. = $6.

6. The interest for $1 is 20 ct.; for $40 it is $8.

7. $9.   (8.) $8.40.

9. $9.   (10.) $36.

LESSON LXXIII.

2. Four mo. = $\frac{1}{3}$ of a year.   The interest on $1 for 4 mo. is $\frac{1}{3}$ of 5 ct. = $1\frac{2}{3}$ ct.; on $60 it is 60 times $1\frac{2}{3}$ ct. = $1.

3. The interest on $1 for 7 mo. at 6% is $3\frac{1}{2}$ ct.; on $80 it is $2.80.

4. On $1 it is $\frac{3}{4}$ of 8 ct. = 6 ct.; on $40 it is $2.40.

5. Two thirds of 9 ct. = 6 ct.; 75 times 6 ct. = $4.50.

7. The interest for 1 year is 180 times 4 ct. = $7.20; for 1 mo. $\frac{1}{12}$ of $7.20 = $0.60; for 10 mo. 10 times 60 ct. = $6; for 10 days $\frac{1}{3}$ of 60 ct. = 20 ct.; for 10 mo. 10 da., $6.20.

9. One year's interest = $12; 1 mo. interest = $1; for 4 mo. $4; for 24 days $\frac{4}{5}$ of $1 = 80 ct.; for 4 mo. 24 da., $4.80.

10. The int. for 1 yr. is $24; for 1 mo. $2; for 9 mo. $18; for $18 $\frac{3}{5}$ of $2 = $1.20; for 9 mo. 18 da. it is $19.20.

11. $8.45.

12. The int. for 1 yr. is $5.76; for 1 mo. 48 ct.; for 8 mo. $3.84; for 25 da. $\frac{5}{6}$ of 48 ct. $= 40$ ct.; for 8 mo. 25 da., $3.84 + $0.40 = $4.24.

13. $3.20.   (14.) $6.75.   (15.) $3.80.

16. The int. for 1 year is $1; for 3 yr. $3.   The amount is $25 + $3 = $28.

17. $44.   (18.) $68.20.   (19.) $32.80.

20. $56.80.   (21.) $99.12.

LESSON LXXIV.

2. The int. for $1 for 3 yr. at 4% is 12 ct. It will take as many dollars to acquire $6 int. as 12 ct. are contained times in 600 ct., which are 50. *Ans.* $50.

3. $60.   (4.) $75.   (5.) $140.

6. $240.   (7.) $350.

8. As many dollars as 5 ct. are contained times in $200, which are 4000. *Ans.* $4000.

LESSON LXXV.

2. The amount of $1 for 3 yr. at 6% is $1.18. It will take as many dollars to amount to $236 as $1.18 is contained times in $236, which are 200.

3. $500.   (4.) $250.

5. $300.   (6.) $25.

7. The amount of $1 for 2 yr. 6 mo. at 8% is $1.20. It will take as many dollars to amount to $60 as $1.20 is contained times in $60, which are 50. If $50 = $\frac{2}{5}$ of the principal, $\frac{5}{5}$, or the whole, = $125.

LESSON LXXVI.

2. The int. on $40 for 1 yr. at 5% is $2. To gain $8, it will take 4 yr.

3. 2 yr. 6 mo.   **(4.)** 2 yr. 8 mo.

5. $3\frac{3}{7}$ years.   **(6.)** $6\frac{2}{3}$ yr. = 6 yr. 8 mo.

9. Any principal to treble itself must gain 200%. At 5% it will take as many years as 5 is contained times in 200 = 40.

LESSON LXXVII.

2. At 1 per cent the int. on $50 for 5 yr. is $2.50. To amount to $20, the rate will be as many times 1% as $2.50 are contained times in $20, which are 8. *Ans.* 8 per cent.

3. Int. at 1% = $2.25; $11.25 ÷ $2.25 = 5.   *Ans.* 5%.

4. 7%.

5. Int. at 1% = $6.75; $54.00 ÷ $6.75 = 8.   *Ans.* 8%.

6. Int. at 1% = $8; $56 ÷ $8 = 7.   *Ans.* 7%.

7. $240 less $200 = $40, the interest; int. at 1% = $8; $40 ÷ $8 = 5.   *Ans.* 5%.

8. \$183 less \$150 = \$33, the int.; int. at $1\% = \$5.50$; \$33 ÷ \$5.50 = 6. *Ans.* 6%.

LESSON LXXVIII.

2. The amount of \$1, for the given time and rate, is $\$1.30 = \frac{13}{10}$. $\$520 = \frac{13}{10}$; $\frac{1}{10} = \$40$; $\frac{3}{10} = \$120$, the discount; $\frac{10}{10} = \$400$, the present worth.

3. $\$30 = \frac{6}{5}$; $\frac{5}{5} = \$25$, present worth; \$30 − \$25 = \$5, discount.

4. Present worth, \$500; discount, \$250.

5. $\$345 = \frac{23}{20}$; $\frac{1}{20} = \$15$; $\frac{20}{20} = \$300$. \$345 − \$300 = \$45, discount.

6. \$96.　　(7.) \$4.　　(8.) \$50.　　(9.) \$44.

10. Int. for 6 yr. 8 mo. = 40 ct.; amt. of \$1 = \$1.40 $= \frac{7}{5}$. $\$77 = \frac{7}{5}$; $\frac{1}{5} = \$11$; $\frac{5}{5} = \$55$, present worth.

11. Amt. of \$1 for 3 yr. 6 mo. at 7% is $\$1.24\frac{1}{2} = \frac{1245}{1000}$ $= \frac{249}{200}$; $\frac{1}{200}$ is $\frac{1}{249}$ of \$1000 = $\$4\frac{4}{249}$; $\frac{200}{200} = \$803\frac{53}{249}$; $\$1000 - \$803\frac{53}{249} = \$196\frac{196}{249}$, discount.

12. Amt. of \$1 is $\$1.22 = \frac{61}{50}$; $\$900 = \frac{61}{50}$; $\frac{1}{50}$ is $\frac{1}{61}$ of \$900 = $\$14\frac{46}{61}$; $\frac{50}{50} = \$737\frac{43}{61}$; $\$900 - \$737\frac{43}{61} = \$162\frac{18}{61}$.

LESSON LXXIX.

1. For 4 yr. 2 mo. 25%; $\frac{25}{100} = \frac{1}{4}$.

2. For 5 yr. 25% int.; $100\% + 25\% = 125\%$, amt.; $\frac{25}{125} = \frac{1}{5}$.

3. For 1 yr. $\frac{1}{2}$ of $\frac{1}{5} = \frac{1}{10}$; $\frac{1}{10}$ of 100% is 10%.

4. Two yr. 6 mo. $= 30$ mo.; $\frac{1}{30}$ of $\frac{1}{4} = \frac{1}{120}$ for 1 mo.; 12 times $\frac{1}{120} = \frac{1}{10}$; $\frac{1}{10}$ of $100\% = 10\%$.

5. The int. at $10\% = \frac{1}{10}$ of the principal in 1 yr.; to equal $\frac{3}{5}$, or $\frac{6}{10}$, it will take 6 yr.

6. The yearly interest is $\frac{1}{3}$ of $\frac{9}{25} = \frac{3}{25}$; $\frac{3}{25} = \frac{12}{100} = 12\%$.

7. The interest for 2 yr. is 5 times $\frac{2}{25} = \frac{20}{25} = \frac{4}{5}$; for 1 yr. $\frac{1}{2}$ of $\frac{4}{5} = \frac{2}{5}$; $\frac{2}{5} = \frac{40}{100} = 40\%$.

8. Five eighths of the interest for 1 yr. $= \frac{3}{80}$ of the principal. If $\frac{3}{80}$ are $\frac{5}{8}$, then $\frac{1}{8}$ is $\frac{1}{5}$ of $\frac{3}{80} = \frac{3}{400}$, and $\frac{8}{8} = \frac{24}{400} = \frac{6}{100} = 6\%$.

9. The int. for 4 mo. is $\frac{1}{50}$ of the principal; for 12 mo. 3 times $\frac{1}{50} = \frac{3}{50} = \frac{6}{100} = 6\%$. Int. for $1 for 1 yr. 4 mo. $= 8$ ct.; for $200 it is 200 times 8 ct. $= $16

10. One yr. 4 mo. $= 16$ mo., or 4 times 4 mo.; $\frac{1}{4}$ of $\frac{3}{25} = \frac{3}{100}$; $\frac{3}{4} = \frac{9}{100} = 9\%$. The interest of $100 for 1 yr. 8 mo. 12 da., at 9%, is $15.30.

11. In 2 times 4 yr. $= 8$ yr.

12. In $3\frac{1}{3}$ are $\frac{10}{3}$; $\frac{1}{3}$ is $\frac{1}{10}$ of $40 = $4; $\frac{3}{3} = $12; $12, the int. for 1 yr. $= 5\%$, or $\frac{1}{20}$ of the principal; the principal $= \frac{20}{20}$, or $240. A has 2 parts; B, 1 part; both, 3 parts. A has $\frac{2}{3}$ of $240 = $160; B has $\frac{1}{3} = $80.

13. In $1\frac{2}{5}$ are $\frac{7}{5}$; $\frac{1}{5} = \frac{1}{7}$ of $49 = $7; $\frac{5}{5} = $35. $35 = \frac{7}{100}$ of the principal; $\frac{1}{100} = $5; $\frac{100}{100} = $500. If twice A's money $= 3$ times B's, then once A's money $= 1\frac{1}{2}$ times B's; B s, $\frac{2}{2}$; A's, $\frac{3}{2}$; both, $\frac{5}{2}$; $\frac{2}{2} = $200, B's money; $\frac{3}{2} = $300, A's money.

14. Two yr. 3 mo. $= 27$ mo. The int. for 1 mo. is $\frac{1}{27}$ of $18 = \$\frac{18}{27} = \$\frac{2}{3}$; for 1 yr. 12 times $\$\frac{2}{3} = \$8$. $8 is 4 per cent, or $\frac{4}{100}$, of $\frac{3}{4}$ of A's and $\frac{1}{2}$ of B's; $\frac{1}{100}$ is $2; $\frac{100}{100}$ is is $200. $\frac{3}{4}$ of A's $+ \frac{1}{2}$ of B's $= \$200$; but $\frac{1}{2}$ of A's $= \frac{2}{3}$ of B's, or $\frac{1}{4}$ of A's $= \frac{1}{3}$ of B's, and B's $= \frac{3}{4}$ of A's. Then, $\frac{6}{4}$ of B's $= \$200$, and B's money $= \$133.33\frac{1}{3}$. Since B's $= \frac{3}{4}$ of A's $= \$133.33\frac{1}{3}$, $\frac{1}{4}$ of A's $= \$44.44\frac{4}{9}$, and $\frac{4}{4}$ or A's money $= \$177.77\frac{7}{9}$.

LESSON LXXX.

1. One apple is worth $\frac{1}{8}$ of 24 plums $= 3$ plums; and 84 apples are worth 84 times 3 plums $= 252$ plums. One peach is worth $\frac{1}{12}$ of 252 plums $= 21$ plums; and 5 peaches are worth 105 plums.

2. Mary has 5 more than James, and Lucy 3 more than James. $5 + 3 = 8$, and $32 - 8 = 24$; $\frac{1}{3}$ of $24 = 8$, James's share; $8 + 3 = 11$, Lucy's; $8 + 5 = 13$, Mary's.

3. Sixteen is twice the number; the number is 8.

4. C has $\frac{6}{6}$; B has $\frac{2}{6}$; A has $\frac{1}{6}$; C has $\frac{5}{6}$ more than A; $\frac{5}{6} = \$15$; $\frac{1}{6} = \$3$, A's; $\frac{6}{6} = \$18$, C's; $\frac{2}{6} = \$6$, B's.

5. Four fourths $=$ James's money; $\frac{4}{4} + \frac{3}{4} = \frac{7}{4}$; $\$34 - \$6 = \$28$; $\$28 = \frac{7}{4}$; $\frac{1}{4} = \$4$; $\frac{4}{4} = \$16$, James's money; $\frac{3}{4} + \$6 = \$18$, Thomas's money.

6. Eight eighths less $\frac{3}{8} = \frac{5}{8}$; $\frac{1}{9}$ of $\frac{5}{8} = \frac{5}{72}$; $\frac{4}{9} = \frac{20}{72}$; $\frac{5}{8} = \frac{45}{72}$; and $\frac{45}{72} + \frac{20}{72} = \frac{65}{72}$; $\frac{1}{72} = \frac{1}{65}$ of 65 sheep $= 1$ sheep; $\frac{72}{72} = 72$ sheep.

7. One man will do the work in 12 da. of 10 hr., or in 120 da. of 1 hr. each; 8 men will do it in 15 da. of 1 hr., or in $2\frac{1}{2}$ da. of 6 hr.

8. At 2 for 3 ct., 1 dozen cost 6 times 3 ct. = 18 ct.; at 2 for 5 ct., 1 doz. cost 6 times 5 ct. = 30 ct., and 2 doz. cost 18 ct. + 30 ct. = 48 ct. At 3 for 7 ct., 1 doz. sold for 4 times 7 ct. = 28 ct.; 2 doz. cost 56 ct.; and 56 ct. — 48 ct. = 8 ct., the gain on 2 doz.; 4 ct., gain on 1 doz.

9. Four horses, 2 mo. = 8 horses 1 mo.; 9 cows, 3 mo. = 27 cows, 1 mo.; 20 sheep, 5 mo. = 100 sheep, 1 mo. If 10 sheep = 2 horses, 5 sheep = 1 horse, and 100 sheep = 20 horses; 1 cow = $\frac{2}{3}$ of a horse, and 27 cows = 18 horses. Then A has the same as 8 horses; B, 18; and C, 20; and all have 46. A pays $\frac{8}{46}$ of $92 = $16; B, $\frac{18}{46}$ = $36; C, $\frac{20}{46}$ = $40.

10. He gave to each pair $5; and $5 in $20 are contained 4 times. He had 4 sons and 4 daughters.

12. Nine less 3 = 6; 4 — 2 = 2; 6 ÷ 2 = 3, number of children.

14. One of John's steps = 1$\frac{1}{4}$ of Henry's; 5 of John's = 6$\frac{1}{4}$ of Henry's. He gains in taking 5 steps, 6$\frac{1}{4}$ steps — 6 steps = $\frac{1}{4}$ step. He will take 4 times 5 steps = 20 steps to gain 1 step, and 7 times 20 steps = 140 steps to gain 7.

15. If 1 ox is worth 8 sheep, 3 oxen are worth 24 sheep, or 2 horses are worth 24 sheep; and 24 sheep are worth 24 times $5 = $120; 1 horse is worth $\frac{1}{2}$ of $120 = $60.

16. Two ct. + 24 ct. = 26 ct., and $\frac{1}{2}$ of 26 ct. = 13 ct., A's money; 13 ct. — 2 ct. = 11 ct., B's money.

17. Let $\frac{6}{6}$ = C's; $\frac{2}{6}$ = B's; $\frac{1}{6}$ = A's; then $\frac{6}{6} - \frac{2}{6} = \frac{4}{6}$, and $\frac{4}{6}$ = 20 yr. $\frac{1}{6}$ = 5 yr., A's age; $\frac{2}{6}$ = 10 yr., B's age; $\frac{6}{6}$ = 30 yr., C's age.

18. If \$15 is $\frac{3}{4}$ of their difference, then \$20 = the whole of the difference. If $\frac{2}{3}$ of A's = $\frac{4}{5}$ of B's, $\frac{3}{3}$ of A's = $\frac{6}{5}$ of B's; $\frac{3}{3} = \frac{5}{5}$, and $\frac{6}{5} - \frac{5}{5} = \frac{1}{5}$, their difference; and $\frac{1}{5}$ = \$20; $\frac{5}{5}$ = 100, B's; $\frac{6}{5}$ = \$120, A's.

19. One half of 17 is $8\frac{1}{2}$; and 10 less $8\frac{1}{2} = 1\frac{1}{2}$; and $1\frac{1}{2}$ in 15 is contained 10 times.

20. If 1 egg cost 2 ct., and 2 cost 6 ct., 3 cost 8 ct., and the average cost is $2\frac{2}{3}$ ct. 1 egg sells for $\frac{1}{3}$ of 10 ct. = $3\frac{1}{3}$ ct. The gain on 1 is $3\frac{1}{3} - 2\frac{2}{3} = \frac{2}{3}$; $\frac{2}{3}$ is $\frac{1}{4}$ of $2\frac{2}{3}$, or 25 per cent.

21. Eight less 5 = 3; 21 ÷ 3 = 7, number of playmates.

22. John gains 2 steps every time he takes 7; to gain 30 steps he must take 7 steps as many times as 2 is contained in 30, or 15 times; 15 times 7 steps = 105 steps.

23. Let $\frac{7}{7}$ = the watch, and $\frac{2}{7}$ = the chain; three times $\frac{2}{7}$ plus 2 times $\frac{7}{7} = \frac{20}{7}$, and $\frac{20}{7}$ = \$100; $\frac{1}{7}$ = \$5; $\frac{2}{7}$ = \$10, price of the chain; $\frac{7}{7}$ = \$35, price of the watch.

24. In $4\frac{1}{2}$ are $\frac{9}{2}$; $2\frac{4}{2} = \frac{18}{7}$; A does $\frac{2}{9}$ in 1 day; both do $\frac{7}{18}$ in 1 day; $\frac{7}{18}$ less $\frac{2}{9} = \frac{3}{18} = \frac{1}{6}$, what B does in 1 day. If B does $\frac{1}{6}$ in 1 day, he would do it all in 6 days.

25. He gave $\frac{1}{2}$ ct. each for the first lot, and $\frac{1}{4}$ ct. each for the second lot; for two he gave $\frac{1}{2}$ ct. + $\frac{1}{4}$ ct. = $\frac{3}{4}$ ct.; average price, $\frac{3}{8}$ ct. He sold them for $\frac{2}{5}$ ct. each; gain on each, $\frac{2}{5} - \frac{3}{8} = \frac{9}{40}$. If he gained $\frac{9}{40}$ ct. on one, to gain 18 ct. it took as many pears as $\frac{9}{40}$ ct. is contained times in 18 ct. = 80.

26. He receives \$59 — \$50 = \$9 for 2 years' interest on \$50, or \$4.50 for each year. $\frac{4.50}{50} = 9\%$.

27. She wished to buy as many yards as $\frac{1}{2}$ is contained times in $5 = 10$.

28. A's money $= \frac{5}{5}$; B's money $= \frac{2}{5} - \$5$; $\frac{5}{5} + \frac{2}{5} - \$5 = \$51$; $\frac{7}{5} = \$56$; $\frac{1}{5} = \$8$; $\frac{5}{5} = \$40$, A's money; \$51 — \$40 = \$11, B's.

29. One third of the gain $= \frac{2}{15}$ of the selling price, and $\frac{3}{3} = \frac{6}{15}$, or $\frac{2}{5}$; $3\frac{3}{4}$ times \$4 = \$15, the cost. If the gain is $\frac{2}{5}$ of the selling price, then $\frac{5}{5} - \frac{2}{5} = \frac{3}{5}$, or the cost; $\frac{3}{5} = \$15$; $\frac{5}{5} = \$25$, the selling price.

30. The hound gains 5 of the hare's leaps every time the hare takes 3; to gain 100, he must take 3 leaps as many times as 5 is contained in $100 = 20$, and 20 times $3 = 60$.

31. Thomas's age $= 3$ parts; James's $= 1$ part; 3 parts $- 1$ part $= 10$, the difference. If $10 = 2$ parts, then 5 yr. $=$ James's age, and 15 yr. $=$ Thomas's.

32. If $\frac{3}{7} = \frac{4}{5}$, then $\frac{7}{7} = \frac{28}{15}$; and $\frac{28}{15} + \frac{15}{15} = \frac{43}{15}$ of George's distance; $\frac{43}{15} = 86$ miles; $\frac{1}{15} = 2$ miles; $\frac{15}{15} = 30$ miles, George's distance; $\frac{28}{15} = 56$ miles, John's distance.

34. The difference between selling the lot at 6 ct. a doz. and 10 ct. a doz. is 12 ct. + 18 ct. = 30 ct. The difference on 1 doz. is 10 ct. — 6 ct. = 4 ct. There were as many doz. as 4 ct. are contained times in 30 ct. = $7\frac{1}{2}$ doz. The cost of the lot was $6 \times 7\frac{1}{2} + 12 = 57$ ct.; and the cost of 1 doz. was 57 ct. $\div 7\frac{1}{2} = 7\frac{3}{5}$ ct.

35. Let $\frac{10}{10}$ = A's age, and $\frac{5}{10}$ = B's; $\frac{3}{5}$ of $\frac{5}{10}$ are $\frac{3}{10}$, and $\frac{3}{10}$ + 44 = $2\frac{1}{2}$ times $\frac{10}{10}$ = $\frac{25}{10}$. If $\frac{3}{10}$ + 44 = $\frac{25}{10}$, then $\frac{22}{10}$ = 44, and $\frac{1}{10}$ = 2, and $\frac{10}{10}$ = 20 yr., A's age; $\frac{5}{10}$ = 10 yr., B's age.

36. Seven eighths of 24 miles = 21 miles. If 21 mi. are $\frac{3}{7}$, then $\frac{1}{7}$ is 7 mi., and $\frac{7}{7}$ are 49 mi., the distance from B to C; 49 mi. + 24 mi. = 73 mi., distance from A to C.

37. A, B, and C together can do $\frac{1}{4}$ in 1 da.; A and B together can do $\frac{1}{8}$ in 1 da.; B and C together can do $\frac{1}{6}$ in 1 da.; C can do in 1 da. $\frac{1}{4} - \frac{1}{8} = \frac{1}{8}$, and the whole in 8 da.; A can do in 1 da. $\frac{1}{4} - \frac{1}{6} = \frac{1}{12}$, and the whole in 12 da.; B can do in 1 da. $\frac{1}{6} - \frac{1}{8} = \frac{1}{24}$, and the whole in 24 da.

38. One duck cost $\$\frac{1}{6}$; 1 chicken, $\$\frac{1}{8}$, and 2 chickens, $\$\frac{2}{8}$; $\frac{1}{6} + \frac{2}{8} = \frac{10}{24}$; $\frac{1}{3}$ of $\frac{10}{24} = \frac{10}{72} = \frac{5}{36}$, the average cost. One third of $\frac{1}{2} = \frac{1}{6}$, the average selling price; $\frac{1}{6} = \frac{6}{36} - \frac{5}{36} = \frac{1}{36}$, the average gain; the whole gain was $\$2\frac{1}{2}$ = $\$\frac{5}{2}$; $\frac{5}{2} = \frac{90}{36}$; $\frac{90}{36} \div \frac{1}{36} = 90$, the whole number; $\frac{2}{3}$ of 90 = 60, the chickens; $\frac{1}{3}$ of 90 = 30, the ducks.

39. Eight ct. — 3 ct. = 5 ct.; 6 ct. + 29 ct. = 35 ct.; 35 ct. = $\frac{5}{8}$ of cost of oranges; $\frac{1}{8}$ = 7 ct., and $\frac{8}{8}$ = 56 ct.; 56 ct. — 6 ct. = 50 ct., James's money.

40. A rides $\frac{1}{5}$ of 10 miles in $\frac{1}{4}$ of an hour, and 8 miles in 1 hour; A will travel 18 miles in 18 ÷ 8 = $2\frac{1}{4}$ hr. B travels $\frac{1}{8}$ of a mile in $\frac{1}{5}$ hr., and 5 miles an hour; B will travel $2\frac{1}{4}$ times 5 mi. = $11\frac{1}{4}$ mi., while A travels 18 mi.

41. Three halves + $\$2\frac{1}{2}$ = $\$40$; then $\frac{3}{2} = \$37\frac{1}{2}$; $\frac{1}{2} = \$12\frac{1}{2}$; $\frac{2}{2} = \$25$, his money.

42. C received $\frac{21}{21} - \frac{6}{21} - \frac{7}{21} = \frac{8}{21}$; $\frac{8}{21} - \frac{6}{21} = \frac{2}{21}$; $\frac{2}{21}$ $= \$160$; $\frac{1}{21} = \$80$; $\frac{6}{21} = \$480$, A's legacy; $\frac{7}{21} = \$560$, B's legacy; $\frac{8}{21} = \$640$, C's legacy.

43. Both consume $\frac{6}{15}$ in 6 days, and $\frac{15}{15}$ less $\frac{6}{15} = \frac{9}{15}$ $= \frac{3}{5}$ remaining. The woman consumes $\frac{1}{24}$ of $\frac{3}{5}$ in one day $= \frac{3}{120} = \frac{1}{40}$, and all in 40 days. Both consume $\frac{1}{15}$ in one day; $\frac{1}{15} - \frac{1}{40} = \frac{5}{120} = \frac{1}{24}$, what the man consumes in one day. It would last him alone 24 days.

44. Three and one half ct. $+ 6\frac{1}{2}$ ct. $= 10$ ct., the price of 2 pounds of the mixture; $100 \div 10 = 10$; 10 times 2 pounds $= 20$, the number of pounds.

45. Let $\frac{1}{10} = $ C's age; $\frac{2}{10} = $ B's; and $\frac{10}{10} = $ C's. $\frac{10}{10} - \frac{1}{10} = \frac{9}{10}$; $\frac{9}{10} = 45$ yr.; $\frac{1}{10} = \frac{1}{9}$ of 45 yr. $= 5$ yr., C's age; $\frac{2}{10} = 10$ yr., B's age; $\frac{10}{10} = 50$ yr. $= $ A's age.

46. Three fifths $=$ Mary's age, and $\frac{5}{5} = $ Ella's; their sum is $\frac{8}{5}$; twice Ella's is $\frac{10}{5}$; $\frac{10}{5} - \frac{8}{5} = \frac{2}{5}$, and $\frac{2}{5} = 6$ yr.; $\frac{1}{5}$ $= 3$ yr.; $\frac{5}{5} = 15$ yr., Ella's age; $\frac{3}{5} = 9$ yr., Mary's age.

47. Both do $\frac{4}{16}$ in 4 days; and $\frac{16}{16} - \frac{4}{16} = \frac{3}{4}$, that B finishes in 36 days. In one day he does $\frac{1}{36}$ of $\frac{3}{4} = \frac{3}{144}$ $= \frac{1}{48}$, and he does all in 48 days; $\frac{1}{16} - \frac{1}{48} = \frac{1}{24}$, what A does in 1 day, and he would do all in 24 days.

48. Three doz. at 1 ct. each $= 36$ ct.; 2 doz. at 4 eggs for 3 ct. $= 18$ ct.; 2 doz., the remainder, at 4 eggs for 5 ct. $= 30$ ct.; 36 ct. $+ 18$ ct. $+ 30$ ct. $= 84$ ct.; $84 = 7$ doz.; $\frac{1}{7}$ of 84 ct. $= 12$ ct. a doz.

50. If he had worked 30 days, he would have received 30 times 30 ct. = $9. Each day he is idle he gives 20 ct. for board and forfeits 30 ct. for not working = 50 ct. $9 — $5 = $4; $4.00 ÷ 50 ct. = 8, number of days idle; 30 days — 8 days = 22, number of days he worked.

51. The difference per yard is $2\frac{1}{2}$ ct.; $40 ÷ 2\frac{1}{2} = 16$, the number of yards.

52. If 4 of Moses's steps = 7 of Noah's, then one of Moses's = $1\frac{3}{4}$ of Noah's, and 5 of Moses's = $8\frac{3}{4}$ of Noah's; Moses gains $8\frac{3}{4} — 7 = 1\frac{3}{4}$ of Noah's steps every time he takes 5 steps; to gain 35 he must take 5 steps as many times as $1\frac{3}{4}$ are contained in 35. $35 = \frac{140}{4}$; $1\frac{3}{4} = \frac{7}{4}$; $\frac{140}{4} ÷ \frac{7}{4} = 20$; 20 times 5 steps = 100 steps.

53. One man will do as much work as 6 boys; 2 men as much as 12 boys; then 2 men would do in a week as much as 12 boys, and to do it in 1 day it would take 6 times 2 men = 12 men.

54. Let $\frac{1}{12}$ = the number in the first field; $\frac{4}{12}$, in the second; and $\frac{12}{12}$, in the third; then $\frac{12}{12} — \frac{1}{12} — \frac{4}{12} = \frac{7}{12}$, and $\frac{7}{12} = 70$; $\frac{1}{12} = 10$, the number in the first field; $\frac{4}{12} = 40$, the number in the second; $\frac{12}{12} = 120$, the number in the third.

55. For 24 days he would have received $48. He loses $2 each day he is idle, and pays 50 ct. for board = $2\frac{1}{2}$; $48 — $38 = $10; $10 ÷ $2\frac{1}{2} = 4$, number of days idle; 24 — 4 = 20, number of days he worked.

56. Since $12 = \frac{2}{7}$ of B's and C's, $\frac{7}{7} = $42; and $42 + $12 = $54, what all had. If $\frac{3}{2}$ of C's = $\frac{3}{10}$ of A's and B's,

then $\frac{1}{8} = \frac{1}{10}$, and the whole of C's $= \frac{8}{10}$ of A's and B's; hence, $\frac{18}{10}$ of A's and B's $= \$54$; $\frac{1}{10} = \$3$, and $\frac{10}{10} = \$30$; $\$30 - \$12 = \$18$, B's share; $\$54 - \$30 = \$24$, C's share.

57. Six and six sevenths pounds cost $6\frac{6}{7}$ times 8 ct. $= 54\frac{6}{7}$ ct.; $\frac{1}{6}$ of $54\frac{6}{7}$ ct. $= 9\frac{1}{7}$ ct.; $54\frac{6}{7}$ ct. $+ 9\frac{1}{7}$ ct. $= 64$ ct.

58. The first has $1200 for 1 mo.; the second has $2400 for 1 mo., or $1200 more than the first; the first must put in for the remaining 6 mo. $\frac{1}{6}$ of $1200 = $200.

59. The difference between selling at 9 ct. and 12 ct. is $1.50 on the whole; on one pound the difference is 3 ct.; there are as many pounds as $1.50 \div 3 = 50$.

60. One of B's steps $= 1\frac{1}{2}$ of A's, and 4 of B's $= 6$ of A's; B gains $6 - 5 = 1$ step every time he takes 4 steps; B takes 4 steps 9 times in taking 36 steps. If he gains 1 step every time he takes 4, then A is 9 steps in advance of B.

61. Both had 9 oranges; each ate $\frac{1}{3}$ of $9 = 3$. Thomas ate 2 of John's oranges, and should give him $\frac{2}{3}$ of 9 ct. $= 6$ ct.; he ate one of James's, and should give him $\frac{1}{3}$ of 9 ct. $= 3$ ct.

SOLUTIONS

TO

QUESTIONS AND PROBLEMS

IN

RAY'S NEW PRACTICAL ARITHMETIC.

NOTATION.

NUMBERS TO BE WRITTEN.

Art. 5.

(1.) 23 ; 24 ; 25 ; 26 ; 27 ; 28 ; 29.

(2.) 37 ; 42 ; 56 ; 69 ; 73 ; 87 ; 94.

(3.) 83 ; 45 ; 99 ; 51 ; 36 ; 78 ; 62.

(4.) 55 ; 93 ; 81 ; 67 ; 49 ; 74 ; 38.

(5.) 76 ; 44 ; 82 ; 57 ; 35 ; 91 ; 63.

NUMBERS TO BE READ.

(1.) Seventy-one; thirty-two; fifty-three; eighty-four; sixty-five; forty-six; ninety-seven.

(2.) Fifty-eight; thirty-four; seventy-nine; sixty-six; forty-one; eighty-five; ninety-two.

(3.) Seventy-five; forty-three; eighty-eight; sixty-one; fifty-nine; thirty-three; ninety-five.

(4.) Thirty-nine; seventy-two; fifty-four; eighty-six; forty-seven; ninety-eight; sixty-four.

(5.) Sixty-eight; seventy-seven; thirty-one; eighty-nine; fifty-two; ninety-six; forty-eight.

NUMBERS TO BE WRITTEN.

Art. 7.

(1.) 130; 140; 150; 160; 170; 180.

(2.) 123; 456; 789; 147; 258; 369.

(3.) 102; 345; 678; 234; 567; 890.

(4.) 453; 786; 912; 230; 450; 670.

(5.) 153; 486; 729; 103; 406; 709.

NUMBERS TO BE READ.

(1.) Two hundred and ten; three hundred and twenty; four hundred and thirty, etc.

(2.) Two hundred and thirteen; five hundred and forty-six; eight hundred and seventy-nine; four hundred and seventeen, etc.

(3.) Two hundred and one; four hundred and thirty-five; seven hundred and sixty-eight; three hundred and twenty-four, etc.

Art. 11.

(2.) 2000; 30000; 400000.

(3.) 5000000; 60000000; 700000000.

(4.) 8000000000; 90000-000000; 100000000000.

(5.) 1200; 2100.

(6.) 3450; 6789.

(7.) 12345.

(8.) 678912.

(9.) 1357924.

(10.) 68143792.

(11.) 1001; 1010; 1100.

(12.) 1101; 1110; 1111.

(13.) 2003; 4050.

(14.) 45026.

(15.) 80201.

(16.) 90001.

(17.) 410205.

(18.) 100010.

(19.) 3070509.

(20.) 45083026.

(21.) 909090000.

(22.) 700010002.

(23.) 40000200005.

(24.) 726050001243.

(25.) 80703000504.

NUMERATION.

Art. 12.

(2.) Forty-one thousand five hundred and eighty-two; seven hundred and sixty-three thousand four hundred and ninety-one; two million five hundred and nineteen thousand eight hundred and thirty-four; three hundred and seventy-five million four hundred and eighty-six thousand nine hundred and twenty-one; four billion nine hundred and twenty-three million one hundred and seventy-six thousand three hundred and fifty-eight.

(3.) Thirty-seven billion five hundred and eighty-four million two hundred and sixteen thousand nine hundred and seventy-four; four hundred and thirty-two billion six hundred and eighty-five million seven hundred and twenty-nine thousand one hundred and forty-five; six trillion two hundred and fifty-three billion nine hundred and seventy-one million four hundred and thirty-eight thousand two hundred and sixty-seven.

(4.) One thousand three hundred; two thousand five hundred and forty; six thousand and seventy; eight thousand and nine; thirteen thousand two hundred; one thousand and five.

(5.) Six hundred and eighty-two thousand three hundred; eight million six hundred thousand and fifty; three thousand and forty; fifty thousand and four; seven hundred and four thousand two hundred and eight.

(6.) Seven thousand and eighty-five; sixty-two thou·

sand and one; four hundred thousand and nine; two million one hundred and two thousand one hundred and two; nine million one thousand and three.

(7.) One hundred and thirty million six hundred and seventy thousand nine hundred and twenty-one; six billion nine hundred million seven hundred and two thousand and three; twenty-three billion four million ninety thousand seven hundred and one; nine billion four hundred and twenty million one hundred and sixty-three thousand and seventy.

(8.) Five hundred and seventy trillion ten million three hundred and twenty-six thousand and forty-nine; two hundred quadrillion one hundred and three trillion four hundred and seventy-eight billion five hundred and eleven million nine hundred and ninety-two thousand four hundred and eighty-five.

(9.) Forty-five quintillion seven hundred and sixty-three quadrillion twenty billion one hundred and eight million five hundred and seven.

(10.) Eight hundred trillion eight hundred and twenty billion twenty million eight hundred and two thousand and eight.

Art. 13. (P. 21.)

(1.) I, II, III, IV, V, VI, VII, VIII, IX, X, XI, XII, XIII, XIV, XV, XVI, XVII, XVIII, XIX, XX.

(2.) XXI, XXII, XXIII, XXIV, etc., XXX.

(3.) XXX, XL, L, LX, LXX, LXXX, XC.

(4.) LVII, XXIX, LXI, XXXVIII, XLVI, LXXII, XCIII.

(5.) C, CI, CVI, CXVII, CXXIX, CLXVIII.

(6.) CXCIX, CCXLVI, CCCIX, CCCCLXXXII, DXXVII, DCXCIII.

(7.) DCCXXXIV, DCCCLIX, DCCCCLXXV, MI, MX.

(8.) MXLVIII, MCXIX, MCCLXXXV, MCCCXXVI.
(9.) MCCCCXCII, MDCCLXXVI, MDCCCLXI, MDCCCC.

ADDITION.

Art. 17.

(2.)	$210	(4.)	50230
	142		3105
	35		423
	$387		53758

Art. 19.

(8.) 21023. (9.) 27910. (10.) 89569.

(11.) 2499593. (12.) 24194086.

(29.) $146 + 607 + 47 = 800$: 1700 yr. + 800 yr. = 2500 yr.

(30)	(31)	(32)	(33)
3005	275432	880000889	8955752
42627	402030	2002002	6917246
105	300005	77436000	94523
307004	872026	206005207	15967521
80079	4002347	49003	
320600	5851840	990019919	
753420		2155513020	

(34)	(35)	(36)	(37)	(38)
$600	$7850	$8785	$7000	30
1325	3275	12789	12875	30
30	3275	878	5600	25
120	2650	1250	4785	25
250	2650	$23702	3500	25
140	2650		$33760	25
120	2650			20
115	$22350			20
$2700				200 yd.

SUBTRACTION.

Art. 26.

(5)	(6)	(8)	(9)
4444444	91516171	153425178	100000000
1234567	15161718	53845248	10001001
3209877	76354453	99579930	89998999

(14)	(15)	16)	(18)	(19)
$1840	$10104	$100000	912010	4000000
475	7426	11	50082	4004
$1365	$2678	$99989	861928	3995996

(20)	(21)	(22)	(23)
2020930	2000687	17102102	$30000
1009006	405022	13000201	26967
1011924	1595665	4101901	$3033

(24)	(25)
18126402	19900900900
9238715	9909090009
8887687	9991810891

ADDITION AND SUBTRACTION.

(1)	(2)	(3)		(4)
275	6723	$2675	$3000	$250
381	479	4375	4947	650
625	6244	1897	$7947	$900
1281	347	$8947		
1098	5897	7947		$1300
183	228	$1000, *Ans.*		900
	5669			$400

(5)	
$450	
725	
1235	
4675	$5935
1727	877
$8812	$6812
6812	
$2000, *Ans.*	

(6)
$350
125
375
150
$1000
$2300
1000
$1300, *Ans.*

(7)
$4875
4875 ⎱
2250 ⎰
3725
$15725
$20838
15725
$5113, *Ans.*

(8)	
$16785	$49570
24937	41722
$41722	$7848, *Ans.*

(9)	
$7895	$10093
175	8073
3	$2020, *Ans.*
$8073	

(10)	
$5750	$10000
925	8925
1575	$1075, *Ans.*
675	
$8925	

(11)		
$4625	$6955	$9395
3785	895	9225
985	1375	$170, *Ans.*
$9395	$9225	

(12)		
Received, $50	Spent, $25	$100
50	7	91
$100	2	$9, *Ans.*
	5	
	35	
	7	
	2	
	8	
	$91	

MULTIPLICATION.

Art. 31.

(25)	(26)	(27)	(28)	(29)
235	346	425	518	279
13	19	29	34	37
705	3114	3825	2072	1953
235	346	850	1554	837
3055	6574	12325	17612	10323

(30)	(31)	(32)	(33)	(34)
869	294	429	485	624
49	57	62	76	85
7821	2058	858	2910	3120
3476	1470	2574	3395	4992
42581	16758	26598	36860	53040

(35)	(36)	(37)	(38)
976	342	376	476
97	364	526	536
6832	1368	2256	2856
8784	2052	752	1428
94672	1026	1880	2380
	124488	197776	255136

(39)	(40)	(41)	(42)
2187	3489	1646	8432
215	276	365	635
10935	20934	8230	42160
2187	24423	9876	25296
4374	6978	4938	50592
470205	962964	600790	5354320

(43)	(44)	(45)	(46)
6874	2873	4786	87603
829	1823	3497	9865
61866	8619	33502	438015
13748	5746	43074	525618
54992	22984	19144	700824
5698546	2873	14358	788427
	5237479	16736642	864203595

(47)	(48)	(51)	(52)
83457	31624	675	496
6835	7138	13	24
417285	252992	2025	1984
250371	94872	675	992
667656	31624	8775 ct.	11904 ct.
500742	221368		
570428595	225732112		

(55)
365
24
1460
730
8760
8
70080 mi.

(53)	(54)		(56)
152	1760		2029
28	209		1007
1216	15840		14203
304	3520		2029
4256 mi.	367840 yd.		2043203

(57)	(58)	(60)	36
80401	101032	36	55
60007	20001	45	180
562807	101032	180	180
482406	202064	144	1980
4824622807	2020741032	1620	1620

Ans. 360 ct.

(61)
95 ct. — 2 ct. = 93 ct.

2650
93
7950
23850
246450 ct.

(62)
$75 × 6 = $450
125 × 5 = 625
$1075

$150 × 11 = $1650
$1650 — $1075 = $575, *Ans.*

(63)
$250
$325 × 2 = 650
175 × 3 = 525
$1425
356
$1781, *Ans.*

(64)
24 × $5 = $120
36 × 14 = 504
9 × 45 = 405
$1029
275
$754, *Ans.*

(65)
75   85
37   54
525   340
225   425
2775   4590
4590
7365
5284
2081, *Ans.*

(66)
69   48
53   27
207   336
345   96
3657   1296
       3657
       4953
       4279
       674, *Ans.*

(67)
63 lb.
50
3150 lb.

3150
34 ct.
12600
9450
107100 ct., *Ans.*

Art. 32.

(2)		(3)	(4)
$124	$124	1512 mi.	**2873 lb.**
6	8	8	**9**
$744 or	$992	12096 mi.	25857 lb.
4	3	7	6
$2976	$2976	84672 mi.	155142 lb.

(5)	(6)
2874	8074
9	12
25866	96888
8	9
206928	871992

Art. 33.

(1)	(2)	(3)
245	138	428
100	1000	10000
24500	138000	4280000

(4)	(5)	(6)
872	9642	10045
100000	1000000	1000000
87200000	9642000000	10045000000

Art. 34.

(3)	(4)	(5)	(6)
2350	80300	10240	9600
60	450	3200	2400
141000	4015	2048	384
	3212	3072	192
	36135000	32768000	23040000

(7)	(8)	(9)
18001	8602	3007
26000	1030	9100
108006	25806	3007
36002	8602	27063
468026000	8860060	27363700

(10)	(11)	(12)
80600	70302	904000
7002	80300	10200
1612	210906	1808
5642	562416	904
564361200	5645250600	9220800000

SHORT DIVISION.

Art. 41.

(24)	(25)	(29)
3) 894	4) 140	4) 321276
298	35	80319

(32)	(33)	(46)
11) 495	9) 3582	4) 144
45	398	3) 36
		12 *Ans.*

(47)
5) 195   3) 39
39   13, *Ans.*

(48)
8) 192   11) 275   25
24   25   24
                1, *Ans.*

LONG DIVISION.

Art. 42.

(5)

14) 11577 (826$\frac{13}{14}$, *Ans.*
112
———
37
28
——
97
84
——
13

(6)

15) 48690 (3246
45
——
36
30
——
69
60
——
90
90
——

(7)

23) 1110960 (48302$\frac{14}{23}$
92
———
190
184
———
69
69
——
60
46
——
14

(8)

67) 122878 (1834
67
———
558
536
———
227
201
———
268
268
———

(9)

53) 12412 (234$\frac{10}{53}$
106
———
181
159
———
222
212
———
10

(10)

72) 146304 (2032
144
———
230
216
———
144
144
———

(11)

54) 47100 (872$\frac{12}{54}$
432
———
390
378
———
120
108
———
12

(12)

88) 71104 (808
704
———
704
704
———

(13)

66) 43956 (666
396
———
435
396
———
396
396
———

(14)

99) 121900 (1231$\frac{31}{99}$
99
———
229
198
———
310
297
———
130
99
———
31

(15)

112) 25312 (226
224
———
291
224
———
672
672
———

(16)

123) 381600 (3102$\frac{54}{123}$
369
———
126
123
———
300
246
———
54

(17)

204) 105672 (518
1020
———
367
204
———
1632
1632
———

(18)

1234) 600000 (486$\frac{276}{1234}$
4936
———
10640
9872
———
7680
7404
———
276

(19)

4321) 1234567 (285$\frac{3082}{4321}$
8642
———
37036
34568
———
24687
21605
———
3082

(20)

819) 50964242 (6518
46914
———
40502
39095
———
14074
7819
———
62552
62552
———

(22)

12345) 4049160 (328
37035
———
34566
24690
———
98760
98760
———

(21)

9876) 48905952 (4952
39504
———
94019
88884
———
51355
49380
———
19752
19752
———

(23)

973) 552160000 (567482$\frac{14}{973}$
4865
‾‾‾‾
6566
5838
‾‾‾‾
7280
6811
‾‾‾‾
4690
3892
‾‾‾‾
7980
7784
‾‾‾‾
1960
1946
‾‾‾‾
14

(24)

15) 3465 (231
30
‾‾
46
45
‾‾
15
15 ·
‾‾

(25)

26) 364 (14 days.
26
‾‾
104
104
‾‾‾

(26)

19) 1083 (57 dollars.
95
‾‾
133
133
‾‾‾

(27)

107) 9523 (89 bu.
856
‾‾‾
963
963
‾‾‾

(28)

63) 14868 (236 hhd.
126
‾‾‾
226
189
‾‾‾
378
378
‾‾‾

(29)

365) 50000 (136
365
‾‾‾
1350
1095
‾‾‾‾
2550
2190
‾‾‾‾
360

Ans. $136 and $360 over.

(30)

365) 379600 ($1040
365
‾‾‾
1460
1460
‾‾‾‾
0

(31)

1235) 6571435 (5321
6175
‾‾‾‾
3964
3705
‾‾‾‾
2593
2470
‾‾‾‾
1235
1235

(32)

405) 1247400 (3080
1215
‾‾‾‾
3240
3240
‾‾‾‾
0

(33)

1006) 10401000 (10338$\frac{972}{1006}$
       1006
       ————
       3410
       3018
       ————
       3920
       3018
       ————
       9020
       8048
       ————
        972

(34)

684) 109440 (160 **A.**
     684
     ————
     4104
     4104
     ————
        0

(35)

56) 8288 (148 **A.**
    56
    ———
    268
    224
    ———
    448
    448

(36)

269) 262275 (975 dollars.
     2421
     ————
     2017
     1883
     ————
     1345
     1345
     ————

(37)

24) 24899 (1037$\frac{11}{24}$ mi.
    24
    ———
    89
    72
    ———
    179
    168
    ———
     11

(38)

238) 3731840 (15680
     238   dollars.
     ————
     1351
     1190
     ————
     1618
     1428
     ————
     1904
     1904
     ————
        0

(39)

24) 27048 (1127 ft.
    24
    ———
    30
    24
    ———
    64
    48
    ———
    168
    168
    ———

(40)

1152000) 92160000 (8 min.
         92160000
         ————————

(41)

94231
86247
————
16) 7984 (499, *Ans.*
    64
    ———
    158
    144
    ———
    144
    144
    ———

```
        (42)                      (43)                        (44)
       46712                      497                        2832
        6848                      583                         987
104) 53560 (515                  1491                        1845
     520                         3976                         678
     ───                         2485                 - 87) 2523 (29
     156               71) 289751 (4081                     174
     104                        284                         ───
     ───                        ───                         783
     520                        575                         783
     520                        568
     ───                        ───
                                 71
        (45)                     71
       4896                      ──
       2384
       2512                      (46)                        (47)
         49                      228                  478     478
     ─────                       786                  296     296
     22608                      1014                  182     774
     10048               ──────                       ───     182
112) 123088 (1099                95                          ───
     112                        5070                         1548
     ────                       9126                         6192
     1108              114) 96330 (845                       774
     1008                      912                   387) 140868 (364
     ────                      ───                        1161
     1008                      513                         ────
     1008                      456                         2476
     ────                      ───                         2322
                               570                         ────
        (48)                   570                         1548
       7560                    ───                         1548
       3885                                                ────
175) 3675 (21 horses.
     350
     ───
     175
     175
     ───
```

(49)	(50)	(51)
7350	58	240
4655	77	26
49) 12005 (245 A.	406	1440
98	406	480
220	4466	6240
196		2820
245	5742	180) 3420 (19 horses.
245	4466	180
	58) 1276 (22 dollars	1620
	116	1620
	116	
	116	

(52)

125 lots.   25) 20625 (825 dolls., gain per acre.
  250 dolls. each.   200

6250   62   125) 20625 (165 dolls., gain
250   50   125   on each lot.

31250   125   812
10625   125   750

$20625, whole gain.   625
                                625

Art. 43.

(3)	(4)	(5)	(6)
9) 2583	4) 6976	4) 2744	6) 6145
7) 287	8) 1744	7) 686	7) 1024—1 rem.
Ans. 41	*Ans.* 218	*Ans.* 98	146—2

$$6 \times 2 + 1 = 13 \text{ rem.}$$
$$\textit{Ans. } 146\tfrac{13}{42}$$

(7)

11)19008

12)1728

Ans. 144

(8)

8)7840   *Ans.*

8)980 $122\frac{32}{64}$

122—4

$8 \times 4 = 32$ rem.

(9)

8)14771   *Ans.*

9)1846—3 $205\frac{11}{72}$

205—1

$8 \times 1 + 3 = 11$ rem.

(10)

9)10206

9)1134

Ans. 126

(11)

11)81344

11)7394—10

672— 2

$2 \times 11 + 10 = 32$

Ans. $672\frac{32}{121}$

or

121)81344($672\frac{32}{121}$
    726
    874
    847
    274
    242
    32

(12)

9)98272

12)10919—1

909—11

$11 \times 9 + 1 = 100$

Ans. $909\frac{100}{108}$

or

108)98272($909\frac{100}{108}$, *Ans.*
    972
    1072
    972
    100

Art. 44.

(2)

1|0)268|2

$268\frac{2}{10}$

(3)

1|00)47|00

47

(4)

1|00)372|01

$372\frac{1}{100}$

(5)

1|00)462|50

$462\frac{50}{100}$

(6)

1|000)18|003

$18\frac{3}{1000}$

Art. 45.

(4)

4|000)73|005

$18\frac{1005}{4000}$

(5)

9|000)36|001

$4\frac{1}{9000}$

(6)

11|000)1078|000

98

(7)

$18|0)4016|7(223\frac{27}{180}$

36
—
41
36
—
56
54
—
2

(9)

$64|00)3640|06(56\frac{5606}{6400}$

320
—
440
384
—
56

(8)

$21|00)9072|37(432\frac{37}{2100}$

84
—
67
63
—
42
42
—

(11)

$634|00)435637|54(687\frac{7954}{63400}$

3804
—
5523
5072
—
4517
4438
—
79

(10)

$25|0000)7654|6037(306\frac{46037}{250000}$

75
—
154
150
—
4

Art. 49.

(1)

$96　$500
120　271
55　$229, *Ans.*
—
$271

(2)

$243 1st.　$243　$1265
61　　　304　　772
—　　　225　$493, *Ans*
$304 2d.　—
79　　　$772
—
$225 3d.

(3)

157　428
264　186
305　614
97
123
—
946
614
—
332, *Ans.*

(4)

9503　57068
586　16967
4794　40101, *Ans.*
1234
850
—
16967

(5)

$12307	$237	$21013
8706	301	5918
$21013, am't with gain.	5380	$15095, *Ans.*
	$5918, am't spent.	

(6)

86) 31173 (362$\frac{41}{86}$
258
———
537
516
———
213
172
———
41

(7)

28
3
—— $
25) 1400 (56 dolls.
125
———
150
150
———

(8)

63 gallons.
5
———
15) 315 (21, *Ans.*
30
———
15
15
———

(9)

73900
70
———
214) 73830 (345, *Ans.*
642
———
963
856
———
1070
1070
———

(10)

148	148
56	56
92	204, sum.
	92, diff.
	408
	1836

23) 18768 (816, *Ans.*
184
———
36
23
———
138
138
———

(11)

$60	$45
8	14
$480	180
630	45
6) 1110	$630
185	*Ans.*, 185 yards.

(12)

$30	$6000		156 acres.
70	2100	$3900 \div 25 = 156$	70 acres.
$2100	$3900		226 acres, *Ans.*

(13)

$360		yr.
300	$1800	800)10400(13, *Ans.*
150	1000	800
100	$800, saved each yr.	2400
90		2400

$1000, spent each yr.

(14)

$40 \times \$15 = \$600$
$80 \times 25 = 2000$
Amt. pd., $2600

$120 - 90 = 30$ acres.
$30 \times 60 = 1800$
$4500 + \$1800 = \$6300$, 1st *Ans.*

$6300
2600
$3700, gain.

(15)

$275 \times \$4 = \$1100$

$250 \times \$5 = \$1250$
$25 \times 6 = \underline{\ \ 150}$
$1400
$\underline{1100}$
$300, *Ans.*

(16)

125	75	175)19250(110, *Ans.*
$85	$115	175
625	375	175
1000	75	175
$10625	75	0
	75	
	$8625	
	10625	
	$19250	

(17)

$150	$125
15	20
750	$2500
150	
$2250	$45
2500	50
$4750	$2250
2250	
$2500	
95	
$2405, *Ans.*	

COMPOUND NUMBERS.

U. S. MONEY.

EXAMPLES TO BE WRITTEN.

Art. 53.

(1.) $12.178

(2.) $ 6.066

(3.) $ 7.007

(4.) $40.535

(5.) $ 2.03

(6.) $ 20.022

(7.) $100.10

(8.) $200.02

(9.) $400.018

EXAMPLES TO BE READ.

Eighteen dollars sixty-two cents five mills; twenty dollars thirty-two cents four mills; seventy-nine dollars five cents; forty-six dollars; seventy dollars one cent five mills; one hundred dollars twenty-eight cents; etc.

Art. 55.   REDUCTION.

Since the operations in this section consist simply in adding ciphers or removing them, or erasing points or inserting them between the different denominations, it is deemed unnecessary to occupy space, as the whole solution, when presented to the eye, would consist in nothing more than writing down the question to be solved, and then placing the answer under it.

Art. 56.   ADDITION.

(2)	(3)	(4)
$17.15	$18.041	$43.75
23.43	16.317	29.18
7.19	100.503	17.63
8.37	87.338	268.95
12.31	$222.199	' 718.07
$68.45		$1077.58

(5)	(6)	(7)
$200.00	$504.06	$5.070
43.87	420.19	30.203
56.93	105.50	100.005
8.50	304.00	60.020
2.31	888.47	700.011
$311.61	$2222.22	1000.100
		40.004
		64.587
		$2000.000

SUBTRACTION.

Art. 57.

(2)	(3)	(4)	(5)
$29.342	$46.28	$20.05	$3.00
17.265	17.75	5.50	.03
$12.077	$28.53	$14.55	$2.97

(6)	(7)	(8)	(9)
$10.000	$50.000	$1000.000	$1000.43
.001	.505	1.011	900.68
$9.999	$49.495	$998.989	$99.75

MULTIPLICATION.

Art. 58.

(2)	(3)	(4)
$7.835	$12.093	$23.018
8	9	16
$62.680	$108.837	138108
		23018

(5)	(6)	$368.288	(7)
$35.14	$125.02		$40.04
53	62		102
10542	25004		8008
17570	75012		4004
$1862.42	$7751.24		$4084.08

(8)	(9)	(10)	(11)
$0.125	$3.28	$1.06	$5.75
17	38	338	38
875	2624	848	4600
125	984	318	1725
$2.125	$124.64	318	$218.50
		$358.28	

(13)	(14)	(15)	(16)
$0.34	$5.67	$2.69	$1.25
89	24	169	691
306	2268	2421	125
272	1134	1614	1125
$30.26	$136.08	269	750
		$454.61	$863.75

(17)
```
      73
      63 gal.
     219
     438
    4599 gal.
    $0.55
   22995
   22995
  $2529.45
```

(18)
```
   281 lb.
     4
  1124 lb.
  $0.065
   5620
   6744
  $73.060
```

(19)
```
    35
    10 yd.
   350 yd.
  $0.01
  $3.50
```

(20)
```
  312      3432
   11 hr.  $0.13
 3432 hr.  10296
           3432
        $446.16, Ans.
```

(21)
```
    18     $1.25
     3 bu.   54
    54 bu.  500
            625
        Ans. $67.50
```

(22)	(23)
$10.001	17 $0.247
150	51 lb. 867
500050	17 1729
10001	85 1482
$1500.150	867 lb. 1976
	$214.149, *Ans.*

DIVISION.

CASE I.

Art. 59.

(2)	(3)	(4)	(5)
9) 72	375)6000(16	8) 280	25)300(12 yd.
8 lb.	375	35 yd.	25
	2250		50
	2250		50

(6)	(7)	(8)
805) 16100 (20 bbl.	75) 1200 (16	1125) 234000 (208 bu.
1610	75	2250
0	450	9000
	450	9000

CASE II.

(3)	(4)	(5)
8)$65.000	23)$29.610($1.287+	4)$92.250
$8.125	23	$23.062+
	66	
	46	(6)
	201	8)$57.500
	184	$7.187+
	170	
	161	
	9	

```
        (7)
16)$25.76($1.61
    16
    ──
    97
    96
    ──
    16
    16
    ──
```

```
              (8)
755)$328.425($0.435
    3020
    2642
    2265
    ────
    3775
    3775
    ────
```

```
              (9)
313)$800.000($2.555+
    626
    ────
    1740
    1565
    ────
    1750
    1565
    ────
    1850
    1565
    ────
    285
```

```
              (10)
133)$10000.000($75.187+
    931
    ───
    690
    665
    ───
    250
    133
    ────
    1170
    1064
    ────
    1060
    931
    ───
    129
```

```
             (11)
154)$2705.010($17.565
    154
    ────
    1165
    1078
    ────
    870
    770
    ────
    1001
    924
    ────
    770
    770
    ───
```

```
        (12)
     25
     15 lb.
     ──
    125
     25
lb. 375)$60.00($0.16
        375
        ────
        2250
        2250
        ────
```

```
           (13)
      235 lb.
        8
        ──
lb. 1880)$122.200($0.065
         11280
         ─────
          9400
          9400
          ────
```

Art. 60.

(1)	(2)	(3)	(4)	
$47.50	$35.25	$18.38	$0.75	$5.00
38.45	23.75	81.62	.35	3.10
15.47	$59.00	$100.00	.50	$1.90, *Ans.*
19.43	59.00	200.00	1.50	
$120.85	1.00	$300.00	$3.10	
	$119.00			

(5)		(6)
$8.10	$20.00	$50.00
5.65	19.75	30.50
$0.25 × 8 = 2.00	$0.25, *Ans.*	$19.50
4.00		6
$19.75		$117.00

(7)	(8)	(9)	(10)
$3.85	$37.06	143	435
1.25	200.85	23 ct.	45 ct.
2.50	400.00	429	2175
1.50	236.75	286	1740
$9.10	124.34	$32.89	$195.75
	$999.00	12.60	
$21.75	889.25	$20.29	$400.00
9.10	$109.75		195.75
$12.65, *Ans.*			*Ans.* $204.25

(11)		(12)	
365	ᵩ400.00	21	63
65 ct.	237.00	3 bu.	35 ct.
1825	$162.75, *Ans.*	63 bu.	315
2190			189
$237.25			*Ans.* $22.05

(13)			(14)
19 yd.	76	$2000.00	5)$1836.25
4	23 ct.	163.75	5)$367.25
76 yd.	228	$1836.25	$73.45, *Ans.*
	152		
	$17.48, *Ans.*		

(15)

4)$516.00

4)$129.00

43)$32.25($0.75, *Ans.*

   301

   215

   215

(16)

4|0)$9|0.00

10)$2.25

$0.225, *Ans.*

(17)

22 = 2 × 11

$1000.00

  500.00

2)$1500.00

11)$750.00

Ans. $68.18+

MERCHANTS' BILLS.

(18.)	9 lb. @ $0.32 =	$2.88	
	4 " " 1.25 =	5.00	
	45 " " .09 =	4.05	
	17 " " .20 =	3.40	$15.33

(19.)	22 yd. @ $1.75 =	$38.50	
	18 " " .15 =	2.70	
	25 " " .65 =	16.25	
	6 " " .18 =	1.08	$58.53

(20.)	4 lb. @ $0.18 =	$0.72	
	8 " " .23 =	1.84	
	7 " " .11 =	.77	
	6 " " .09 =	.54	
	13 " " .35 =	4.55	
	26 " " .12 =	3.12	$11.54

(21.)

$$43 \text{ yd. @ } \$0.13 = \$5.59$$
$$28 \text{ " " } .09 = 2.52$$
$$23 \text{ " " } .23 = \underline{5.29} \qquad \$13.40$$

DRY MEASURE.

Art. 63.

(5.) 4 bu. $\times 4 + 2$ pk. $= 18$ pk.: 18 pk. $\times 8 + 1$ qt. $=$ 145 qt.: 145 qt. $\times 2 = 290$ pt., *Ans.*

(6.) 7 bu. $\times 4 + 3$ pk. $= 31$ pk.: 31 pk. $\times 8 + 7$ qt. $=$ 255 qt.: 255 qt. $\times 2 + 1$ pt. $= 511$ pt., *Ans.*

(7.) 3 bu. $\times 4 = 12$ pk.: 12 pk. $\times 8 = 96$ qt.: 96 qt. $\times 2 + 1$ pt. $= 193$ pt., *Ans.*

(8.) 384 pt. $\div 2 = 192$ qt.: 192 qt. $\div 8 = 24$ pk.: 24 pk. $\div 4 = 6$ bu., *Ans.*

(9.) 47 pt. $\div 2 = 23$ qt. 1 pt.: 23 qt. $\div 8 = 2$ pk. 7 qt. *Ans.* 2 pk. 7 qt. 1 pt.

(10.) 95 pt. $\div 2 = 47$ qt. 1 pt.: 47 qt. $\div 8 = 5$ pk. 7 qt.: 5 pk. $\div 4 = 1$ bu. 1 pk. Collecting the different remainders, the *Ans.* is 1 bu. 1 pk. 7 qt. 1 pt.

(11.) 508 pt. $\div 2 = 254$ qt.: 254 qt. $\div 8 = 31$ pk. 6 qt.: 31 pk. $\div 4 = 7$ bu. 3 pk. *Ans.* 7 bu. 3 pk. 6 qt.

LIQUID MEASURE.

Art. 64.

(1.) 17 gal. $\times 4 \times 2 = 136$ pt., *Ans.*

(2.) 13 gal. $\times 4 \times 2 \times 4 = 416$ gi., *Ans.*

(3.) 126 gal. $\times 4 \times 2 = 1008$ pt., *Ans.*

(4.) 1260 gal. $\times 4 \times 2 \times 4 = 40320$ gi., *Ans.*

(5.) 1120 gi. $\div 4 = 280, \div 2 = 140, \div 4 = 35$ gal., *Ans.*

(6.) 1848 cu. in. ÷ 231 = 8 gal., *Ans.*

(7.) 138138 cu. in. ÷ 231 = 598 gal., *Ans.*

AVOIRDUPOIS WEIGHT.

Art. 65.

(1.) 2 cwt. × 4 × 25 = 200 lb., *Ans.*

(2.) 3 cwt. × 100 = 300 lb. + 75 lb. = 375 lb., *Ans.*

(3.) 1 T. × 20 + 2 cwt. = 22 cwt. × 100 = 2200 lb., *Ans.*

(4.) 3 T. × 20 × 100 = 6000 lb. + 75 lb. = 6075 lb., *Ans.*

(5.) 4 cwt. × 100 + 44 lb. = 444 lb., *Ans.*

(6.) 5 T. × 20 × 100 + 90 lb. = 10090 lb., *Ans.*

(7.) 2 cwt. × 100 + 77 lb. = 277 lb.: 277 lb. × 16 + 12 oz. = 4444 oz., *Ans.*

(8.) 2 cwt. × 100 + 17 lb. = 217 lb.: 217 lb. × 16 + 3 oz. = 3475 oz., *Ans.*

(9.) 1 T. × 20 + 6 cwt. = 26 cwt., × 100 + 4 lb. = 2604 lb., × 16 + 2 oz. = 41666 oz., *Ans.*

(10.) 4803 lb. ÷ 100 = 48 cwt. and 3 lb. over, *Ans.*

(11.) 22400 lb. ÷ 100 ÷ 20 = 11 T. and 4 cwt., *Ans.*

(12.) 2048000 ÷ 16 = 128000 lb., ÷ 100 = 1280 cwt., ÷ 20 = 64 T., *Ans.*

(13.) 64546 oz. ÷ 16 = 4034 lb. 2 oz.: 4034 ÷ 100 = 40 cwt. 34 lb. *Ans.* 40 cwt. 34 lb. 2 oz.

(14.) 97203 oz. ÷ 16 = 6075 lb. 3 oz.: 6075 ÷ 100 = 60 cwt. 75 lb.: 60 ÷ 20 = 3 T. *Ans.* 3 T. 75 lb. 3 oz.

(15.) 544272 oz. ÷ 16 = 34017 lb., ÷ 100 = 340 cwt. **17** lb.: 340 ÷ 20 = 17 T. *Ans.* 17 T. 17 lb.

(16.) $52 \times 18 = 936$ lb.: $936 \div 100 = 9$ cwt. 36 lb., *Ans.*

(17.) $180 \times 75 = 13500$ lb.: $13500 \div 100 = 135$ cwt. $\div$ $20 = 6$ T. 15 cwt., *Ans.*

Long Measure.

Art. 66.

(1.) 2 yd. $\times 3 + 2$ ft. $= 8$ ft.: 8 ft. $\times 12 + 7$ in. $= 103$ in., *Ans.*

(2.) 7 yd. $\times 3 = 21$ ft., $\times 12 + 11$ in: $= 263$ in., *Ans.*

(3.) 12 mi. $\times 320 = 3840$ rd., *Ans.*

(4.) 7 mi. $\times 320 + 240$ rd. $= 2480$ rd., *Ans.*

(5.) 9 mi. $\times 320 + 31$ rd. $= 2911$ rd., *Ans*

(6.) 133 in. $\div 12 = 11$ ft. 1 in.: 11 ft. $\div 3 = 3$ yd. 2 ft. *Ans.* 3 yd. 2 ft. 1 in.

(7.) 181 in. $\div 12 = 15$ ft. 1 in.: 15 ft. $\div 3 = 5$ yd. *Ans.* 5 yd. 1 in.

(8.) 2240 rd. $\div 320 = 7$ mi., *Ans.*

(9.) 2200 rd. $\div 320 = 6$ mi. 280 rd., *Ans.*

(10.) 1 mi. $\times 320 \times 5\frac{1}{2} = 1760$ yd., *Ans.*

(11.) 1 mi. $\times 320 \times 5\frac{1}{2} \times 3 = 5280$ ft. *Ans.*

Square Measure.

Art. 67.

(1.) 8 sq. yd. $\times 9 \times 144 = 10368$ sq. in., *Ans.*

(2.) 4 A. $\times 160 = 640$ sq. rd., *Ans.*

(3.) 1 sq. mi. $\times 640 \times 160 = 102400$ sq. rd., *Ans.*

(4.) 2 sq. yd. $\times 9 + 3$ sq. ft. $= 21$ sq. ft.: 21 sq. ft. $\times 144 = 3024$ sq. in., *Ans.*

(5.) 5 A. $\times 160 + 100$ sq. rd. $= 900$ sq. rd., *Ans.*

(6.) 960 sq. rd. ÷ 160 = 6 A., *Ans.*

(7.) 3888 sq. in. ÷ 144 = 27 sq. ft.: 27 sq. ft. ÷ 9 = 3 sq. yd., *Ans.*

(8.) 20000 sq. rd. ÷ 160 = 125 A., *Ans.*

(9.) 515280 sq. rd. ÷ 160 ÷ 640 = 5 sq. mi. 20 A. 80 sq. rd., *Ans.*

(10.) 4176 sq. in. ÷ 144 = 29 sq. ft.: 29 sq. ft. ÷ 9 = 3 sq. yd. 2 sq. ft., *Ans.*

Art. 68.

(2.) 16 ft. × 12 ft. = 192 sq. ft., *Ans.*

(3.) 5 yd. × 4 yd. = 20 sq. yd., *Ans.*

(4.) 18 ft. ÷ 3 = 6 yd.: 12 ft. ÷ 3 = 4 yd.: 21 ft. ÷ 3 = 7 yd.: 15 ft. ÷ 3 = 5 yd. 6 yd. × 4 yd. = 24 sq. yd.: 7 yd. × 5 yd. = 35 sq. yd.: 24 sq. yd. + 35 sq. yd. = 59 sq. yd., *Ans.*

(5.) 18 ft. × 14 ft. = 252 sq. ft.: 252 sq. ft. ÷ 9 = 28 sq. yd., *Ans.*

(6.) 35 rd. × 32 rd. = 1120 sq. rd.: 1120 sq. rd. ÷ 160 = 7 A., *Ans.*

(7.) 18 ft. ÷ 3 = 6 yd.: 15 ft. ÷ 3 = 5 yd. 5 yd. × 6 yd. × 2 = 60 sq. yd.: 60 × $1.25 = $75, *Ans.*

(8.) 21 ft. = 7 yd.: 18 ft. = 6 yd.; 7 yd. × 6 yd. = 42 sq. yd.: 42 × $0.17 = $7.14, *Ans.*

Art. 69.

(1.) 132 sq. ft. ÷ 11 ft. = 12 ft., *Ans.*

(2.) 30 sq. yd. × 9 = 270 sq. ft.: 270 sq. ft. ÷ 18 ft. = 15 ft., *Ans.*

(3.) 9 A. $\times$ 160 $=$ 1440 sq. rd.: 1440 sq. rd. $\div$ **45 rd.** $=$ 32 rd., *Ans.*

(4.) 21 A. $\times$ 160 $=$ 3360 sq. rd.: 3360 sq. rd. $\div$ **35 rd.** $=$ 96 rd., *Ans.*

Cubic Measure.

Art. 70.

(1.) 2 cu. yd. $\times$ 27 $\times$ 1728 $=$ 93312 cu. in., *Ans.*

(2.) 28 C. $\times$ 128 $=$ 3584 cu. ft., *Ans.*

(3.) 34 C. $\times$ 128 $\times$ 1728 $=$ 7520256 cu. in., *Ans.*

(4.) 1 C. $\times$ 128 $\times$ 1728 $=$ 221184 cu. in., *Ans.*

(5.) 63936 cu. in. $\div$ 1728 $=$ 37 cu. ft.: 37 cu. ft. $\div$ 27 $=$ 1 cu. yd. 10 cu. ft., *Ans.*

(6.) 8 ft. $\times$ 5 ft. $\times$ 4 ft. $=$ 160 cu. ft., *Ans.*

(7.) 8 yd. $\times$ 5 yd. $\times$ 2 yd. $=$ 80 cu. yd., *Ans.*

(8.) 18 ft. $\times$ 15 ft. $\times$ 7 ft. $=$ 1890 cu. ft.: 1890 cu. ft. $\div$ 27 $=$ 70 cu. yd., *Ans.*

(9.) 40 ft. $\times$ 12 ft. $\times$ 8 ft. $=$ 3840 cu. ft.: 3840 cu. ft. $\div$ 128 $=$ 30 C., *Ans.*

(10.) 80 ft. $\times$ 8 ft. $\times$ 4 ft. $=$ 2560 cu. ft.: 2560 cu. ft. $\div$ 128 $=$ 20 C.: 20 $\times$ \$5.50 $=$ \$110, *Ans.*

(11.) 24 ft. $=$ 8 yd., 15 ft. $=$ 5 yd., 6 ft. $=$ 2 yd.: 8 yd. $\times$ 5 yd. $\times$ **2 yd.** $=$ 80 cu. yd.: 80 $\times$ \$1.25 $=$ \$100, *Ans.*

Time Measure.

Art. 71.

(1.) 2 hr. $\times$ 60 $\times$ 60 $=$ 7200 sec., *Ans.*

(2.) 7 da. $\times$ 24 $\times$ 60 $=$ 10080 min., *Ans.*

(3.) 1 da. $\times$ 24 $+$ 3 hr. $=$ 27 hr.: 27 hr. $\times$ 60 $+$ 44 min. $=$ 1664 min.: 1664 min. $\times$ 60 $+$ 3 sec. $=$ 99843 sec., *Ans.*

(4.) 9 wk. $\times$ 7 + 6 da. = 69 da.: 69 da. $\times$ 24 + 10 hr. = 1666 hr.: 1666 hr. $\times$ 60 + 40 min. = 100000 min., *Ans.*

(5.) 4 wk. $\times$ 7 + 3 da. = 31 da. : 31 da. $\times$ 24 = 744 hr. : 744 hr. $\times$ 60 + 4 min. = 44644 min., *Ans.*

(6.) 10800 sec. ÷ 60 = 180 min.: 180 min. ÷ 60 = 3 hr., *Ans.*

(7.) 432000 sec. ÷ 60 = 7200 min.: 7200 min. ÷ 60 = 120 hr.: 120 hr. ÷ 24 = 5 da., *Ans.*

(8.) 7322 sec. ÷ 60 = 122 min. 2 sec.: 122 min. ÷ 60 = 2 hr. 2 min. *Ans.* 2 hr. 2 min. 2 sec.

(9.) 4323 min. ÷ 60 = 72 hr. 3 min.: 72 hr. ÷ 24 = 3 da. *Ans.* 3 da. 3 min.

(10.) 20280 min. ÷ 60 = 338 hr.: 338 hr. ÷ 24 = 14 da. 2 hr.: 14 da. ÷ 7 = 2 wk. *Ans.* 2 wk. 2 hr.

(11.) 41761 min. ÷ 60 = 696 hr. 1 min.: 696 hr. ÷ 24 = 29 da.: 29 da. ÷ 7 = 4 wk. 1 da.: 4 wk. ÷ 4 = 1 mo. *Ans.* 1 mo. 1 da. 1 min.

MISCELLANEOUS TABLES.

Art. 73.

(1.) 5 lb. $\times$ 12 + 4 oz. = 64 oz., *Ans.*

(2.) 9 lb. $\times$ 12 + 3 oz. = 111 oz.: 111 oz. $\times$ 20 + 5 pwt. = 2225 pwt., *Ans.*

(3.) 8 lb. $\times$ 12 + 9 oz. = 105 oz.: 105 oz. $\times$ 20 + 13 pwt. = 2113 pwt.: 2113 pwt. $\times$ 24 + 17 gr. = 50729 gr., *Ans.*

(4.) 805 pwt. ÷ 20 = 40 oz. 5 pwt.: 40 oz. ÷ 12 = 3 lb. 4 oz. *Ans.* 3 lb. 4 oz. 5 pwt.

(5.) 12530 gr. ÷ 24 = 522 pwt. 2 gr.: 522 pwt. ÷ 20 = 26 oz. 2 pwt.: 26 oz. ÷ 12 = 2 lb. 2 oz. *Ans.* 2 lb. 2 oz. 2 pwt. 2 gr.

(6.) 4 ℔. × 12 + 5 ℥ = 53 ℥: 53 × 8 × 3 × 20 + 2 gr. = 25442 gr., *Ans.*

(7.) 7 ℔. × 12 + 2 ℥ = 86 ℥: 86 ℥ × 8 = 688 ʒ: 688 ʒ × 3 + 1 ℈ = 2065 ℈: 2065 ℈ × 20 = 41300 gr., *Ans.*

(8.) 431 ʒ ÷ 8 = 53 ℥ 7 ʒ: 53 ℥ ÷ 12 = 4 ℔. 5 ℥. *Ans.* 4 lb. 5 ℥ 7 ʒ.

(9.) 975 ℈ ÷ 3 = 325 ʒ: 325 ʒ ÷ 8 = 40 ℥ 5 ʒ: 40 ℥ ÷ 12 = 3 ℔. 4 ℥. *Ans.* 3 ℔. 4 ℥ 5 ʒ.

(10.) 6321 gr. ÷ 20 = 316 ℈ 1 gr.: 316 ℈ ÷ 3 = 105 ʒ 1 ℈: 105 ʒ ÷ 8 = 13 ℥ 1 ʒ: 13 ℥ ÷ 12 = 1 ℔. 1 ℥. *Ans.* 1 ℔. 1 ℥ 1 ʒ 1 ℈ 1 gr.

(11.) 4 cong. × 8 × 16 + 7 f. ℥ × 8 = 4152 f. ʒ., *Ans.*

(12.) 5 O. × 16 + 6 f. ℥ = 86 f. ℥: 86 f. ℥ × 8 + 3 f. ʒ = 691 f. ʒ: 691 × 60 = 41460 minims, *Ans.*

(13.) 2469 f. ʒ ÷ 8 = 308 f. ℥ 5 f. ʒ: 308 ÷ 16 = 19 O. 4 f. ℥: 19 ÷ 8 = 2 cong. 3 O. *Ans.* 2 cong. 3 O. 4 f. ℥ 5 f. ʒ.

(14.) 3 yd. × 3 = 9 ft., × 12 = 108 in., × 3 = 324 barleycorns, *Ans.*

(15.) 1 ft. × 12 + 6 in. = 18 in.: 18 × 12 = 216 lines, *Ans.*

(16.) 16½ hands × 4 = 66 in.: 66 ÷ 12 = 5 ft. 6 in., *Ans.*

(17.) 24 chains × 4 = 96 rd.: 15 chains × 4 = 60 rd.: 96 rd. × 60 rd. = 5760 sq. rd.: 5760 ÷ 160 = 36 A., *Ans.*

(18.) 267 cu. ft. × 1728 + 624 cu. in. = 462000 cu. in.: 462000 ÷ 231 = 2000 gal., *Ans.*

(19.) 8° × 60 + 41′ = 521′: 521′ × 60 + 45″ = 31305″, *Ans.*

(20.) 61° × 60 + 59′ = 3719′: 3719′ × 60 + 28″ = 223168″, *Ans.*

(21.) $915' \div 60 = 15°$ $15'$, *Ans.*

(22.) $3661'' \div 60 = 61'$ $1''$: $61' \div 60 = 1°$ $1'$. *Ans.* $1°$ $1'$ $1''$.

(23.) 6 gross $\times$ 12 = 72 doz., $\times$ 5 ct. = \$3.60, *Ans.*

(24.) 4 score $\times$ 20 + 10 yr. = 90 yr., *Ans.*

(25.) 3 bdl. $\times$ 2 = 6 rm., $\times$ 20 = 120 qr.: 120 @ 18 ct. = \$21.60, *Ans.*

(26.) 336 pp. $\div$ 2 = 168 leaves: $168 \div 12 = 14$ sheets, *Ans.*

(27.) $512 + 528 + 528 + 512 + 496 = 2576$ pp., $\div$ 2 = 1288 leaves: $1288 \div 8 = 161$ sheets, $\div$ 24 = 6 qr. 17 sheets, *Ans.*

Art. 74.

(1.) 2 bu. $\times$ 4 $\times$ 8 $\times$ 2 = 128 pt.: 5 ct. $\times$ 128 = 640 ct. = \$6.40, *Ans.*

(2.) 3 bu. $\times$ 4 + 2 pk. = 14 pk.: 50 ct. $\times$ 14 = 700 ct. = \$7.00, *Ans.*

(3.) 3 pk. $\times$ 8 + 3 qt. = 27 qt.: 27 qt. $\times$ 2 = 54 pt.: 3 ct. $\times$ 54 = \$1.62, *Ans.*

(4.) \$3 = 300 ct.: 300 ct. $\div$ 15 ct. = 20 pk.: 20 pk. $\div$ 4 = 5 bu., *Ans.*

(5.) \$1.66 = 166 ct.: 166 ct. $\div$ 4 = 41 qt. and 2 ct. over, which will buy 1 pt. at 4 ct. a qt. 41 qt. $\div$ 8 = 5 pk. 1 qt.: 5 pk. $\div$ 4 = 1 bu. 1 pk. *Ans.* 1 bu. 1 pk. 1 qt. 1 pt.
Or thus: 4 ct. a qt. is 2 ct. a pt.; and 166 ct. $\div$ 2 ct. = 83 pt. = 1 bu. 1 pk. 1 qt. 1 pt., *Ans.*

(6.) 3 bu. 2 pk. = 14 pk.: 91 bu. = 364 pk.: 364 pk. $\div$ 14 pk. = 26 bags, *Ans.*

(7.) 15 lb. $\times$ 16 + 12 oz. = 252 oz.: 252 ÷ 4 = 63, *Ans.*

(8.) 44 cwt. 52 lb. = 71232 oz.: 9 lb. 15 oz. = 159 oz.: 71232 ÷ 159 = 448, *Ans.*

(9.) 14 cwt. 28 lb. = 1428 lb.: 1428 ÷ 84 = 17, *Ans.*

(10.) 7 cwt. 56 lb. = 756 lb.: 756 ÷ 12 = 63, *Ans.*

(11.) 6 cwt. 10 lb. = 9760 oz.: 3 lb. 13 oz. = 61 oz.: 9760 ÷ 61 = 160, *Ans.*

(12.) 2 A. 125 sq. rd. = 445 sq. rd.: 20 ct. $\times$ 445 = 8900 ct. = \$89, *Ans.*

(13.) 16 A. 53 sq. rd. = 2613 sq. rd.: 1 A. 41 sq. rd. = 201 sq. rd.: 2613 ÷ 201 = 13, *Ans.*

(14.) 2 ft. $\times$ 2 ft. $\times$ 2 ft. = 8 cu. ft.: 8 cu. ft. $\times$ 1728 = 13824 cu. in., *Ans.*

(15.) 1000 oz. $\times$ 5 = 5000 oz. = 312 lb. 8 oz., *Ans.*

(16.) 1000 oz. $\times$ 128 = 128000 oz. = 4 T., *Ans.*

(17.) 2 C. $\times$ 128 = 256 cu. ft.: 950 oz. $\times$ 256 = 243200 oz. = 7 T. 12 cwt., *Ans.*

(18.) 63 gal. $\times$ 4 $\times$ 2 = 504 pt.: 20 ct. $\times$ 504 = 10080 ct. = \$100.80, *Ans.*

(19.) 31 gal. 2 qt. = 126 qt.: 126 qt. $\times$ 5 = 630 qt.: 10 ct. $\times$ 630 = 6300 ct. = \$63, *Ans.*

(20.) \$2 = 200 ct.: 200 ÷ 5 = 40 pt.: 40 pt. = 5 gal., *Ans.*

(21.) 63 gal. = 504 pt.: 3 qt. 1 pt. = 7 pt.: 7 pt. $\times$ 12 = 84 pt. in 1 doz. bottles: 504 ÷ 84 = 6 doz., *Ans.*

(22.) 4 gal. 3 qt. 1 pt. = 39 pt.: 58 gal. 2 qt. = 468 pt.: 468 ÷ 39 = 12, *Ans.*

(23.) 1 da. = 1440 min.:   70 beats × 1440 = 100800 beats, *Ans.*

(24.) 1876 is a leap year, because it is exactly divisible by 4; hence, February has 29 days: 29 days = 2505600 seconds, *Ans.*

(25.) 3 wk. 2 da. 3 hr. = 555 hr.: 8 mi. × 555 = 4440 mi., *Ans.*

(26.) A peck is ¼ bushel, and will, therefore, cost ¼ of 44 ct. = 11 ct. per day: 365 × 11 = $40.15, *Ans.*

(27.) 40 bbl. × 196 = 7840 lb.   The gain equals 5 ct. — 3 ct., or 2 ct., a pound.   7840 × 2 ct. = $156.80, *Ans.*

Art. 75.

(4.) 17 bu. 3 pk. 7 qt., *Ans.*

(5.) 26 bu. 1 qt. 1 pt., *Ans.*

(6.) 24 qt., *Ans.*

(7.) 128 gal. 3 qt. 1 pt. 3 gi., *Ans.*

(8.) 79 T. 15 cwt. 48 lb. 6 oz., *Ans.*

(9.) 57 cwt. 51 lb. 7 oz., *Ans.*

(10.) 111 mi. 44 rd., *Ans.*

(11.) 14 yd. 4 in., *Ans.*

(12.) 299 A. 150 sq. rd., *Ans.*

(13.) 51 sq. yd. 4 sq. ft. 73 sq. in., *Ans.*

(14.) 49 C. 58 cu. ft. 519 cu. in., *Ans.*

(15.) 143 cu. yd. 2 cu. ft. 990 cu. in., *Ans.*

(16.) 50 da. 3 hr. 12 min. 28 sec., *Ans.*

(17.) 8 mo. 4 da. 8 hr. 49 min. 35 sec., *Ans.*

(18)	
bu.	pk.
21	3
14	1
23	2
18	1
22	1
100	0

(19)	
bu.	pk.
200	3
143	1
400	3
255	1
1000	0

(20)	
cwt.	lb.
8	36
4	64
5	19
7	75
7	84
33	78

(21)	
lb.	oz.
13	11
17	13
14	14
16	0
19	7
17	9
99	6

(22)	
mi.	rd.
104	50
95	270
200	0

(23)	
A.	sq. rd.
186	134
286	17
113	89
586	80

(24)		
sq. yd.	sq. ft.	sq. in.
17	3	119
18	0	141
23	7	0
29	5	116
88	8	88

(25)	
C.	cu. ft.
7	78
16	24
35	127
29	10
88	111

(26)			
hhd.	gal.	qt.	pt.
	4642	3	1
	945	0	0
	1707	0	1
	10206	1	0
277	50	1	0

Art. 76.

(4.) 3 gal. 3 qt. 1 pt., *Ans.*

(5.) 19 gal. 1 qt. 1 pt. 3 gi., *Ans.*

(6.) 3 T. 18 cwt. 75 lb., *Ans.*

(7.) 11 T. 42 lb. 15 oz., *Ans.*

(8.) 6 mi. 282 rd., *Ans.*

(9.) 1 yd. 2 ft. 11 in., *Ans.*

(10.) 249 A. 153 sq. rd., *Ans.*

(11.) 2 sq. yd. 8 sq. ft. 104 sq. in., *Ans.*

(12.) 8 C. 125 cu. ft., *Ans.*

(13.) 8 cu. yd. 18 cu. ft. 1727 cu. in., *Ans.*

(14.) 51 min. 42 sec., *Ans.*

(15.) 55 da. 5 hr. 55 min. 55 sec., *Ans.*

(16)				(17)				(18)	
bu.	pk.	qt.		bu.	pk.	qt.	pt.	lb.	oz.
4	0	0		100	0	0	0	46	4
2	1	1		24	0	0	1	19	8
1	2	7		75	3	7	1	26	12

(19)		(20)		(21)	
cwt.	lb.	mi.	**rd.**	A.	sq. rd.
32	66	24899	0	146	80
8	67	100	41	86	94
23	99	24798	279	59	146

(22)		(23)				(24)			
C.	cu. ft.	gal.	qt.	pt.	gi.	da.	hr.	min.	sec.
8	50	63	0	0	0	5	10	27	15
3	75	51	1	0	2	2	4	13	29
4	103	11	2	1	2	3	6	13	46

Art. 77.

(2)			(3)			(4)		
yr.	mo.	da.	yr.	mo.	da.	yr.	mo.	da.
1876	9	1	1191	7	12	1587	2	8
1776	7	4	1099	7	15	1215	6	15
100	1	27	91	11	27	371	7	23

	(5)				(6)	
	yr.	mo.	da.		yr.	mo.	da.
	1688	11	5		1815	6	18
	1066	10	14		1805	12	2
	622	0	21		9	6	16

Art. 78.

(2)	(3)	(4)	(5)	(6)
da.	da.	da.	da.	da.
Mar. 14	12	25	19	11
Apr. 30	31	31	30	30
May 31	20	30	31	31
June 30	63 da.	7	31	30
July 31		93 da.	28	31
Aug. 31			31	31
Sept. 12			30	29
179 da.			25	8
			225 da.	201 da.

Art. 79.

(2)				(3)			(4)			
bu.	pk.	qt.	pt.	bu.	pk.	qt.	bu.	pk.	qt.	pt.
2	1	1	1	2	2	2	4	3	3	1
			6			9				12
13	3	1	0	23	0	2	58	1	2	0

(5)			(6)			(7)	
T.	cwt.	lb.	T.	cwt.	lb.	mi.	rd.
	8	62		10	89	208	176
		9			7		15
3	17	58	3	16	23	3128	80

(8)		
cu. yd.	cu. ft.	cu. in.
23	9	228
		12
280	1	1008

(9)		
T.	cwt.	lb.
	16	74
		119
99	12	6

(10)		
gal.	qt.	pt.
47	3	1
		59
2824	2	1

(11)	
mi.	rd.
27	155
	31
852	5

(12)	
C.	cu. ft.
7	98
	17
132	2

(13)					
mo.	wk.	da.	hr.	min.	sec.
2	4	13	48	39
					75
49	3	0	3	48	45

(14)

cwt.	lb.
10	84
	75
813	0

813 cwt. = 81300 lb.

8 ct. — 6 ct. = 2 ct., gain on 1 lb.

2 ct. × 81300 = 162600 ct. = \$1626, *Ans.*

(15)

4 cwt. 85 lb. = 485 lb.

485 lb. × 425 = 206125 lb.

206125 × 13 ct. = \$26796.25

\$26796.25 — \$24735 = \$2061.25, *Ans.*

DIVISION.

Art. 80.

(4)			
bu.	pk.	qt.	pt.
5)67	3	4	1
13	2	2	1

(5)		
cwt.	lb.	oz.
11)35	44	12
3	22	4

(6)	
mi.	rd.
7)39	288
5	224

(7)	(8)	(9)
A. sq. rd.	bu. pk. qt.	lb. oz.
16)69 64	10)490 2 4	5)265 10
4 54	10)49 0 2	10)53 2
	Ans. 4 3 5	Ans. 5 5

(10)

T. cwt.

17)45   18

2   14

(12)

lb.   oz.

27   13

10 cwt. = 1000

23)1027(44 lb.

92

107

92

15

(11)

dr.   hr.   min.   sec.

6)114   22   45   18

9)19   3   47   33

Ans. 2   3   5   17

$15 \times 16 + 13$ oz. $\div 23 = 11$ oz.

Ans. 44 lb. 11 oz.

(13)

bu.   pk.   qt. bu.   pk.   qt.

78)309   2   2 (3   3   7, Ans.

234

75

4

78)302(3 pk.

234

68

8

78)546(7 qt.

546

(14)

gal.   qt.   pt.   gi.

63)127   3   1   3

gal. 2 . . 1

4   qt. qt.

4+3=7

pt.   2   pt. pt.

15   14+1=15

4

60+3gi.=63 gi.

63÷63=1 gi

Ans. 2 gal. 1 gi.

(15)

```
        mi.  rd.  mi.  rd.
319)788   169 ( 2    151, Ans.
    638
    ───
    150×320=48000 rd.
                169
        319)48169(151 rd.
            319
            ───
            1626
            1595
            ────
             319
             319
```

(16)

```
            A.   sq. rd.
           104   117
            87    78
           ───   ───
           191   195
            40    40
         3)151   155
           ─────────
           50 .. 1=160 sq. rd.

160 sq. rd.+155 sq. rd.=315 sq. rd.
315 sq. rd.÷3=105 sq. rd.
    Ans. 50 A. 105 sq. rd.
```

(17)

```
 bu.    pk.
5000     3
7245     2
─────   ──
12245    5
8022     1
─────   ──
4223     4=4224 bu.
4224÷8=528 bu., Ans.
```

(18)

```
            A.   sq. rd.
             4    80
           160
           ───
           640+80=720 sq. rd.
           720 sq. rd.×6=4320 sq. rd.
        54)4320(80 sq. rd. in each lot.
           432
           ───
             0

        80×$5=$400, Ans.
```

(19)

```
 lb.   oz.
 35     9
 75    14
 85    15      84 lb.÷64=1 lb. 5 oz., Ans.
───    ──
195    38
186    14
───    ──
  9    24
        8
───   ───
 72   192=84 lb.
```

Art. 81.

(1)

15)18°   25'   30''
_____
1 hr. 13 min. 42 sec.

(2)

30° ÷ 15 = 2.   *Ans.* 2 hr.

(3)

15)71°   4'   0''
_____
4 hr. 44 min. 16 sec.

(4)

15)10°   35'   0''
_____
0 hr. 42 min. 20 sec.

(5)

min. sec.
    37   20
         15
_____
9°   20'   0''

(6)

hr. min. sec.
 1   4   56
          15
_____
16° 14'   0''

(7)

hr. min. sec.
 5   8   4
          15
_____
77°   1'   0''

Art. 82.

(8)

            hr. min. sec.
Time at C. 12   0   0
Add diff.   37   20
            _____
            12 37   20
(See **Ex. 5**, Art. 81.)

(9)

              hr. min. sec.
Time at N. Y. 11   0   0 A. M.
30°=   2   0   0 to be added.
              _____
               1   0   0 P. M.

(10)

            hr. min. sec.
Time at Ph. 12   0   0
Subtr. diff.   37   20
            _____
            11   22   40 A. M.

(11)

              hr. min. sec.
Time at N. Y. 11   0   0
Subtr. diff.   1   4   56
              _____
               9 55   4 A. M.
(See **Ex. 6**, Art. 81.)

(12)

$124° - 80° 42' = 43° 18'$: $43° 18' \div 15 = 2$ hr. 53 min. 12 sec.

	hr.	min.	sec.
Time at W.	1	0	0
Subtr. diff.	2	53	12
Ans.	10	6	48 A. M.

NOTE. — In performing the subtraction, we can not take 3 hr. from 1 hr., but 1 P. M. is the 13th hour from midnight, from which, after taking 3 hr., the remainder is the 10th hr. from midnight, or 10 A. M.

FACTORING.

Arts. 87 and 88.

NOTE.—The principles and processes of factoring are so simple, and are so fully explained in the Arithmetic, that it seems unnecessary to give any solutions here.

Art. 89.

(2)

```
2)16    2)24    2)40
─────   ─────   ─────
2)8     2)12    2)20
─────   ─────   ─────
2)4     2)6     2)10
─────   ─────   ─────
2)2      3       5
─────
 1
```

$2 \times 2 \times 2 = 8$, G. C. D.

(3)

```
2)24    2)36    2)60
─────   ─────   ─────
2)12    2)18    2)30
─────   ─────   ─────
3)6     3)9     3)15
─────   ─────   ─────
2)2     3)3      5
─────   ─────
 1       1
```

$2 \times 2 \times 3 = 12$, G. C. D.

(4)

```
2)36    54    90
─────
3)18    27    45
─────
3)6      9    15
─────
 2       3     5
```

$2 \times 3 \times 3 = 18$, G. C. D.

(5)

```
2)40    60    100
─────
2)20    30    50
─────
5)10    15    25
─────
 2       3     5
```

$2 \times 2 \times 5 = 20$, G. C. D.

(6)

3)54	81	108
3)18	27	36
3)6	9	12
2	3	4

$3\times3\times3=27$, G. C. D.

(7)

2)60	90	120
3)30	45	60
5)10	15	20
2	3	4

$2\times3\times5=30$, G. C. D.

(8)

2)32	48	80	112
2)16	24	40	56
2)8	12	20	28
2)4	6	10	14
2	3	5	7

$2\times2\times2\times2=16$, G. C. D.

(9)

2)48	72	96	120
2)24	36	48	60
2)12	18	24	30
3)6	9	12	15
2	3	4	5

$2\times2\times2\times3=24$, G. C. D.

(10)

2)72	108	144	180
2)36	54	72	90
3)18	27	36	45
3)6	9	12	15
2	3	4	5

$2\times2\times3\times3=36$, G. C. D.

(11)
(By 2d method.)
62)93(1
62
31)62(2
62
31 = G. C. D.

(12)
78)130(1
78
52)78(1
52
26)52(2
52
26 = G. C. D.

(13)
161)253(1
161
92)161(1
92
69)92(1
69
23)69(3
69
23 = G. C. D.

(14)
247)323(1
247
76)247(3
228
19)76(4
76
19 = G. C. D.

```
        (16)                      (15)
   2145)3471(1            391)697(1
        2145                   391              17 = G. C. D.
        1326)2145(1            306)391(1
             1326                  306
             819)1326(1           85)306(3
39 = G. C. D.    819                 255
                 507)819(1           51)85(1
   (17)              507                  51
16571)38363(2       312)507(1           34)51(1
     33142               312                 34
     5221)16571(3        195)312(1          17)34(2
          15663               195                34
          908)5221(5          117)195(1
               4540                117
               681)908(1           78)117(1
227 = G. C. D.     681                  78
                   227)681(3            39)78(2
                        681                  78

        (18)                       (19)
72)120(1    24)132(5        75)125(1    25)165(6
   72          120             75          150
   48)72(1     12)24(2         50)75(1     15)25(1
      48          24              50           15
      24)48(2  12 = G. C. D.      25)50(2     10)15(1
         48                          50          10
                                               5)10(2
            (20)                                 10
      2)64    96   112   136           5 = G. C. D.
      2)32    48    56    68
      2)16    24    28    34
         8    12    14    17
      2×2×2=8, G. C. D.
```

Art. 90.

(2)

```
2)4   6   8
2)2   3   4
   2)3   2
      3
```

$2\times2\times2\times3=24$, L. C. M.

(3)

```
3)6   9   12
2)2   3   4
   3   2
```

$3\times2\times3\times2=36$, L. C. M.

(4)

```
2)4   8   10
2)2   4   5
   2   5
```

$2\times2\times2\times5=40$, L. C. M.

(5)

```
5)6   10   15
3)6    2    3
2)2    2
```

$5\times3\times2=30$, L. C. M.

(6)

```
3)6   8   9   12
2)2   8   3   4
   2)4   3   2
      2   3
```

$3\times2\times2\times2\times3=72$, L. C. M.

(7)

```
5)10   12   15   20
 2)2   12    3    4
    3)6    3    2
    2)2         2
```

$5\times2\times3\times2=60$, L. C. M.

(8)

```
3)9   15   18   30
5)3    5    6   10
3)3         6    2
       2)2         2
```

$3\times5\times3\times2=90$, L. C. M.

(9)

```
3)12   18   27   36
3)4     6    9   12
2)4     2    3    4
2)2          3    2
        3
```

$3\times3\times2\times2\times3=108$, L. C. M.

(10)

5)15	25	30	50
5)3	5	6	10
2)3		2	2
3			

$5\times5\times2\times3=150$, L. C. M.

(11)

7)14	21	30	35
5)2	3	30	5
3)2	3	6	
2)2		2	

$7\times5\times3\times2=210$, L. C. M.

(12)

7)15	20	21	28
5)15	20	3	4
3)3	4	3	4
	2)4		4
	2)2		2

$7\times5\times3\times2\times2=420$, L. C. M.

(13)

5)20	24	28	30
3)4	24	28	6
2)4	8	28	2
2)2	4	14	
	2	7	

$5\times3\times2\times2\times2\times7=840$,
L. C. M.

(14)

7)45	30	35	42
5)45	30	5	6
3)9	6		6
2)3	2		2
3			

$7\times5\times3\times2\times3=630$, L. C. M.

(15)

5)36	40	45	50
3)36	8	9	10
2)12	8	3	10
2)6	4	3	5
3)3	2	3	5
	2	3	5

$5\times3\times2\times2\times3\times2\times5=1800$, L. C. M.

(16)

7)42	56	63
3)6	8	9
2)2	8	3
	2)4	3
	2	3

$7\times3\times2\times2\times2\times3=504$,
L. C. M.

(17)

13)78	104	117
3)6	8	9
2)2	8	3
	2)4	3
	2	3

$13\times3\times2\times2\times2\times3=936$,
L. C. M.

	(18)		
5)125	150	200	
5)25	30	40	
2)5	6	8	
2)5	3	4	
5	3	2	

$5\times5\times2\times2\times5\times3\times2=3000$, L. C. M.

	(19)			
5)10	24	25	32	45
3)2	24	5	32	9
2)2	8	5	32	3
	2)4	5	16	3
	2)2	5	8	3
	2)5	4	3	
	5	2	3	

$5\times3\times2\times2\times2\times2\times5\times2\times3=7200$, L. C. M.

	(20)						
3)2	3	4	5	6	7	8	9
2)2		4	5	2	7	8	3
	2)2	5		7	4	3	
	5		7	2	3		

$3\times2\times2\times5\times7\times2\times3=2520$, L. C. M.

	(21)		
3)16	27	42	108
2)16	9	14	36
3)8	9	7	18
3)8	3	7	6
2)8		7	2
2)4		7	
2		7	

$3\times2\times3\times3\times2\times2\times2\times7=3024$, L. C. M.

	(22)		
13)13	29	52	87
29)29	4	87	
	2)4	3	
	2	3	

$13\times29\times2\times2\times3=4524$,
L. C. M.

$$(23)$$

5)120	360	144	720	72
3)24	72	144	144	72
3)8	24	48	48	24
2)8	8	16	16	8
2)4	4	8	8	4
2)2	2	4	4	2
		2)2	2	

$5\times3\times3\times2\times2\times2\times2=720$, L. C. M.

CANCELLATION.

Art. 91.

(4.) $\dfrac{1\!\!\!/3 \times 4}{1\!\!\!/3} = 4$, *Ans.*

(5.) $\dfrac{\overset{3}{17 \times 1\!\!\!/8}}{\underset{}{6\!\!\!/}} = 51$, *Ans.*

(6.) $\dfrac{\overset{2}{15 \times 8\!\!\!/}}{4\!\!\!/} = 30$, *Ans.*

(7.) $\dfrac{\overset{3}{2\!\!\!/4 \times 4}}{8\!\!\!/} = 12$, *Ans.*

(8.) $\dfrac{\overset{3}{37 \times 1\!\!\!/5}}{5\!\!\!/} = 111$, *Ans.*

(9.) $\dfrac{\overset{6}{3\!\!\!/6} \times \overset{5\!\!\!/}{4\!\!\!/0}}{\underset{5\!\!\!/}{3\!\!\!/0} \times 8\!\!\!/} = 6$, *Ans.*

(10.) $\dfrac{\overset{12}{3\!\!\!/6} \times 5\!\!\!/}{\underset{3\!\!\!/}{1\!\!\!/5}} = 12$, *Ans.*

(11.) $\dfrac{\overset{2}{4\!\!\!/2} \times \overset{5}{2\!\!\!/5} \times \overset{6}{1\!\!\!/8}}{\underset{3\!\!\!/}{2\!\!\!/1} \times 1\!\!\!/5} = 60$, *Ans.*

(12.) $\dfrac{23 \times \overset{2}{1\!\!\!/0}}{5\!\!\!/} = 46$, *Ans.*

(13.) $\dfrac{\overset{3}{1\!\!\!/5} \times \overset{2}{1\!\!\!/4}}{\underset{7\!\!\!/}{3\!\!\!/5\!\!\!/}} = 6$, *Ans.*

(14.) $\cancel{3}$ 3 $\cancel{2}$

$$\frac{\cancel{21} \times 11 \times \cancel{6} \times \cancel{26}}{\cancel{13} \times \cancel{3} \times \cancel{14} \times \cancel{2}} = 33, \; Ans.$$

                 $\cancel{2}$

(15.)   7 $\cancel{3}$ $\cancel{3}$ $\cancel{2}$ 7

$$\frac{\cancel{21} \times \cancel{15} \times \cancel{33} \times \cancel{8} \times \cancel{14} \times 17}{\cancel{20} \times \cancel{34} \times \cancel{22} \times \cancel{27}} = 49, \; Ans.$$

         4   17   2 $\cancel{9}$

                        $\cancel{3}$

(16.) $\cancel{3}$ 19   2

$$\frac{\cancel{21} \times \cancel{95} \times \cancel{6}}{\cancel{35} \times \cancel{9}} = 38, \; Ans.$$

         5    $\cancel{3}$

(17.) $\cancel{2}$

      5    $\cancel{3}$ 4

$$\frac{\cancel{35} \times \cancel{39} \times \cancel{40}}{\cancel{26} \times \cancel{30} \times \cancel{42}} = \tfrac{5}{3} = 1\tfrac{2}{3}, \; Ans.$$

     $\cancel{2}$ $\cancel{3}$ $\cancel{6}$

               3

(18.) 13   11   7

$$\frac{\cancel{26} \times \cancel{33} \times \cancel{35}}{\cancel{4} \times \cancel{9} \times \cancel{25}} = \frac{13 \times 11 \times 7}{2 \times 3 \times 5} = \tfrac{1001}{30} = 33\tfrac{11}{30}, \; Ans.$$

   2   3   5

(19.)   3   3

$$\frac{\cancel{6} \times 9 \times \cancel{15} \times \cancel{21}}{4 \times \cancel{6} \times \cancel{10} \times \cancel{14}} = 5\tfrac{1}{16}, \; Ans.$$

          2   2

(20.)   2

    $\cancel{3}$ $\cancel{4}$ 7   7

$$\frac{\cancel{21} \times \cancel{24} \times \cancel{28} \times \cancel{35}}{\cancel{14} \times \cancel{18} \times \cancel{20} \times \cancel{25}} = \tfrac{98}{25} = 3\tfrac{23}{25}, \; Ans.$$

    $\cancel{2}$ $\cancel{3}$ 5   5

FRACTIONS.

Art. 103.

(8.) 4 times $\frac{7}{7} = \frac{28}{7}$, or $\frac{7}{7} \times 4 = \frac{28}{7}$.

(9.) 8 times $\frac{9}{9} = \frac{72}{9}$, or $\frac{9}{9} \times 8 = \frac{72}{9}$.

(10.) 19 times $\frac{13}{13} = \frac{247}{13}$, or $\frac{13}{13} \times 19 = \frac{247}{13}$.

(11.) $\frac{20}{20} \times 25 = \frac{500}{20}$.

(12.) $\frac{23}{23} \times 37 = \frac{851}{23}$.

Art. 104.

(2.) $\frac{2}{2} \times 4 + \frac{1}{2} = \frac{9}{2}$.

(3.) $\frac{3}{3} \times 2 + \frac{1}{3} = \frac{7}{3}$.

(8.) $\frac{6}{6} \times 15 + \frac{5}{6} = \frac{95}{6}$.

(9.) $\frac{24}{24} \times 26 + \frac{13}{24} = \frac{637}{24}$.

(12.) $\frac{583}{583} \times 21 + \frac{117}{583} = \frac{12360}{583}$.

(14.) $\frac{71}{71} \times 14 + \frac{6}{71} = \frac{1000}{71}$.

Art. 105.

(3)	(4)	(5)	(6)
3)6	4)12	4)15	5)17
2	3	$3\frac{3}{4}$	$3\frac{2}{5}$

(7)	(8)	(13)	(14)
7)19	10)23	24)611($25\frac{11}{24}$	75)3000(40
$2\frac{5}{7}$	$2\frac{3}{10}$	48	300
		131	0
		120	
		11	

(15)	(16)	(17)	(18)
25)775(31	12)171	11)509($46\frac{3}{11}$	298)6437($21\frac{179}{298}$
75	$14\frac{3}{12}$	44	596
25		69	477
25		66	298
		3	179

(19)	(20)	(21)
125)7536($60\frac{36}{125}$	19)3781(199	101)1325($13\frac{12}{101}$
750	19	101
36	188	315
	171	303
	171	12
	171	

Art. 106.

(2.) $\frac{1}{2} \times \frac{2}{2} = \frac{2}{4}$, *Ans.*   (3.) $\frac{2}{3} \times \frac{2}{2} = \frac{4}{6}$, *Ans.*

(4.) $\frac{3}{4} \times \frac{3}{3} = \frac{9}{12}$, *Ans.*   (5.) $\frac{5}{6} \times \frac{4}{4} = \frac{20}{24}$, *Ans.*

(6.) $\frac{5}{7} \times \frac{4}{4} = \frac{20}{28}$, *Ans.*   (7.) $\frac{4}{21} \times \frac{4}{4} = \frac{16}{84}$, *Ans.*

(8.) $\frac{7}{8} \times \frac{9}{9} = \frac{63}{72}$, *Ans.*   (9.) $\frac{3}{5} \times \frac{12}{12} = \frac{36}{60}$, *Ans.*

(10.) $\frac{9}{10} \times \frac{10}{10} = \frac{90}{100}$, *Ans.*

(11.) 2Ø)72Ø; $\frac{9}{20} \times \frac{36}{36} = \frac{324}{720}$, *Ans.*
           36

(12.) 14)2016(144; $\frac{13}{24} \times \frac{144}{144} = \frac{1872}{2016}$, *Ans.*
          14
          61
          56
          56
          56

(13.) $43\overline{)1935}(45$; $\quad \frac{22}{43} \times \frac{45}{45} = \frac{990}{1935}$, *Ans.*
$$\begin{array}{r} 172 \\ \hline 215 \\ 215 \end{array}$$

(14.) $41\overline{)8118}(198$; $\quad \frac{35}{41} \times \frac{198}{198} = \frac{6930}{8118}$, *Ans.*
$$\begin{array}{r} 41 \\ \hline 401 \\ 369 \\ \hline 328 \\ 328 \end{array}$$

(15.) $17\overline{)5134}(302$; $\quad \frac{16}{17} \times \frac{302}{302} = \frac{4832}{5134}$, *Ans.*
$$\begin{array}{r} 51 \\ \hline 34 \\ 34 \end{array}$$

(16.) $81\overline{)23328}(288$; $\quad \frac{77}{81} \times \frac{288}{288} = \frac{22176}{23328}$, *Ans.*
$$\begin{array}{r} 162 \\ \hline 712 \\ 648 \\ \hline 648 \\ 648 \end{array}$$

(17.) $21\overline{)2541}(121$; $\quad \frac{13}{21} \times \frac{121}{121} = \frac{1573}{2541}$, *Ans.*
$$\begin{array}{r} 21 \\ \hline 44 \\ 42 \\ \hline 21 \\ 21 \end{array}$$

Art. 107.

 (2.) The G. C. D. of 18 and 30 is 6: $6)\frac{18}{30} = \frac{3}{5}$, *Ans.*

 (3.) $10)\frac{60}{90} = \frac{6}{9}$: $3)\frac{6}{9} = \frac{2}{3}$, *Ans.*

 (4.) G. C. D. of 12 and $18 = 6$: $6)\frac{12}{18} = \frac{2}{3}$, *Ans.*

 (5.) $5)\frac{30}{45} = \frac{6}{9}$: $3)\frac{6}{9} = \frac{2}{3}$, *Ans.*

 (6.) G. C. D. of 60 and $150 = 30$: $30)\frac{60}{150} = \frac{2}{5}$, *Ans.*

 (7.) G. C. D. of 42 and $70 = 14$: $14)\frac{42}{70} = \frac{3}{5}$, *Ans.*

 (8.) G. C. D. of 96 and $112 = 16$: $16)\frac{96}{112} = \frac{6}{7}$, *Ans.*

 (9.) $5)\frac{60}{125} = \frac{12}{25}$, *Ans.*

 (10.) $2)\frac{126}{198} = \frac{63}{99}$: $9)\frac{63}{99} = \frac{7}{11}$, *Ans.*

 (11.) $2)\frac{182}{196} = \frac{91}{98}$: $7)\frac{91}{98} = \frac{13}{14}$, *Ans.*

 (12.) $5)\frac{615}{815} = \frac{123}{183}$: $3)\frac{123}{183} = \frac{41}{61}$, *Ans.*

 (13.) G. C. D. of 873 and $1067 = 97$: $97)\frac{873}{1067} = \frac{9}{11}$, *Ans.*

 (14.) G. C. D. of 777 and $1998 = 111$: $111)\frac{777}{1998} = \frac{7}{18}$, *Ans.*

 (15.) G. C. D. of 909 and $2323 = 101$: $101)\frac{909}{2323} = \frac{9}{23}$, *Ans.*

 (16.) $\frac{391}{667}$: G. C. D. $= 23$: $23)\frac{391}{667} = \frac{17}{29}$, *Ans.*

 (17.) $\frac{585}{1287}$: G. C. D. $= 117$: $117)\frac{585}{1287} = \frac{5}{11}$, *Ans.*

 (18.) $\frac{796}{14129}$: G. C. D. $= 199$: $199)\frac{796}{14129} = \frac{4}{71}$, *Ans.*

 (19.) $\frac{1457}{5921}$: G. C. D. $= 31$: $31)\frac{1457}{5921} = \frac{47}{191}$, *Ans.*

 (20.) $5)\frac{6465}{7335} = \frac{1293}{1467}$, $\div 3 = \frac{431}{489}$, *Ans.*

Art. 108.

 (2.) $2)2 \quad 3 \quad 4$

    $\overline{\;\;1 \quad 3 \quad 2}$; $2 \times 3 \times 2 = 12$, L. C. Denominator.
Each must be changed to twelfths. If there are $\frac{12}{12}$ in 1,
in $\frac{1}{2}$ there are $\frac{1}{2}$ of $\frac{12}{12} = \frac{6}{12}$: $\frac{1}{3}$ of $\frac{12}{12} = \frac{4}{12}$, and $\frac{2}{3} = \frac{8}{12}$:
$\frac{1}{4}$ of $\frac{12}{12} = \frac{3}{12}$, and $\frac{3}{4} = \frac{9}{12}$.

(3.) L. C. M. of 3, 6, and 9 is 18; $\frac{1}{3} = \frac{6}{18}$, and $\frac{2}{3} = \frac{12}{18}$: $\frac{1}{6} = \frac{3}{18}$, and $\frac{5}{6} = \frac{15}{18}$: $\frac{1}{9} = \frac{2}{18}$, and $\frac{7}{9} = \frac{14}{18}$.

(4.) The L. C. M. of 2, 4, and 5 = 20; $\frac{1}{2} = \frac{10}{20}$: $\frac{1}{4} = \frac{5}{20}$, and $\frac{3}{4} = \frac{15}{20}$: $\frac{1}{5} = \frac{4}{20}$, and $\frac{4}{5} = \frac{16}{20}$.

(5.) L. C. M. of 8, 5, and 10 = 40: $\frac{1}{8} = \frac{1}{8}$ of $\frac{40}{40} = \frac{5}{40}$, and $\frac{3}{8} = \frac{15}{40}$: $\frac{1}{5} = \frac{1}{5}$ of $\frac{40}{40} = \frac{8}{40}$, and $\frac{4}{5} = \frac{32}{40}$: $\frac{1}{10} = \frac{1}{10}$ of $\frac{40}{40} = \frac{4}{40}$, and $\frac{9}{10} = \frac{36}{40}$.

(6.) The L. C. M. of 3, 4, and 8 is 24; $\frac{1}{3} = \frac{8}{24}$, and $\frac{2}{3} = \frac{16}{24}$: $\frac{1}{4} = \frac{6}{24}$, and $\frac{3}{4} = \frac{18}{24}$: $\frac{1}{8} = \frac{3}{24}$, and $\frac{7}{8} = \frac{21}{24}$.

(7.) L. C. M. of 4, 8, and 9 = 72; $\frac{1}{4} = \frac{18}{72}$, and $\frac{3}{4} = \frac{54}{72}$: $\frac{1}{8} = \frac{9}{72}$, and $\frac{5}{8} = \frac{45}{72}$: $\frac{1}{9} = \frac{8}{72}$, and $\frac{5}{9} = \frac{40}{72}$.

(12.) L. C. M. of 3, 5, 7, and 8 = 840; $\frac{1}{3} = \frac{280}{840}$, and $\frac{2}{3} = \frac{560}{840}$: $\frac{1}{5} = \frac{168}{840}$, and $\frac{2}{5} = \frac{336}{840}$: $\frac{1}{7} = \frac{120}{840}$, and $\frac{3}{7} = \frac{360}{840}$: $\frac{1}{8} = \frac{105}{840}$, and $\frac{5}{8} = \frac{525}{840}$.

(13.) First reduce $\frac{9}{21}$ to lowest terms = $\frac{3}{7}$. L. C. M. of 7, 14, 7, and 28 is 28; $\frac{1}{7} = \frac{4}{28}$, and $\frac{2}{7} = \frac{8}{28}$: $\frac{1}{14} = \frac{2}{28}$, and $\frac{5}{14} = \frac{10}{28}$: $\frac{1}{7} = \frac{4}{28}$, and $\frac{3}{7} = \frac{12}{28}$: $\frac{11}{28}$ is already reduced.

(14.) $\frac{6}{9} = \frac{2}{3}$: $\frac{15}{18} = \frac{5}{6}$; the L. C. M. of 5, 4, 3, and 6 is 60; $\frac{1}{5} = \frac{12}{60}$, and $\frac{2}{5} = \frac{24}{60}$: $\frac{1}{4} = \frac{15}{60}$, and $\frac{3}{4} = \frac{45}{60}$: $\frac{1}{3} = \frac{20}{60}$, and $\frac{2}{3} = \frac{40}{60}$: $\frac{1}{6} = \frac{10}{60}$, and $\frac{5}{6} = \frac{50}{60}$.

(15.) The L. C. M. of 4, 9, and 12 = 36; $1 = \frac{36}{36}$, and $2 = \frac{72}{36}$: $\frac{1}{4} = \frac{9}{36}$, and $\frac{3}{4} = \frac{27}{36}$: $\frac{1}{9} = \frac{4}{36}$, and $\frac{5}{9} = \frac{20}{36}$: $\frac{1}{12} = \frac{3}{36}$, and $\frac{7}{12} = \frac{21}{36}$.

(16.) $2\frac{2}{3} = \frac{8}{3}$: $5\frac{5}{6} = \frac{35}{6}$; L. C. M. of 3, 5, and 6 is 30; $\frac{1}{3} = \frac{10}{30}$, and $\frac{8}{3} = \frac{80}{30}$: $\frac{1}{5} = \frac{6}{30}$, and $\frac{3}{5} = \frac{18}{30}$: $1 = \frac{30}{30}$, and $4 = \frac{120}{30}$: $\frac{1}{6} = \frac{5}{30}$, and $\frac{35}{6} = \frac{175}{30}$.

(17.) $2\frac{1}{2} = \frac{5}{2}$: $3\frac{1}{3} = \frac{10}{3}$: $4\frac{1}{4} = \frac{17}{4}$; L. C. M. of 2, 3, and 4 is 12; $\frac{1}{2} = \frac{6}{12}$, and $\frac{5}{2} = \frac{30}{12}$: $\frac{1}{3} = \frac{4}{12}$, and $\frac{10}{3} = \frac{40}{12}$: $\frac{1}{4} = \frac{3}{12}$, and $\frac{17}{4} = \frac{51}{12}$: $1 = \frac{12}{12}$, and $5 = \frac{60}{12}$.

(18.) L. C. M. of 16, 18, 24, 36, and 48 is 144; $\frac{1}{16} = \frac{9}{144}$, and $\frac{7}{16} = \frac{63}{144}$: $\frac{1}{18} = \frac{8}{144}$, and $\frac{11}{18} = \frac{88}{144}$: $\frac{1}{24} = \frac{6}{144}$, and $\frac{17}{24} = \frac{102}{144}$: $\frac{1}{36} = \frac{4}{144}$, and $\frac{19}{36} = \frac{76}{144}$: $\frac{1}{48} = \frac{3}{144}$, and $\frac{25}{48} = \frac{75}{144}$.

(19.) L. C. M. of 7, 10, 12, 35, 63, and 28 is 1260: $\frac{1}{7} = \frac{180}{1260}$, and $\frac{4}{7} = \frac{720}{1260}$: $\frac{1}{10} = \frac{126}{1260}$, and $\frac{3}{10} = \frac{378}{1260}$: $\frac{1}{12} = \frac{105}{1260}$, and $\frac{5}{12} = \frac{525}{1260}$: $\frac{1}{35} = \frac{36}{1260}$, and $\frac{17}{35} = \frac{612}{1260}$: $\frac{1}{63} = \frac{20}{1260}$, and $\frac{4}{63} = \frac{80}{1260}$: $\frac{1}{28} = \frac{45}{1260}$, and $\frac{15}{28} = \frac{675}{1260}$.

(20.) L. C. M. of 5, 10, 25, 30, 45, and 60 is 900; $\frac{1}{5} = \frac{180}{900}$, and $\frac{3}{5} = \frac{540}{900}$: $\frac{1}{10} = \frac{90}{900}$, and $\frac{7}{10} = \frac{630}{900}$: $\frac{1}{25} = \frac{36}{900}$, and $\frac{6}{25} = \frac{216}{900}$: $\frac{1}{30} = \frac{30}{900}$, and $\frac{11}{30} = \frac{330}{900}$: $\frac{1}{45} = \frac{20}{900}$, and $\frac{13}{45} = \frac{260}{900}$: $\frac{1}{60} = \frac{15}{900}$, and $\frac{23}{60} = \frac{345}{900}$.

Art. 110.

(6.) $\frac{3}{11} + \frac{7}{11} + \frac{8}{11} + \frac{10}{11} = \frac{28}{11} = 2\frac{6}{11}$, *Ans.*

(7.) $\frac{5}{13} + \frac{8}{13} + \frac{9}{13} + \frac{11}{13} = \frac{33}{13} = 2\frac{7}{13}$, *Ans.*

(8.) $\frac{7}{15} + \frac{8}{15} + \frac{11}{15} + \frac{13}{15} = \frac{39}{15} = 2\frac{9}{15} = 2\frac{3}{5}$, *Ans.*

(9.) $\frac{9}{20} + \frac{11}{20} + \frac{13}{20} + \frac{17}{20} = \frac{50}{20} = 2\frac{10}{20} = 2\frac{1}{2}$, *Ans.*

(10.) $\frac{12}{25} + \frac{16}{25} + \frac{18}{25} + \frac{24}{25} = \frac{70}{25} = 2\frac{20}{25} = 2\frac{4}{5}$, *Ans.*

Art. 111.

(2.) The least common denominator is 6; $\frac{1}{2} = \frac{3}{6}$, $\frac{1}{3} = \frac{2}{6}$: $\frac{3}{6} + \frac{2}{6} = \frac{5}{6}$, *Ans.*

(4.) The L. C. D. is 10; $\frac{1}{2} = \frac{5}{10}$, $\frac{3}{5} = \frac{6}{10}$: $\frac{6}{10} + \frac{5}{10} = \frac{11}{10} = 1\frac{1}{10}$, *Ans.*

(8.) $2\frac{1}{2} = \frac{5}{2}$, $3\frac{2}{3} = \frac{11}{3}$; the L. C. D. $= 6$; $\frac{5}{2} = \frac{15}{6}$, $\frac{11}{3} = \frac{22}{6}$: $\frac{15}{6} + \frac{22}{6} = \frac{37}{6} = 6\frac{1}{6}$, *Ans.*

(9.) L. C. D. $= 12$; $\frac{2}{3} = \frac{8}{12}$, $\frac{3}{4} = \frac{9}{12}$, $\frac{5}{6} = \frac{10}{12}$: $\frac{8+9+10}{12} = \frac{27}{12} = 2\frac{3}{12} = 2\frac{1}{4}$, *Ans.*

(10.) L. C. D. $= 24$; $\frac{1}{4} = \frac{6}{24}$, $\frac{7}{8} = \frac{21}{24}$, $\frac{11}{12} = \frac{22}{24}$: $\frac{6+21+22}{24} = \frac{49}{24} = 2\frac{1}{24}$, *Ans.*

(11.) L. C. D. $= 792$; $\frac{1}{8} = \frac{99}{792}$, $\frac{1}{9} = \frac{88}{792}$, $\frac{2}{11} = \frac{144}{792}$: $\frac{99+88+144}{792} = \frac{331}{792}$, *Ans.*

(12.) $\frac{4}{5} = \frac{16}{20}$, $\frac{1}{2} = \frac{10}{20}$, $\frac{3}{4} = \frac{15}{20}$; $\frac{16}{20} + \frac{10}{20} + \frac{15}{20} = \frac{41}{20} = 2\frac{1}{20}$: $7 + 8 + 2\frac{1}{20} = 17\frac{1}{20}$, *Ans.*

(13.) L. C. D. $= 5460$; $\frac{1}{12} = \frac{455}{5460}$, $\frac{1}{13} = \frac{420}{5460}$, $\frac{1}{14} = \frac{390}{5460}$, $\frac{1}{15} = \frac{364}{5460}$: $\frac{455+420+390+364}{5460} = \frac{1629}{5460} = \frac{543}{1820}$, *Ans.*

(14.) L. C. D. $= 180$; $\frac{13}{18} = \frac{130}{180}$, $\frac{8}{15} = \frac{96}{180}$, $\frac{11}{20} = \frac{99}{180}$, $\frac{13}{30} = \frac{78}{180}$: $\frac{130+96+99+78}{180} = \frac{403}{180} = 2\frac{43}{180}$, *Ans.*

(15)		

$$\begin{array}{ll} \frac{7}{12} & \frac{7}{12} = \frac{42}{72} \\ 2\frac{5}{6} & \frac{5}{6} = \frac{60}{72} \\ 3\frac{3}{8} & \frac{3}{8} = \frac{27}{72} \\ 3\frac{4}{9} & \frac{4}{9} = \frac{32}{72} \\ \hline 8 & \frac{161}{72} = 2\frac{17}{72} \\ 2\frac{17}{72} & \\ \hline 10\frac{17}{72}, \text{ Ans.} \end{array}$$

(16)

$$\begin{array}{ll} 16\frac{2}{3} & \frac{2}{3} = \frac{40}{60} \\ 12\frac{3}{4} & \frac{3}{4} = \frac{45}{60} \\ 8\frac{3}{5} & \frac{3}{5} = \frac{36}{60} \\ 2\frac{1}{4} & \frac{1}{4} = \frac{15}{60} \\ \hline 38 & \frac{136}{60} = 2\frac{4}{15} \\ 2\frac{4}{15} & \\ \hline 40\frac{4}{15}, \text{ Ans.} \end{array}$$

(17.) L. C. D. $= 60$; $\frac{1}{2} = \frac{30}{60}$, $\frac{1}{3} = \frac{20}{60}$, $\frac{1}{4} = \frac{15}{60}$, $\frac{1}{5} = \frac{12}{60}$, $\frac{1}{6} = \frac{10}{60}$: $\frac{30+20+15+12+10}{60} = \frac{87}{60} = 1\frac{27}{60} = 1\frac{9}{20}$, *Ans.*

(18.) $\frac{2}{5} = \frac{1120}{2800}$, $\frac{7}{16} = \frac{1225}{2800}$, $\frac{7}{50} = \frac{392}{2800}$, $\frac{3}{140} = \frac{60}{2800}$, $\frac{3}{2800}$: $\frac{1120+1225+392+60+3}{2800} = \frac{2800}{2800} = 1$, *Ans.*

(19.) $\frac{1}{20} = \frac{36}{720}$, $\frac{7}{16} = \frac{315}{720}$, $\frac{11}{12} = \frac{660}{720}$, $\frac{2}{15} = \frac{96}{720}$, $\frac{11}{18} = \frac{440}{720}$: $\frac{36}{720} + \frac{315}{720} + \frac{660}{720} + \frac{96}{720} + \frac{440}{720} = \frac{1547}{720} = 2\frac{107}{720}$: $1 + 2 + 2\frac{107}{720} = 5\frac{107}{720}$, *Ans.*

(20.) $\frac{2}{3} = \frac{40}{60}$, $\frac{1}{2} = \frac{30}{60}$, $\frac{1}{5} = \frac{12}{60}$, $\frac{1}{3} = \frac{20}{60}$, $\frac{1}{4} = \frac{15}{60}$: $\frac{40}{60} + \frac{30}{60} + \frac{12}{60} + \frac{20}{60} + \frac{15}{60} = \frac{117}{60} = 1\frac{57}{60} = 1\frac{19}{20}$: $2 + 4 + 6 + 8 + 1\frac{19}{20} = 21\frac{19}{20}$, *Ans.*

(21.) $\frac{1}{3} = \frac{35}{105}$, $\frac{2}{7} = \frac{30}{105}$, $\frac{1}{5} = \frac{21}{105}$, $\frac{1}{21} = \frac{5}{105}$: $\frac{35}{105} + \frac{30}{105} + \frac{21}{105} + \frac{5}{105} = \frac{91}{105} = \frac{13}{15}$: $1 + 4 + 2 + 2 + \frac{13}{15} = 9\frac{13}{15}$, *Ans.*

Art. 113.

(2.) $\frac{3}{4} - \frac{1}{4} = \frac{2}{4} = \frac{1}{2}$, *Ans.*

(7.) $4\frac{1}{4} - 2\frac{3}{4}$. $\frac{3}{4}$ can not be taken from $\frac{1}{4}$; so borrow 1 from 4. $1 = \frac{4}{4}$; $\frac{4}{4} + \frac{1}{4} = \frac{5}{4}$; $\frac{3}{4}$ from $\frac{5}{4} = \frac{2}{4}$ or $\frac{1}{2}$. Since we took 1 from 4, only 3 remain, and $3 - 2 = 1$. *Ans.* $1\frac{1}{2}$.

	(8)		(9)
$8\frac{1}{3}$	$\frac{1}{3} + \frac{3}{3} = \frac{4}{3}$	$23\frac{7}{20}$	$\frac{7}{20} + \frac{20}{20} = \frac{27}{20}$
$3\frac{2}{3}$	$\frac{4}{3} - \frac{2}{3} = \frac{2}{3}$	$17\frac{11}{20}$	$\frac{27}{20} - \frac{11}{20} = \frac{16}{20} = \frac{4}{5}$
$\overline{4\frac{2}{3}}$, *Ans.*		$\overline{5\frac{4}{5}}$, *Ans.*	

Art. 114.

(9.) L. C. D. $= 30$; $\frac{4}{15} = \frac{8}{30}$, $\frac{1}{10} = \frac{3}{30}$: $\frac{8}{30} - \frac{3}{30} = \frac{5}{30} = \frac{1}{6}$, *Ans.*

(10.) L. C. D. $= 42$; $\frac{16}{21} = \frac{32}{42}$, $\frac{5}{14} = \frac{15}{42}$: $\frac{32}{42} - \frac{15}{42} = \frac{17}{42}$, *Ans.*

(12.) $5 = \frac{15}{3}$: $\frac{15}{3} - \frac{2}{3} = \frac{13}{3} = 4\frac{1}{3}$, *Ans.*

(13.) $5\frac{2}{3} = \frac{17}{3} = \frac{34}{6}$, $4\frac{1}{2} = \frac{9}{2} = \frac{27}{6}$: $\frac{34}{6} - \frac{27}{6} = \frac{7}{6} = 1\frac{1}{6}$, *Ans.*

(14.) $7\frac{2}{3} = \frac{23}{3} = \frac{92}{12}$, $4\frac{3}{4} = \frac{19}{4} = \frac{57}{12}$: $\frac{92}{12} - \frac{57}{12} = \frac{35}{12} = 2\frac{11}{12}$, *Ans.*

(15.) $14\frac{1}{4} = \frac{57}{4} = \frac{171}{12}$, $12\frac{2}{3} = \frac{38}{3} = \frac{152}{12}$: $\frac{171}{12} - \frac{152}{12} = \frac{19}{12} = 1\frac{7}{12}$, *Ans.*

(16.) $5\frac{3}{14} = \frac{73}{14} = \frac{219}{42}$, $2\frac{10}{21} = \frac{52}{21} = \frac{104}{42}$: $\frac{219}{42} - \frac{104}{42} = \frac{115}{42} = 2\frac{31}{42}$, *Ans.*

(17.) $4\frac{1}{24} = \frac{97}{24} = \frac{194}{48}$, $3\frac{1}{16} = \frac{49}{16} = \frac{147}{48}$: $\frac{194}{48} - \frac{147}{48} = \frac{47}{48}$, *Ans.*

(18.) $56\frac{1}{3} = \frac{169}{3} = \frac{676}{12}$, $42\frac{1}{4} = \frac{169}{4} = \frac{507}{12}$: $\frac{676}{12} - \frac{507}{12} = \frac{169}{12} = 14\frac{1}{12}$, *Ans.*

(19.) $60\frac{4}{5} = \frac{304}{5} = \frac{608}{10}$, $41\frac{3}{10} = \frac{413}{10}$: $\frac{608}{10} - \frac{413}{10} = \frac{195}{10} = 19\frac{1}{2}$, *Ans.*

(20.) $97\frac{1}{2} = \frac{195}{2} = \frac{585}{6}$, $48\frac{5}{6} = \frac{293}{6}$: $\frac{585}{6} - \frac{293}{6} = \frac{292}{6} = 48\frac{2}{3}$, *Ans.*

Art. 115.

(5.) $\frac{3}{4} \times 3 = \frac{9}{4} = 2\frac{1}{4}$, *Ans.*

(6.) $8 \times \frac{2}{3} = \frac{16}{3} = 5\frac{1}{3}$, *Ans.*

(7.) $\frac{3}{4} \times \frac{5}{7} = \frac{15}{28}$, *Ans.*

(8.) $\frac{2}{3} \times 4 = \frac{8}{3} = 2\frac{2}{3}$, *Ans.*

(9.) $5 \times \frac{3}{4} = \frac{15}{4} = 3\frac{3}{4}$, *Ans.*

(11.) $\frac{2}{3} \times 6 = \frac{12}{3} = 4$, *Ans.*

(12.) $20 \times \frac{3}{4} = \frac{60}{4} = 15$, *Ans.*

(13.) $\dfrac{\cancel{8}}{13} \times \dfrac{11}{\underset{2}{\cancel{16}}} = \frac{11}{26}$, *Ans.*

(14.) $\frac{3}{5} \times 10 = \frac{30}{5} = 6$, *Ans.*

(15.) $12 \times \frac{2}{3} = \frac{24}{3} = 8$, *Ans.*

(16.) $\frac{9}{13} \times \frac{3}{7} : \frac{9}{13} \times \frac{3}{7} = \frac{27}{91}$, *Ans.*

(17.) $\frac{3}{7} \times 6 = \frac{18}{7} = 2\frac{4}{7}$, *Ans.*

(18.) $7 \times \frac{2}{3} = \frac{14}{3} = 4\frac{2}{3}$, *Ans.*

(21.) 8 times $3 = 24$: 8 times $\frac{2}{3} = \frac{16}{3} = 5\frac{1}{3}$: $24 + 5\frac{1}{3} = 29\frac{1}{3}$, *Ans.*

(22.) $2\frac{1}{2} = \frac{5}{2}$: $\frac{5}{2} \times \frac{5}{2} = \frac{25}{4} = 6\frac{1}{4}$, *Ans.*

(23.) $10 \times 7 = 70$: $\frac{7}{9} \times 7 = \frac{49}{9} = 5\frac{4}{9}$: $70 + 5\frac{4}{9} = 75\frac{4}{9}$, *Ans.*

(24.) $25 \times 8 = 200$: $25 \times \frac{3}{5} = \frac{75}{5} = 15$: $200 + 15 = 215$, *Ans.*

(25.)
$$17\frac{3}{11} = \frac{190}{11} : \dfrac{9}{\cancel{10}} \times \dfrac{\overset{19}{\cancel{190}}}{11} = \frac{171}{11} = 15\frac{6}{11}, \textit{Ans.}$$

(26.) $10 \times 9 = 90$: $\frac{5}{6} \times 9 = \frac{45}{6} = 7\frac{3}{6} = 7\frac{1}{2}$: $90 + 7\frac{1}{2} = 97\frac{1}{2}$, *Ans.*

(27.) 8 times $64 = 512$: $\frac{1}{8}$ of $64 = 8$: $\frac{7}{8} = 56$: $512 + 56 = 568$, *Ans.*

(28.) $8\frac{3}{4} = \frac{35}{4}$: $\frac{1}{7}$ of $\frac{35}{4} = \frac{5}{4}$: $\frac{3}{7} = \frac{15}{4} = 3\frac{3}{4}$, *Ans.*

(29.)
$$2\frac{2}{11} = \frac{24}{11}: \quad \frac{5}{\overset{}{\underset{4}{12}}} \times \frac{9}{\overset{}{\underset{2}{16}}} \times \frac{\overset{3}{\cancel{24}}}{11} = \frac{45}{88}, \textit{ Ans.}$$

(30.)
$$2\frac{1}{16} = \frac{33}{16}: \quad \frac{\overset{3}{\cancel{33}}}{\cancel{16}} \times \frac{\cancel{3}}{\cancel{11}} \times \frac{\cancel{16}}{\underset{3}{\cancel{9}}} = 1, \textit{ Ans.}$$

(31.)
$$\overset{3}{\underset{2}{\frac{\cancel{27}}{\cancel{4}}}} \times \frac{\overset{13}{\cancel{26}}}{\cancel{9}} \times \frac{21}{1} = \frac{819}{2} = 409\frac{1}{2}, \textit{ Ans.}$$

(32.)
$$\frac{5}{\cancel{2}} \times \frac{11}{3} \times \frac{19}{\cancel{4}} \times \frac{\overset{2}{\cancel{8}}}{7} = \frac{1045}{21} = 49\frac{16}{21}, \textit{ Ans.}$$

(33.)
$$\frac{\cancel{11}}{\cancel{5}} \times \frac{\overset{11}{\cancel{55}}}{\underset{2}{\cancel{26}}} \times \frac{\overset{13}{\cancel{13}}}{\cancel{4}} \times \frac{\overset{4}{\cancel{16}}}{\cancel{11}} = 22, \textit{ Ans.}$$

(34) $\dfrac{\cancel{7}}{\cancel{8}} \times \dfrac{\cancel{3}}{\underset{2}{\cancel{10}}} \times \dfrac{\cancel{8}}{9} \times \dfrac{\cancel{5}}{\cancel{6}} \times \dfrac{\cancel{2}}{\cancel{3}} \times \dfrac{\cancel{6}}{\cancel{7}} = \frac{1}{9}$, *Ans.*

(35.)
$$\frac{\cancel{1}}{\underset{2}{\cancel{4}}} \times \frac{\cancel{9}}{\cancel{7}} \times \frac{\cancel{4}}{\cancel{5}} \times \frac{\cancel{7}}{\cancel{9}} \times \frac{\cancel{5}}{\cancel{4}} \times \frac{\cancel{2}}{\cancel{3}} \times \frac{\overset{2}{\cancel{6}}}{\cancel{1}} = 1, \textit{ Ans.}$$

(36.)
$$\frac{\cancel{6}}{\cancel{7}}\times\frac{4}{9}\times\frac{\cancel{7}}{4}\times\frac{1}{\cancel{6}}\times\frac{3}{4}\times\frac{\cancel{5}}{\cancel{6}}\times\frac{2}{5}\times\frac{\overset{5}{\cancel{20}}}{1}=\tfrac{5}{9},\ Ans.$$

(37.)
$$\frac{5}{\cancel{2}}\times\frac{\overset{8}{\cancel{32}}}{5}\times\frac{\cancel{13}}{\cancel{4}}\times\frac{\cancel{7}}{\cancel{13}}\times\frac{2}{1}\times\frac{3}{\cancel{7}}=24,\ Ans.$$

Art. 116.

(2.) $\frac{1}{4}$ of $5 = \frac{5}{4}$; then $\frac{3}{4}$ of $5 = 3$ times $\frac{5}{4} = \frac{15}{4} = 3\frac{3}{4}$, *Ans.*

(3.) $\frac{2}{5}$ of $7 = \frac{14}{5} = 2\frac{4}{5}$, *Ans.*

(4.) $\frac{4}{5}$ of $10 = \frac{40}{5} = 8$, *Ans.*

(5.) $\frac{1}{6}$ of $12 = 2$: $\frac{5}{6} = 2 \times 5 = 10$, *Ans.*

(6.) $\frac{5}{6}$ of $15 = \frac{75}{6} = 12\frac{3}{6} = 12\frac{1}{2}$, *Ans.*

(7.) $\frac{8}{9}$ of $21 = \frac{168}{9} = 18\frac{6}{9} = 18\frac{2}{3}$, *Ans.*

(8.) $\frac{1}{10}$ of $25 = \frac{25}{10} = \frac{5}{2}$: $\frac{7}{10} = \frac{35}{2} = 17\frac{1}{2}$, *Ans.*

(9.) $\frac{5}{12}$ of $27 = \frac{135}{12} = 11\frac{3}{12} = 11\frac{1}{4}$, *Ans.*

(10.) $\frac{7}{12}$ of $28 = \frac{196}{12} = 16\frac{4}{12} = 16\frac{1}{3}$, *Ans.*

Art. 117.

(4.) $\frac{1}{2}$ of $\frac{3}{5}$ of $\frac{11}{4} = \frac{1}{2} \times \frac{3}{5} \times \frac{11}{4} = \frac{33}{40}$, *Ans.*

(7.) $\frac{2}{3}$ of $\frac{5}{7}$ of $\frac{13}{9} = \frac{2}{3} \times \frac{5}{7} \times \frac{13}{9} = \frac{130}{189}$, *Ans.*

(8.) $\frac{2}{\cancel{3}}$ of $\frac{\cancel{3}}{\cancel{4}}$ of $\frac{\cancel{4}}{5} = \tfrac{2}{5}$, *Ans.*

(9.) $\frac{1}{\cancel{3}}$ of $\frac{\cancel{3}}{4}$ of $\frac{5}{6} = \tfrac{5}{24}$, *Ans.*

(10.) $\frac{3}{\cancel{5}}$ of $\frac{\cancel{5}}{\cancel{7}}$ of $\frac{\cancel{7}}{8} = \tfrac{3}{8}$, *Ans.*

(11.)
$$\frac{\cancel{3}}{\cancel{5}} \text{ of } \frac{\cancel{4}}{\cancel{9}} \text{ of } \frac{\cancel{7}}{\underset{\cancel{3}}{\cancel{12}}} \text{ of } \frac{\overset{2}{\cancel{18}}}{\underset{\cancel{5}}{\cancel{35}}} = \tfrac{2}{25}, \textit{Ans.}$$

(12.) $\dfrac{1}{\cancel{3}} \text{ of } \dfrac{\cancel{3}}{\cancel{4}} \text{ of } \dfrac{\cancel{4}}{9} = \tfrac{1}{9}, \textit{Ans.}$

(13.) $\dfrac{1}{9} \text{ of } \dfrac{\cancel{3}}{\cancel{4}} \text{ of } \dfrac{\cancel{4}}{\cancel{3}} = \tfrac{1}{9}, \textit{Ans.}$

(14.)
$$\frac{\cancel{3}}{\cancel{5}} \text{ of } \frac{\cancel{6}}{\cancel{7}} \text{ of } \frac{\overset{5}{\cancel{35}}}{\underset{\cancel{3}}{\cancel{18}}} = 1, \textit{Ans.}$$

(15.)
$$\frac{\cancel{3}}{\cancel{7}} \text{ of } \frac{\overset{2}{\cancel{8}}}{\cancel{3}} \text{ of } \frac{\cancel{7}}{4} = 2, \textit{Ans.}$$

(16.) $\dfrac{\cancel{9}}{\cancel{13}} \text{ of } \dfrac{\cancel{7}}{\underset{2}{\cancel{18}}} \text{ of } \dfrac{\cancel{13}}{\cancel{7}} = \tfrac{1}{2}, \textit{Ans.}$

(17.) $\dfrac{1}{2} \text{ of } \dfrac{\cancel{4}}{\cancel{5}} \text{ of } \dfrac{1}{\underset{2}{\cancel{8}}} \text{ of } \dfrac{\cancel{5}}{1} = \tfrac{1}{4}, \textit{Ans.}$

(18.) $\dfrac{1}{\cancel{2}} \text{ of } \dfrac{\cancel{2}}{\cancel{3}} \text{ of } \dfrac{\cancel{3}}{\cancel{4}} \text{ of } \dfrac{\cancel{4}}{\cancel{5}} \text{ of } \dfrac{\cancel{5}}{8} \text{ of } \dfrac{\cancel{5}}{\cancel{9}} \text{ of } \dfrac{\cancel{9}}{\underset{2}{\cancel{10}}} = \tfrac{1}{16}, \textit{Ans.}$

Art. 118.

(1.)
$$2\tfrac{1}{3} = \tfrac{7}{3},\ 13\tfrac{1}{5} = \underset{5}{\cancel{\tfrac{66}{5}}} : \frac{7}{\cancel{3}} \times \frac{\overset{22}{\cancel{66}}}{5} = \tfrac{154}{5} = 30\tfrac{4}{5} \text{ ct., } \textit{Ans.}$$

(2.) 3 times $\frac{2}{3} = \frac{6}{3} = \$2$:   5 times $\frac{2}{3} = \frac{10}{3} = \$3\frac{1}{3}$:   7 times $\frac{2}{3} = \frac{14}{3} = \$4\frac{2}{3}$: $\dfrac{13}{\cancel{2}} \times \dfrac{\cancel{2}}{3} = \frac{13}{3} = \$4\frac{1}{3}$: $\dfrac{23}{\cancel{4}_2} \times \dfrac{\cancel{2}}{3} = \frac{23}{6} = \$3\frac{5}{6}$.

(3.) $\dfrac{\overset{2}{\cancel{10}}}{\cancel{3}} \times \dfrac{\overset{8}{\cancel{24}}}{\cancel{5}} = 16$ ct., *Ans.*

(4.) $\dfrac{\overset{4}{\cancel{16}}}{\cancel{5}} \times \dfrac{\overset{15}{\cancel{75}}}{\cancel{4}} = \$60$, *Ans.*

(5.) $\dfrac{\cancel{5}}{\cancel{3}} \times \dfrac{\cancel{3}}{\cancel{20}_4} = \$\frac{1}{4}$, *Ans.*

(6.) $\dfrac{\cancel{5}}{\cancel{2}} \times \dfrac{\overset{2}{\cancel{4}}}{\cancel{5}} = \$2$, *Ans.*

(7.) $\dfrac{\overset{10}{\cancel{50}}}{\cancel{9}_3} \times \dfrac{\overset{2}{\cancel{6}}}{\cancel{5}} = \frac{20}{3} = \$6\frac{2}{3}$, *Ans.*

(8.) $\frac{11}{2} \times \frac{31}{4} = \frac{341}{8} = 42\frac{5}{8}$ mi., *Ans.*

(9.) $\dfrac{\cancel{3}}{5}$ of $\dfrac{2}{\cancel{3}} = \frac{2}{5}$, *Ans.*

(10.) $\frac{2}{9}$ of $\frac{11}{2} = \frac{11}{9}$: $\dfrac{11}{\cancel{9}} \times \dfrac{\overset{3}{\cancel{27}}}{4} = \frac{33}{4} = \$8\frac{1}{4}$, *Ans.*

(11.) $\dfrac{\cancel{3}}{\cancel{7}} \times \dfrac{5}{\cancel{9}_3} \times \dfrac{\overset{11}{\cancel{33}}}{\cancel{2}} \times \dfrac{\cancel{2}}{\cancel{3}} \times \dfrac{\cancel{7}}{8} \times \dfrac{\overset{5}{\cancel{15}}}{1} = \frac{275}{8} = 34\frac{3}{8}$, *Ans.*

(12.) $\frac{2}{3} = \frac{8}{12}$, $\frac{3}{4} = \frac{9}{12}$: $\frac{8}{12} + \frac{9}{12} = \frac{17}{12}$: $\dfrac{2}{\cancel{3}} \times \dfrac{\cancel{3}}{4}_2 = \frac{1}{2}$: $\frac{1}{2} = \frac{6}{12}$: $\frac{17}{12} \times \frac{6}{12} = \frac{23}{12} = 1\frac{11}{12}$. *Ans.*

Art. 119.

REMARK.—Pupils are often at a loss to understand, why it is that the quotient of one proper fraction, divided by another, is sometimes a whole number, or greater than unity. The teacher should be careful to explain this subject, by means of familiar examples, such as may be found in "Ray's New Intellectual Arithmetic," Lessons XXXIII—XXXVIII.

It should also be shown, that if we take any dividend, and divide it by different numbers, that as the divisor becomes less, the quotient becomes greater; so that, by making the divisor sufficiently small, the quotient may be made as large as we please. Thus, the quotient of $\frac{1}{2}$ divided by $\frac{1}{4}$ is 2; by $\frac{1}{8}$, is 4; by $\frac{1}{16}$ is 8; by $\frac{1}{4000000}$, is 2000000, etc. It is on this principle, that mathematicians, say, that the quotient of any number, divided by 0, is infinitely large.

(6.) 1 yd. will cost $\frac{1}{4}$ of $\$\frac{8}{9} = \$\frac{2}{9}$, *Ans.*

(7.) $3 \div \frac{1}{2} = 3 \times \frac{2}{1} = 6$, *Ans.*

(8.) $\frac{9}{10} \div \frac{1}{5} = \frac{9}{\underset{2}{10}} \times \frac{\overset{}{5}}{1} = \frac{9}{2} = 4\frac{1}{2}$ yd., *Ans.*

(9.) One cent will buy $\frac{1}{3}$ of an orange: $\frac{1}{2}$ cent will buy $\frac{1}{2}$ of $\frac{1}{3} = \frac{1}{6}$, *Ans.*

(10.) $6 \div \frac{3}{4} = 6 \times \frac{4}{3} = \frac{24}{3} = 8$ yd., *Ans.*

(11.) $\frac{3}{4} \div \frac{1}{5} = \frac{3}{4} \times \frac{5}{1} = \frac{15}{4} = 3\frac{3}{4}$ yd., *Ans.*

(12.) 1 lb. will cost $\frac{1}{7}$ of $\$\frac{14}{25} = \$\frac{2}{25}$, *Ans.*

(14.)
$$2\frac{2}{5} = \frac{12}{5} : \quad \frac{1}{\cancel{6}} \text{ of } \frac{\overset{2}{\cancel{12}}}{5} = \frac{2}{5}, \textit{Ans.}$$

(15.)
$$5\frac{1}{2} = \frac{11}{2} : \quad \frac{\overset{2}{\cancel{22}}}{1} \times \frac{2}{\cancel{11}} = 4, \textit{Ans.}$$

(16.)
$$\frac{5}{\cancel{2}} \times \frac{\cancel{16}^{\;8}}{1} = 40, \; Ans.$$

(17.) 3
$$\frac{\cancel{24}}{5} \times \frac{1}{\cancel{8}} = \tfrac{3}{5}, \; Ans.$$

(18.) $\dfrac{\cancel{6}}{1} \times \dfrac{5}{\underset{2}{\cancel{12}}} = \tfrac{5}{2} = 2\tfrac{1}{2}, \; Ans.$

(19.)
$$\frac{19}{\cancel{4}} \times \frac{\cancel{8}^{\;2}}{41} = \tfrac{38}{41}, \; Ans.$$

(20.) 8
$$\frac{\cancel{88}}{7} \times \frac{1}{\cancel{11}} = \tfrac{8}{7} = 1\tfrac{1}{7}, \; Ans.$$

(21.) 2
$$\frac{\cancel{30}}{1} \times \frac{4}{\cancel{15}} = 8, \; Ans.$$

(22.) 3
$$\frac{\cancel{9}}{\underset{2}{\cancel{4}}} \times \frac{2}{\underset{5}{\cancel{15}}} = \tfrac{3}{10}, \; Ans.$$

(23.) $\tfrac{11}{3} \times \tfrac{1}{7} = \tfrac{11}{21}, \; Ans.$

(24.) $\tfrac{50}{1} \times \tfrac{7}{31} = \tfrac{350}{31} = 11\tfrac{9}{31}, \; Ans.$

(25.) 25
$$\frac{1}{2} \times \frac{\cancel{50}}{1} = 25, \; Ans.$$

(26.) $\tfrac{237}{5} \times \tfrac{1}{15} = \tfrac{237}{75} = 3\tfrac{12}{75} = 3\tfrac{4}{25}, \; Ans.$

(27.) 8
$$\frac{\cancel{56}}{1} \times \frac{9}{\underset{7}{\cancel{49}}} = \tfrac{72}{7} = 10\tfrac{2}{7}, \; Ans.$$

(28.) 2
$$\frac{\cancel{14}}{15} \times \frac{1}{\underset{3}{\cancel{21}}} = \tfrac{2}{45}, \; Ans.$$

(29.) $\frac{392}{8} \times \frac{1}{18} = \frac{392}{54} = \frac{196}{27} = 7\frac{7}{27}$, *Ans.*

(31.)

$$\frac{\cancel{3}}{5} \times \frac{\overset{4}{\cancel{8}}}{\underset{3}{\cancel{9}}} \times \frac{7}{\underset{3}{\cancel{6}}} \times \frac{4}{3} = \frac{112}{135}, \; Ans.$$

(32.) $\frac{1}{3} \times \frac{41}{\underset{2}{\cancel{8}}} \times \frac{\cancel{4}}{3} \times \frac{\cancel{2}}{35} = \frac{41}{315}, \; Ans.$

(33.)

$$\frac{\cancel{5}}{\underset{6}{\cancel{18}}} \times \frac{\cancel{2}}{\cancel{5}} \times \frac{\overset{\overset{3}{\cancel{6}}}{\cancel{123}}}{\underset{2}{\cancel{10}}} \times \frac{\cancel{5}}{1} \times \frac{5}{\cancel{41}} = \frac{5}{6}, \; Ans.$$

(34.) $\frac{\cancel{2}}{\cancel{7}} \times \frac{\cancel{7}}{\underset{2}{\cancel{8}}} \times \frac{4}{\cancel{3}} \times \frac{\cancel{3}}{1} \times \frac{1}{5} = \frac{1}{5}, \; Ans.$

(35.)

$$\frac{\cancel{5}}{\underset{6}{\cancel{18}}} \times \frac{\cancel{2}}{\cancel{5}} \times \frac{\overset{\overset{3}{\cancel{6}}}{\cancel{123}}}{\cancel{10}} \times \frac{\cancel{5}}{1} \times \frac{\cancel{10}}{\cancel{41}} \times \frac{1}{\underset{\underset{2}{4}}{\cancel{20}}} = \frac{1}{12}, \; Ans.$$

Art. 120.

(6.) $\frac{3}{4} \times \frac{1}{5} = \frac{3}{20}$, *Ans.*

(7.) $\frac{1}{\underset{2}{\cancel{4}}} \times \frac{\cancel{2}}{1} = \frac{1}{2}$, *Ans.*

(8.) $\frac{2}{\cancel{3}} \times \frac{\overset{2}{\cancel{6}}}{5} = \frac{4}{5}$, *Ans.*

(9.) $\frac{\overset{3}{\cancel{15}}}{4} \times \frac{1}{\cancel{5}} = \frac{3}{4}$, *Ans.*

(10.) $\frac{5}{\underset{2}{\cancel{6}}} \times \frac{\overset{3}{\cancel{9}}}{8} = \frac{15}{16}$, *Ans.*

(11.) 7

$$\frac{\cancel{77}}{9} \times \frac{1}{\cancel{11}} = \frac{7}{9}, \textit{ Ans.}$$

(12.)   3

3   $\cancel{6}$

$$\frac{\cancel{21}}{\cancel{32}} \times \frac{\cancel{48}}{\cancel{35}} = \frac{9}{10}, \textit{ Ans.}$$

4   5

2

Art. 121.

(2.) $\frac{6}{7} \times \frac{5}{11} = \frac{30}{77}, \textbf{ Ans.}$

(3.) $\frac{2}{3} \times \frac{1}{5} = \frac{2}{15}, \textbf{ Ans.}$

(4.) $\frac{2}{1} \times \frac{3}{11} = \frac{6}{11}, \textbf{ Ans.}$

(5.) $\frac{25}{8} \times \frac{7}{33} = \frac{175}{264}, \textbf{ Ans.}$

(6.) $\frac{7}{3} \times \frac{2}{9} = \frac{14}{27}, \textbf{ Ans.}$

(7.)   2

$$\frac{\cancel{15}}{4} \times \frac{8}{\cancel{45}} = \frac{2}{3}, \textbf{ Ans.}$$

3

(8.) 8   3

$$\frac{\cancel{88}}{9} \times \frac{\cancel{27}}{\cancel{55}} = \frac{24}{5} = 4\frac{4}{5}, \textbf{ Ans.}$$

5

(9.) 7   2

$$\frac{\cancel{35}}{4} \times \frac{8}{\cancel{45}} = 1\frac{5}{9}, \textbf{ Ans.}$$

9

(10.) $\frac{47}{6} \times \frac{11}{97} = \frac{517}{582}, \textbf{ Ans.}$

Art. 122.

(1.) $3\frac{1}{4} \div \frac{1}{2} = \frac{13}{4} \times \frac{2}{1} = \frac{13}{2} = 6\frac{1}{2}$ yd., *Ans.*

(2.) $2\frac{3}{10} \div \frac{3}{5} = \frac{23}{10} \times \frac{5}{3} = \frac{23}{6} = 3\frac{5}{6}$ lb., *Ans.*

(3.) $42\frac{1}{2} \div 3\frac{3}{4} = \frac{85}{2} \div \frac{15}{4} = \frac{85}{2} \times \frac{4}{15} = \frac{17}{1} \times \frac{2}{3} = \frac{34}{3} =$ $11\frac{1}{3}$ yd., *Ans.*

(4.) $10 \div \frac{3}{8} = \frac{10}{1} \times \frac{8}{3} = \frac{80}{3} = 26\frac{2}{3}$, *Ans.*

(5.) $\frac{3}{7}$ of $1\frac{1}{2} = \frac{3}{7}$ of $\frac{3}{2} = \frac{9}{14}$: $3\frac{3}{7} = \frac{24}{7}$: $\frac{24}{7} \div \frac{9}{14} = \frac{24}{7} \times \frac{14}{9} = \frac{8}{1} \times \frac{2}{3} = \frac{16}{3} = 5\frac{1}{3}$, *Ans.*

(6.) $\frac{4}{11}$ of $27\frac{1}{2} = \frac{4}{11}$ of $\frac{55}{2} = 10$: $\frac{3}{10}$ of $21\frac{1}{4} = \frac{3}{10}$ of $\frac{85}{4}$ $= \frac{51}{8}$: $10 \div \frac{51}{8} = \frac{10}{1} \times \frac{8}{51} = \frac{80}{51} = 1\frac{29}{51}$, *Ans.*

(7.) $\dfrac{3}{\cancel{2}} \times \dfrac{\cancel{5}}{7} \times \dfrac{\cancel{5}}{7} \times \dfrac{\cancel{2}}{\cancel{9}} = \frac{3}{49}$, Ans.

(8.)
$$\dfrac{\cancel{11\frac{3}{5}}}{\cancel{15}} \times \dfrac{\overset{4}{\cancel{12}}}{\cancel{11\frac{3}{5}}} \times \dfrac{19}{\cancel{9}} \times \dfrac{\cancel{15}}{47} \times \dfrac{\cancel{5}}{\cancel{4}} \times \dfrac{\overset{2}{\cancel{6}}}{\cancel{5}} = \frac{38}{47}, Ans.$$

(9.) $\dfrac{1\frac{1}{2}}{\frac{2}{3}} = \frac{3}{2} \times \frac{3}{2} = \frac{9}{4}$: $\dfrac{2\frac{2}{5}}{2\frac{1}{6}} = \frac{12}{5} \times \frac{6}{13} = \frac{72}{65}$: $\frac{9}{4} \div \frac{72}{65} =$

$\frac{9}{4} \times \frac{65}{72} = \frac{1}{4} \times \frac{65}{8} = \frac{65}{32} = 2\frac{1}{32}$, Ans.

(10.) $\dfrac{\cancel{5}}{3} \times \dfrac{2}{\cancel{5}} = \frac{2}{3}$: $\dfrac{\overset{2}{\cancel{36}}}{\cancel{7}} \times \dfrac{\cancel{7}}{\underset{33}{\cancel{594}}} = \frac{2}{33}$: $\dfrac{\cancel{2}}{\cancel{3}} \times \dfrac{\overset{11}{\cancel{33}}}{\cancel{2}} = 11$, Ans.

Art. 123.

(1)	(2)	(3)	(4)	(5)
$\$16\frac{1}{16}$	$\$9\frac{1}{8}$	$\$50\frac{1}{4}$	$\$32.31\frac{1}{4}$	$\$5.81\frac{1}{4}$
$9\frac{1}{8}$	$4\frac{7}{16}$	$27\frac{3}{16}$	$15.12\frac{1}{2}$	$1.18\frac{3}{4}$
$5\frac{7}{16}$	$0\frac{3}{8}$	$\$23\frac{1}{16}$	$\$17.18\frac{3}{4}$	$\$4.62\frac{1}{2}$
$2\frac{13}{16}$	$1\frac{5}{8}$			
$\$33\frac{7}{16}$	$\$15\frac{9}{16}$			

(6.) $12\frac{1}{2} \times 9 = 108 + 4\frac{1}{2} = 112\frac{1}{2}$ ct. $= \$1.12\frac{1}{2}$, Ans.

(7.) $21 \times 6\frac{1}{4} = 126 + 5\frac{1}{4} = 131\frac{1}{4}$ ct. $= \$1.31\frac{1}{4}$, Ans.

(8.) $\$3.18\frac{3}{4} \times 15 = \$47.70 + \$0.11\frac{1}{4} = \$47.81\frac{1}{4}$, Ans.

(9.) $62\frac{1}{2} \times 5\frac{1}{2} = \frac{125}{2} \times \frac{11}{2} = \frac{1375}{4} = 343\frac{3}{4}$ ct. $= \$3.43\frac{3}{4}$, Ans.

(10.) $18\frac{3}{4} = \frac{75}{4}$: $12\frac{1}{2} = \frac{25}{2}$: $\frac{75}{4} \times \frac{25}{2} = \frac{1875}{8} = 234\frac{3}{8}$ ct. $= \$2.34\frac{3}{8}$, Ans.

(11.) $16\frac{2}{3} = \frac{50}{3}$: $13\frac{1}{2} = \frac{27}{2}$: $\frac{50}{3} \times \frac{27}{2} = 25 \times 9 = 225$ ct. $= \$2.25$, Ans.

(12.) $\$3.37\frac{1}{2} \times 10\frac{1}{4} = \frac{675}{2} \times \frac{41}{4} = \frac{27675}{8} = 3459\frac{3}{8}$ ct. = $\$34.59\frac{3}{8}$, *Ans.*

(13.) $17\frac{2}{3} = \frac{53}{3}$: $\frac{375}{1} \times \frac{53}{3} = 125 \times 53 = 6625$ ct. = $\$66.25$, *Ans.*

(14.) $225 \div 18\frac{3}{4} = \frac{225}{1} \times \frac{4}{75} = \frac{3}{1} \times \frac{4}{1} = 12$ yd., *Ans.*

(15.) $581\frac{1}{4} \div 37\frac{1}{2} = \frac{2325}{4} \times \frac{2}{75} = \frac{31}{2} \times \frac{1}{1} = 15\frac{1}{2}$ bu., *Ans.*

(16.) $\$11.56\frac{1}{4} \div 5 = \$2.31\frac{1}{4}$, *Ans.*

(17.) $\$31.06\frac{1}{4} \div 7 = \$4.43\frac{3}{4}$, *Ans.*

(18.) 5 mi. $\times$ 320 = 1600 rd.: 1600 rd. $\times 16\frac{1}{2} = 26400$ ft.: 26400 ft. $\times 12 = 316800$ in., *Ans.*

(19.) 2 mi. $\times$ 320 + 2 rd. = 642 rd.: 642 rd. $\times 16\frac{1}{2} + 2$ ft. = 10595 ft., *Ans.*

(21.) 15875 ft. $\div 16\frac{1}{2} = 962$ rd. 2 ft.: 962 rd. $\div 320 = 3$ mi. 2 rd. *Ans.* 3 mi. 2 rd. 2 ft.

(22.) 142634 in. $\div 12 = 11886$ ft. 2 in.: 11886 ft. $\div 3 = 3962$ yd.: 3962 yd. $\div 5\frac{1}{2} = 720$ rd. 2 yd.: 720 rd. $\div 320 = 2$ mi. 80 rd. *Ans.* 2 mi. 80 rd. 2 yd. 2 in.

(23.) 2 mi. = 126720 in.: 2 ft. 8 in. = 32 in.: 126720 in. $\div 32$ in. = 3960, *Ans.*

(24.) 65 mi. = 4118400 in.: 9 ft. 2 in. = 110 in.: 4118400 in. $\div 110$ in. = 37440, *Ans.*

(25.) 1 A. $\times$ 160 + 136 sq. rd. = 296 sq. rd.: 296 sq. rd. $\times 30\frac{1}{4} + 25$ sq. yd. = 8979 sq. yd., *Ans.*

(26.) 7506 sq. yd. $\div 30\frac{1}{4} = 248$ sq. rd. 4 sq. yd.: 248 sq. rd. $\div 160 = 1$ A. 88 sq. rd. *Ans.* 1 A. 88 sq. rd. 4 sq. yd.

(27.) 5 ch. 15 l. = 515 l.: $7\frac{92}{100}$ in. = $\frac{792}{100}$ in.: $\frac{792}{100}$ in. $\times 515 = \frac{407880}{100} = 4078\frac{4}{5}$ in., *Ans.*

(28.) $40\frac{1}{2} = \frac{81}{2}$: $\frac{81}{2} \times \frac{32}{1} = 81 \times 16 = 1296$ sq. rd.: 1296 sq. rd. $\div 160 = 8$ A. 16 sq. rd., *Ans.*

(29.) $365\frac{1}{4}$ da. $\times 4 = 1461$ da.: 1461 da. $\times 24 = 35064$ hr., *Ans.*

(30.) 914092 hr. $\div 24 = 38087$ da. 4 hr.: 38087 da. $\div$ $365\frac{1}{4} = 104$ yr. 101 da.: 104 yr. $\div 100 = 1$ cen. 4 yr. *Ans.* 1 cen. 4 yr. 101 da. 4 hr.

(31.) $238545 \div 31 = 7695$ da.: $7695 \div 365\frac{1}{4} = 21$ yr., and 99 quarter days remaining, which, reduced to days, by dividing by 4, makes $24\frac{3}{4}$ days. *Ans.* 21 yr. $24\frac{3}{4}$ da.

Art. 124.

(3.) $\frac{1}{28}$ lb. $\times 16 = \frac{16}{28} = \frac{4}{7}$ oz., *Ans.*

(4.) $\frac{1}{16}$ lb. $\times 12 = \frac{12}{16} = \frac{3}{4}$ oz., *Ans.*

(5.) $\frac{1}{20}$ rd. $\times 5\frac{1}{2} = \frac{11}{40}$ yd. $\times 3 = \frac{33}{40}$ ft., *Ans.*

(6.) $\frac{7}{1280}$ A. $\times 160 = \frac{7}{8}$ sq. rd., *Ans.*

(7.) $\$\frac{3}{350} \times 100 = \frac{300}{350} = \frac{6}{7}$ ct., *Ans.*

(8.) $\frac{1}{1584}$ da. $\times 24 = \frac{1}{66}$ hr.: $\frac{1}{66}$ hr. $\times 60 = \frac{60}{66} = \frac{10}{11}$ min., *Ans.*

(9.) $\frac{3}{320}$ bu. $\times 4 = \frac{3}{80}$ pk.: $\frac{3}{80}$ pk. $\times 8 = \frac{3}{10}$ qt.: $\frac{3}{10}$ qt. $\times 2 = \frac{3}{5}$ pt., *Ans.*

Art. 125.

(2.) $\frac{4}{5}$ mi. $\times 320 = \frac{1280}{5}$ rd. $= 256$ rd., *Ans.*

(3.) $\$\frac{3}{5} \times 100 = \frac{300}{5}$ ct. $= 60$ ct., *Ans.*

(4.) $\frac{2}{5}$ mi. $\times 320 = \frac{640}{5}$ rd. $= 128$ rd., *Ans.*

(5.) $\frac{4}{5}$ lb. $\times 12 = \frac{48}{5}$ oz. $= 9\frac{3}{5}$ oz.: $\frac{3}{5}$ oz. $\times 20 = \frac{60}{5}$ pwt. $= 12$ pwt. *Ans.* 9 oz. 12 pwt.

(6.) $\frac{7}{16}$ T. $\times 20 = \frac{140}{16} = 8\frac{3}{4}$ cwt.; $\frac{3}{4}$ cwt. $\times 100 = \frac{300}{4}$ lb. $= 75$ lb. *Ans.* 8 cwt. 75 lb.

(7.) $\frac{5}{8}$ A. $\times 160 = \frac{800}{8}$ sq. rd. $= 100$ sq. rd., *Ans.*

(8.) $\frac{1}{8}$ of 63 gal. $= 7\frac{7}{8}$, and $\frac{7}{8} = 55\frac{1}{8}$ gal.: $\frac{1}{8}$ gal. $\times 4 = \frac{4}{8}$ or $\frac{1}{2}$ qt.: $\frac{1}{2}$ qt. $\times 2 = \frac{2}{2}$ or 1 pt. *Ans.* 55 gal. 1 pt.

Art. 126.

(2.) $\dfrac{\cancel{4}}{5} \times \dfrac{1}{8} \times \dfrac{1}{\cancel{4}} = \frac{1}{40}$ bu., *Ans.*

(3.) $\frac{4}{5} \times \frac{2}{33} = \frac{8}{165}$ rd., *Ans.*   ($16\frac{1}{2}$ ft. in a rd. $= \frac{33}{2}$ ft.)

(4.) $\frac{3}{80} \times \frac{1}{16} = \frac{3}{1280}$ lb., *Ans.*

(5.) $\dfrac{\cancel{4}}{9} \times \dfrac{1}{100} \times \dfrac{1}{\underset{5}{\cancel{20}}} = \frac{1}{4500}$ T., *Ans.*

(6.) $\frac{3}{5} \times \frac{1}{2} \times \frac{1}{8} \times \frac{1}{4} = \frac{3}{320}$ bu., *Ans.*

(7.) $\dfrac{\cancel{4}}{7} \times \dfrac{1}{\underset{4}{\cancel{16}}} \times \dfrac{1}{100} = \frac{1}{2800}$ cwt., *Ans.*

(8.) $\dfrac{\underset{2}{\cancel{3}}}{\cancel{4}} \times \dfrac{1}{12} \times \dfrac{\cancel{2}}{\underset{11}{\cancel{33}}} = \frac{1}{264}$ rd., *Ans.*

(9.) $\dfrac{\cancel{8}}{9} \times \dfrac{1}{60} \times \dfrac{1}{\underset{3}{\cancel{24}}} = \frac{1}{1620}$ da., *Ans.*

(10.) $\dfrac{\cancel{5}}{112} \times \dfrac{1}{16} \times \dfrac{1}{\underset{20}{\cancel{100}}} = \frac{1}{35840}$ cwt., *Ans.*

Art. 127.

(2.) 2 ft. 6 in. $= 30$ in.: 6 ft. 8 in. $= 80$ in.: $\frac{30}{80} = \frac{3}{8}$, *Ans.*

(3.) 2 pk. 4 qt. $= 20$ qt.: 1 bu. $= 32$ qt.: $\frac{20}{32} = \frac{5}{8}$, *Ans.*

(4.) 2 yd. 9 in. = 81 in.: 8 yd. 2 ft. 3 in. = 315 in.: $\frac{81}{315} = \frac{9}{35}$, *Ans.*

(5.) 13 hr. 30 min. = 810 min.: 1 da. × 24 × 60 = 1440 min.: $\frac{810}{1440} = \frac{9}{16}$, *Ans.*

(6.) $\frac{145}{320} = \frac{29}{64}$, *Ans.*

(7.) 2 ft. 8 in. = 32 in.: 1 yd. = 36 in.: $\frac{32}{36} = \frac{8}{9}$, *Ans.*

(8.) 15 mi. 123 rd. = 4923 rd.: 35 mi. 287 rd. = 11487 rd.: $\frac{4923}{11487} = \frac{3}{7}$, *Ans.*

(9.) 37 A. 94 sq. rd. = 6014 sq. rd.: 168 A. 28 sq. rd. = 26908 sq. rd.: $\frac{6014}{26908} = \frac{97}{434}$, *Ans.*

(10.)   4
$$\frac{\cancel{64}}{9} \text{ oz.} \times \frac{1}{\cancel{16}} = \frac{4}{9}, \text{ } Ans.$$

(11.) 2 qt. 1⅓ pt. = 5⅓ or $\frac{16}{3}$ pt.: 1 bu. 1 qt. 1⅔ pt. = 67⅔ or $\frac{203}{3}$ pt.: $\frac{16}{\cancel{3}} \times \frac{\cancel{3}}{203} = \frac{16}{203}$, *Ans.*

(12.) 1 yd. 1 ft. 1$\frac{9}{11}$ in. = 49$\frac{9}{11}$ in. = $\frac{548}{11}$: 3 yd. 2 ft. 8$\frac{6}{7}$ in. = 140$\frac{6}{7}$ = $\frac{986}{7}$: $\frac{548}{11} \times \frac{7}{986} = \frac{3836}{10890} = \frac{1918}{5423}$, *Ans.*

Art. 128.

(3)		
	hr.	min.
⅔ da. =	16	0
¾ hr. =		45
Ans.	16	45

(4)			
	da.	hr.	min.
¼ wk. =	1	18	0
¼ da. =		6	0
¼ hr. =			15
Ans.	2	0	15

(5)

	da.	hr.	min.	sec.
$\frac{2}{3}$ wk. =	4	16	0	0
$\frac{5}{9}$ da. =		13	20	0
$\frac{2}{3}$ hr. =			40	0
$\frac{2}{3}$ min.=				40
Ans.	5	6	0	40

(6)

	qt.	pt.	gi.
$\frac{11}{12}$ gal.=	3	1	$1\frac{1}{3}$
$\frac{1}{12}$ qt. =		0	$\frac{2}{3}$
Ans.	3	1	2

(7)

	hr.	min.	sec.
$\frac{7}{9}$ da.=	18	40	0
$\frac{1}{18}$ hr.=		3	20
Ans.	18	36	40

(8)

	ct.
$\$\frac{5}{8}$ =	$62\frac{1}{2}$
$\$\frac{3}{40}$ =	$7\frac{1}{2}$
Ans.	55

(9.) $\frac{3}{8}$ lb. = 6 oz. : 6 oz. $-\frac{7}{8}$ oz. = $5\frac{1}{8}$ oz., *Ans.*

(10.) $\frac{1}{7}$ da. = $\frac{24}{7}$ hr.: $\frac{24}{7} - \frac{6}{7} = \frac{18}{7} = 2\frac{4}{7}$ hr.: $\frac{4}{7}$ hr. $\times$ 60 = $\frac{240}{7}$ or $34\frac{2}{7}$ min.: $\frac{2}{7}$ min. $\times$ 60 = $\frac{120}{7}$ or $17\frac{1}{7}$ sec. *Ans.* 2 hr. 34 min. $17\frac{1}{7}$ sec.

Promiscuous Examples.

Art. 129.

(1.) $\frac{32989}{56981} = \frac{2999 \times 11}{2999 \times 19} = \frac{11}{19}$, *Ans.*

(2.) $2 + 3 = 5$: $\frac{1}{2} + \frac{2}{3} + \frac{5}{14} + \frac{8}{21} = \frac{21}{42} + \frac{28}{42} + \frac{15}{42} + \frac{16}{42} = \frac{80}{42} = \frac{40}{21} = 1\frac{19}{21}$: $5 + 1\frac{19}{21} = 6\frac{19}{21}$, *Ans.*

(3.) $\frac{25}{7} = \frac{125}{35}$: $\frac{9}{5} = \frac{63}{35}$: $\frac{125-63}{35} = \frac{62}{35} = 1\frac{27}{35}$, *Ans.*

(4.) $3\frac{5}{8} = \frac{29}{8}$: $\frac{1}{3}$ of $3\frac{1}{2} = \frac{1}{3}$ of $\frac{7}{2} = \frac{7}{6}$: $\frac{29}{8} - \frac{7}{6} = \frac{87}{24} - \frac{28}{24} = \frac{59}{24} = 2\frac{11}{24}$, *Ans.*

(5.) $\frac{5}{9}$ of $\frac{7}{\cancel{10}}_{2} = \frac{7}{18}$: $\frac{2}{5}$ of $\frac{7}{\cancel{12}}_{6} = \frac{7}{30}$: $\frac{7}{18} + \frac{7}{30} = \frac{35}{90} + \frac{21}{90} = \frac{56}{90} = \frac{28}{45}$, *Ans.*

(6.)

$$1\tfrac{3}{4} \div 2\tfrac{1}{2} = \frac{7}{\underset{2}{\cancel{4}}} \times \frac{\cancel{2}}{5} = \tfrac{7}{10} : \quad 5\tfrac{1}{2} \div 3\tfrac{1}{8} = \frac{11}{\cancel{2}} \times \frac{\overset{4}{\cancel{8}}}{25} = \tfrac{44}{25} :$$

$\tfrac{7}{10} + \tfrac{44}{25} = \tfrac{35}{50} + \tfrac{88}{50} = \tfrac{123}{50} = 2\tfrac{23}{50}$, *Ans.*

(7.) $10 \times \tfrac{3}{5} = \tfrac{30}{5} = 6$, *Ans.*

(8.) $10 \div \tfrac{3}{5} = 10 \times \tfrac{5}{3} = \tfrac{50}{3} = 16\tfrac{2}{3}$, **Ans.**

(9.) Any number less $\tfrac{3}{7} = \tfrac{4}{7}$: then 16 is $\tfrac{4}{7}$ of the number: 4 is $\tfrac{1}{7}$, and 28 is $\tfrac{7}{7}$, the number.

(10.) Any number plus $\tfrac{3}{7} = \tfrac{10}{7}$: then $20 = \tfrac{10}{7}$: $\tfrac{1}{7} = \tfrac{1}{10}$ of 20 = 2: $\tfrac{7}{7} = 14$, the number.

(11.) $\tfrac{1}{3}$ of $\tfrac{5}{8} = \tfrac{5}{24}$, and $\tfrac{5}{8} - \tfrac{5}{24} = \tfrac{15}{24} - \tfrac{5}{24} = \tfrac{10}{24} = \tfrac{5}{12}$, part left.

Or, the part left may be found thus: If he sell $\tfrac{1}{3}$ of his share, he has $\tfrac{2}{3}$ of it left, and $\tfrac{2}{3}$ of $\tfrac{5}{8} = \tfrac{10}{24} = \tfrac{5}{12}$. $\tfrac{5}{12}$ of $\$900 = \tfrac{4500}{12} = \$375$, *Ans.*

(12.) I sell $\tfrac{1}{3}$ of $\tfrac{7}{12}$ of the ship $= \tfrac{7}{36}$ of the ship for $\$1944\tfrac{4}{9}$; at that rate, $\tfrac{1}{36}$ of the ship is worth $\tfrac{1}{7}$ of $\$1944\tfrac{4}{9}$ $= \$277\tfrac{4}{9}$, and $\tfrac{36}{36}$ is worth 36 times $\$277\tfrac{4}{9} = \$10000$.

(13.) $\tfrac{2}{3}$ of $2 = \tfrac{4}{3} = 1\tfrac{1}{3}$: $\quad \dfrac{1\tfrac{1}{3}}{3} = \tfrac{4}{3} \times \tfrac{1}{3} = \tfrac{4}{9}$, *Ans.*

(14.) $\tfrac{176}{368} = \dfrac{16 \times 11}{16 \times 23} = \tfrac{11}{23}$, *Ans.*

(15.) $\tfrac{1}{8} + \tfrac{1}{18} + \tfrac{13}{111} = \tfrac{333}{2664} + \tfrac{148}{2664} + \tfrac{312}{2664} = \tfrac{793}{2664} : \tfrac{25}{37} - \tfrac{793}{2664} = \tfrac{1800}{2664} - \tfrac{793}{2664} = \tfrac{1007}{2664}$, *Ans.*

(16.)

$$4\tfrac{9}{14} = \tfrac{65}{14} : \quad \frac{\cancel{3}}{\underset{2}{\cancel{10}}} \text{ of } \frac{\cancel{7}}{\underset{4}{\cancel{12}}} \text{ of } \frac{\overset{13}{\cancel{65}}}{\underset{2}{\cancel{14}}} = \tfrac{13}{16} : \quad 1 - \tfrac{13}{16} = \tfrac{3}{16}, \, Ans.$$

(17.) $\frac{2}{3} \div \frac{5}{7} = \frac{2}{3} \times \frac{7}{5} = \frac{14}{15}$: $\frac{5}{8} \div \frac{10}{11} = \frac{\cancel{5}}{8} \times \frac{11}{\cancel{10}} = \frac{11}{16}$: $\frac{14}{15} -$
$\frac{11}{16} = \frac{224}{240} - \frac{165}{240} = \frac{59}{240}$, $Ans.$

(18.) In $\frac{1}{15}$ of an hour he walks $\frac{1}{7}$ of 2044 rd., which is 292 rd.: $1\frac{14}{15} = \frac{29}{15}$: in $\frac{29}{15}$ hr. he will walk 29 times 292 rd. = 8468 rd., $Ans.$

(19.) $1\frac{1}{4}$ ft. = 15 in. = $\frac{45}{3}$: $3\frac{1}{3} = \frac{10}{3}$: $\frac{10}{45} = \frac{2}{9}$, $Ans.$

(20.) $3\frac{1}{5} + 3\frac{2}{3} = \frac{16}{5} + \frac{11}{3} = \frac{48}{15} + \frac{55}{15} = \frac{103}{15}$. $Ans.$ $\frac{48}{103}$ and $\frac{55}{103}$.

(21.) $\frac{5}{8}$ of $2400 = $1500: $1500 + $500 = $2000. If $\frac{5}{4}$ of B's money = $2000, $\frac{1}{4}$ is $\frac{1}{5}$ of $2000, which is $400, and the whole will be 4 times $400, which are $1600, $Ans.$

(22.) If $2200 are $\frac{5}{12}$ of the elder one's share, $\frac{1}{12}$ is $440, and $\frac{12}{12}$, the elder one's share = $5280; if $5280 are $\frac{16}{35}$ of the whole estate, $\frac{1}{35}$ is $330, and $\frac{35}{35} = $11550; $2200 + $5280 = $7480; $11550 - $7480 = $4070; each daughter had $\frac{1}{3}$ of $4070 = 1356\frac{2}{3}$, $Ans.$

PRACTICE.

Art. 130.

(3.) $12\frac{1}{2} = \frac{25}{2}$: $18\frac{3}{4}$ ct. = $\$\frac{3}{16}$: $\frac{25}{2} \times \frac{3}{16} = \$\frac{75}{32} = 2.34\frac{3}{8}$, $Ans.$

(4.)
$$\$2.25 = \$2\frac{1}{4} = \frac{\overset{3}{\cancel{9}}}{\cancel{4}} \times \frac{\overset{4}{\cancel{16}}}{\cancel{3}} = 12 \text{ yd., } Ans.$$

(5.) $\frac{11}{2} \times \frac{5}{8} = \frac{55}{16}$: $\$\frac{1}{16} = 6\frac{1}{4}$ ct.; $\$\frac{55}{16} = 3.43\frac{3}{4}$, $Ans.$

(6.)
$$53$$
$$\$66.25 = \tfrac{2\,6\,5}{4}: \quad \$3.75 = 3\tfrac{3}{4} = \tfrac{1\,5}{4}: \quad \frac{\cancel{265}}{\cancel{4}} \times \frac{\cancel{4}}{\cancel{15}} = \tfrac{5\,3}{3}$$
$$= 17\tfrac{2}{3} \text{ doz., } Ans.$$
$$3$$

(7.)
$$10$$
$$\$2.37\tfrac{1}{2} = 2\tfrac{3}{8} = \tfrac{1\,9}{8}: \quad \frac{19}{\cancel{8}} \times \frac{\cancel{80}}{1} = \$190, \; Ans.$$

(8.) $\$4.87\tfrac{1}{2} = 4\tfrac{7}{8} = \tfrac{3\,9}{8}: \quad \dfrac{\cancel{39}}{1} \times \dfrac{8}{\cancel{39}} = 8$ men, $Ans.$

(9.)
$$12$$
$$\$8.33\tfrac{1}{3} = 8\tfrac{1}{3} = \tfrac{2\,5}{3}: \quad \frac{25}{\cancel{3}} \times \frac{\cancel{36}}{1} = \$300, \; Ans.$$

(10.) $\$246.66\tfrac{2}{3} = 246\tfrac{2}{3} = \tfrac{7\,4\,0}{3}: \quad \$1.33\tfrac{1}{3} = 1\tfrac{1}{3} = \tfrac{4}{3}:$
$$185$$
$$\frac{\cancel{740}}{\cancel{3}} \times \frac{\cancel{3}}{\cancel{4}} = 185 \text{ yd., } Ans.$$

(12.)
$$275$$
$$\$18\tfrac{1}{3} = \tfrac{5\,5}{3}: \quad \$229\tfrac{1}{6} = \tfrac{1\,3\,7\,5}{6}: \quad \frac{\cancel{1375}}{\cancel{6}} \times \frac{3}{\cancel{55}} = \tfrac{2\,7\,5}{2\,2} =$$
$$2 \qquad 11$$
$12\tfrac{1}{2}, \; Ans.$

(13.) 120 sq. rd. $= \tfrac{3}{4}$ A. $\$125.60 \times 11 = \$1381.60 =$ cost of 11 A.: $\tfrac{3}{4}$ of $\$125.60 = \$94.20 =$ cost of 120 sq. rd.: $\$1381.60 + \$94.20 = \$1475.80, \; Ans.$

(14.) $\dfrac{10000}{250} = 40$ lots. 50 ft. $\times$ 150 ft. $= 7500$ sq. ft.: 7500 sq. ft. $\times 40 = 300000$ sq. ft., $\div 9 = 33333$ sq. yd. $+ 3$ sq. ft.: 33333 sq. yd. $\div 30\tfrac{1}{4} = 1101$ sq. rd. $+ 27\tfrac{3}{4}$ sq. yd.: $\tfrac{3}{4}$ sq. yd. $= \tfrac{2\,7}{4}$ sq. ft. $= 6$ sq. ft. $+ \tfrac{3}{4}$; $\tfrac{3}{4}$ sq. ft. $\times 144 = 108$ sq. in.; 6 sq. ft. $+ 3$ sq. ft. $= 9$ sq. ft. $= 1$ sq. yd., which added to $27 = 28$ sq. yd.: 1101 sq. rd. $\div 160 = 6$ A. 141 sq. rd. $Ans.$ 6 A. 141 sq. rd. 28 sq. yd. 108 sq. in.

(15.) 2 qt. $=\frac{1}{4}$ pk. $=\frac{1}{16}$ bu.: 3 pk. $=\frac{3}{4}$ or $\frac{12}{16}$ bu.: \$6.20 $=\$6\frac{1}{5}=\frac{31}{5}$: $83\frac{13}{16}=\frac{1341}{16}$, $\times \frac{31}{5}=\frac{41571}{80}=\$519.63\frac{3}{4}$, *Ans.*

(16.)

$$167\frac{1}{2}=\frac{335}{2}: \quad \frac{\overset{2}{335}}{\underset{7}{2}} \times \frac{4}{3}=\frac{670}{3}=223\frac{1}{3} \text{ bu.}: \frac{1}{3} \text{ bu.}=\frac{4}{3}$$

or $1\frac{1}{3}$ pk.: $\frac{1}{3}$ pk. $=\frac{8}{3}$ or $2\frac{2}{3}$ qt.: $\frac{2}{3}$ qt. $=\frac{4}{3}$ or $1\frac{1}{3}$ pt. *Ans.*
223 bu. 1 pk. 2 qt. $1\frac{1}{3}$ pt.

(17.) \$1.75 $=1\frac{3}{4}$ or $\frac{7}{4}$: $\frac{7}{2} \times \frac{7}{4}=\frac{49}{8}=\$6.12\frac{1}{2}$, *Ans.*

(18.)

$$\$1.50=\frac{3}{2}; \$7.12\frac{1}{2}=\frac{57}{8}: \quad \frac{\overset{19}{57}}{\underset{4}{8}} \times \frac{2}{3}=\frac{19}{4}=4\frac{3}{4} \text{ yd., } Ans.$$

(19.) 12 oz. $=\frac{12}{16}$ or $\frac{3}{4}$ lb.: $45\frac{3}{4}$ lb. $=\frac{183}{4}$: $\frac{183}{4} \times \frac{3}{8}=\frac{549}{32}=\$17.15\frac{5}{8}$, *Ans.*

(20.) \$0.93$\frac{3}{4}$ $=\left\{ \begin{array}{l} 87\frac{1}{2}=\frac{7}{8}=\frac{14}{16} \\ 6\frac{1}{4}=\frac{1}{16} \end{array} \right\}=\frac{15}{16}$: \$2$\frac{15}{16}$ $=\$\frac{47}{16}$:
$\frac{47}{\underset{2}{16}} \times \frac{8}{1}=\frac{47}{2}=23\frac{1}{2}$ lb., *Ans.*

(21.) 2 T. 9 cwt. $=49$ cwt.: $37\frac{1}{2}$ ct. per lb. $=\$37\frac{1}{2}$ per cwt.: $\frac{49}{1} \times \frac{75}{2}=\$1837.50$, *Ans.*

(22.)

$$\$3.90=3\frac{9}{10}=\frac{39}{10}: \quad \frac{\overset{5}{\overset{10}{\cancel{100}}}}{\underset{2}{\underset{4}{\cancel{12}}}} \times \frac{\overset{13}{39}}{\cancel{10}}=\$32.50, Ans.$$

(23.)

$$3\frac{3}{4}=\frac{15}{4}; \$5.40=5\frac{4}{10}=\frac{54}{10}: \quad \frac{\overset{3}{15}}{\underset{2}{4}} \times \frac{\overset{27}{54}}{\underset{2}{\cancel{10}}}=\$20.25, Ans.$$

(24.)　　　　　　　　2

$$\frac{13}{2} \times \frac{1}{3} \times \frac{12}{1} \text{ (1 doz.)} = \$26. \left.\rule{0pt}{14pt}\right\} = \$40.06\tfrac{1}{4}:$$

$$\frac{75}{2} \times \frac{3}{8} = \frac{225}{16} = \$14.06\tfrac{1}{4} \left.\rule{0pt}{10pt}\right\}$$

$$\$40.06\tfrac{1}{4} - \$36 = \$4.06\tfrac{1}{4} = \$4\tfrac{1}{16} = \$\tfrac{65}{16}: \quad \frac{65}{16} \times \frac{8}{1} = \frac{65}{2} =$$

$32\tfrac{1}{2}$ lb., *Ans.*

DECIMAL FRACTIONS.

Art. 135.

REMARKS.—Pupils must have a thorough knowledge of common fractions, before they can understand fully the reason of the rules in decimals.

When a pupil is in doubt with regard to the accuracy of the result in any operation involving decimals, let him convert the decimals into common fractions, and then perform the work; the results in both cases ought to be the same.

It is a useful exercise to perform the same operations in equivalent common and decimal fractions. Thus, they may be required to perform the operations indicated in the following examples, by the rules for common fractions; then to convert the common fractions into decimals, and work by the rules for decimals.

(5.) .26		(16.) .00009
(6.) .35		(17.) .900
(7.) .87		(18.) .00605
(8.) 4.19		(19.) .20304
(9.) .005		(20.) .000007
(10.) .054		(21.) .000203
(11.) .304		(22.) .300004
(12.) 7.293		(23.) .0000024
(13.) 25.047		(24.) .0080006
(14.) .0205		(25.) .000200
(15.) .4125		(26.) .00000002

(27.) .00000907

(28.) .20020003

(29.) 1.010100

(30.) .01010001

(31.) 106.037

(32.) 1000.001

(33.) .225

(34.) 200.025

(35.) .002929

(36.) 2900.000029

(37.) .001000005

(38.) .0000000202

(39.) 200.0000000002

(40.) 65.006005

(41.) .3 .7 .09 .17 .23 .41 .53

(42.) .87 .97. .123. .289 .487 .733

(43.) .003 .0101 .00053 .000503

Art. 136.

(4.) Twenty-eight *thousandths;* three hundred and forty-one *thousandths;* two and three hundred and twenty-seven *thousandths;* fifty and five *thousandths;* one hundred and eighty-four and one hundred and seventy-three *thousandths.*

(5.) Three *ten-thousandths;* six hundred and twenty-five *ten-thousandths;* two thousand three hundred and seventy-four *ten-thousandths;* two thousand and six *ten-thousandths;* one hundred and four *ten-thousandths.*

(6.) Three and two hundred and five *ten-thousandths;* eight hundred and ten and two thousand four hundred and six *ten-thousandths;* ten thousand seven hundred and twenty and nine hundred and five *ten-thousandths.*

(7.) Four *hundred-thousandths;* one hundred and thirty-seven *hundred-thousandths;* two thousand three hundred and seventy-six *hundred-thousandths;* one thousand and seven *hundred-thousandths.*

(8.) One thousand seven hundred and sixty-eight *millionths;* forty thousand and thirty-five *millionths;* seventy and three hundred and sixty thousand and four *millionths.*

(9.) One million ten thousand one hundred and one *ten-millionths;* forty thousand and five *hundred-millionths;* one hundred thousand three hundred and four *hundred-millionths.*

(10.) Thirty-one thousand four hundred and fifty-six *hundred-thousandths;* one hundred and thirty-three *millionths;* sixty and four *hundredths;* forty-five and one thousand and three *ten-thousandths.*

(11.) Three hundred and fifty-seven and seventy-five *hundredths;* four thousand nine hundred and twenty-eight *ten-thousandths;* five and nine hundred and forty-five *thousandths;* six hundred and eighty-one and two *ten-thousandths.*

(12.) Seventy and one million two hundred thousand seven hundred and sixty-four *ten-millionths;* nine hundred and fifty-four and two hundred and three *thousandths;* thirty-eight and twenty-seven *thousandths.*

(13.) One thousand and seven and three thousand one hundred and fifty-four *ten-thousandths;* seven thousand four hundred and ninety-six and thirty-five million four hundred and ninety-one thousand seven hundred and sixty-eight *hundred-millionths.*

(14.) Seven hundred and fifteen *hundred-thousandths;* three and five *hundred-thousandths;* twenty-eight and ten million sixty-five thousand seven hundred and one *hundred-millionths.*

(15.) Thirteen and eight trillion two hundred and forty-one billion ninety-four million seven hundred and ten thousand nine hundred and forty-seven *ten-quad-rillionths.*

(16.) $\frac{9}{10}$; $\frac{13}{100}$; $\frac{19}{100}$; etc.

(17.) $\frac{91}{100}$; $\frac{347}{1000}$; $\frac{513}{1000}$; etc.

(18.) $\frac{7}{1000}$; $\frac{207}{10000}$; $\frac{79}{100000}$; $\frac{1007}{1000000}$.

(19.) $1\frac{36}{100}$; $\frac{3421}{10000}$; $\frac{3401}{100000}$; $\frac{900}{10000}$.

(20.) $\frac{1}{1000}$; $\frac{5302}{10000}$; $8\frac{1}{100}$; $\frac{53}{1000000}$.

Art. 141.

(2.) $.6 = \frac{6}{10} = \frac{3}{5}$, *Ans.*   (3.) $.25 = \frac{25}{100} = \frac{1}{4}$, *Ans.*

(4.) $.375 = \frac{375}{1000} = \frac{3}{8}$, *Ans.*

(5.) $.035 = \frac{35}{1000} = \frac{7}{200}$, *Ans.*

(6.) $.5625 = \frac{5625}{10000} = \frac{9}{16}$, *Ans.*

(7.) $.34375 = \frac{34375}{100000} = \frac{11}{32}$, *Ans.*

(8.) $.1484375 = \frac{1484375}{10000000} = \frac{19}{128}$, *Ans.*

(9.) $4.02 = 4\frac{2}{100} = 4\frac{1}{50}$, *Ans.*

(10.) $8.415 = 8\frac{415}{1000} = 8\frac{83}{200}$, *Ans.*

Art. 142.

(2.) $\frac{4}{5} = \frac{4.0}{5} = .8$, *Ans.*   (3.) $\frac{5}{8} = \frac{5.000}{8} = .625$, *Ans.*

(4.) $\frac{7}{25} = \frac{7.00}{25} = \frac{1.40}{5} = .28$, *Ans.*

(5.) $\frac{3}{40} = \frac{3.000}{40} = .075$, *Ans.*

(6.) $\frac{15}{16} = \frac{15.0000}{16} = .9375$, *Ans.*

(7.) $\frac{1}{1250} = \frac{1.0000}{1250} = .0008$, *Ans.*

(8.) $\frac{9}{400} = \frac{9.0000}{400} = .0225$, *Ans.*

(9.) $\frac{1}{256} = \frac{1.00000000}{256} = .00390625$, *Ans.*

(10.) $\frac{5}{6} = \frac{5.0000}{6} = .8333+$, *Ans.*

(11.) $\frac{1}{11} = \frac{1.000000}{11} = .090909+$, *Ans.*

(12.) $\frac{4}{33} = \frac{4.000000}{33} = .121212+$, *Ans.*

Art. 143.

(2)	(3)	(4)	(5)
37.1065	4.0004	3.25	21.611
432.07	28.035	6.4	6888.32
4.20733	8.07	.35	3.4167
11.706	.09404	10.00	6913.3477
485.08983	40.19944		

(6)	(7)	(8)	(9)
6.61	4.8	45.019	432.432
636.1	43.31	7.00071	61.0793
6516.14	74.019	93.4327	100.07794
67.1234	11.204	6.0401	6.009
5.1233	133.333	151.49251	1000.1001
7231.0967			1599.69834

(10)	(11)	(12)
16.041	204.0009	.0035
9.000094	103.00000009	.00035
33.27	42.009099	.000035
8.969	430.99	.0000035
32.719906	220.0000009	.0038885
100.000000	999.99999999	

Art. 144.

(2)	(3)	(4)	(5)
97.5168	20.014	5.03	24.0042
38.25942	7.0021	2.115	13.7013
59.25738	13.0119	2.915	10.3029

(6)	(7)	(8)	(9)
170.0035	.0142	.05	13.5
68.00181	.005	.0024	8.037
102.00169	.0092	.0476	5.463

(10)	(11)	(12)
3.00000	29.0029	5.000
.00003	19.003	.125
2.99997	9.9999	4.875

(13)	(14)	(15)
1000.0000	1.000000	.025
.0001	.000001	.000025
999.9999	.999999	.024975

Art. 147.

(4)	(5)	(6)	(7)
33.21	32.16	.125	.35
4.41	22.5	9	7
3321	16080	1.125	2.45
13284	6432		
13284	6432		
146.4561	723.600		

(10.) $.15 \times .7 = \frac{15}{100} \times \frac{7}{10} = \frac{105}{1000} = .105$, *Ans.*

(13.) $1.035 \times 17 = 17.595$, *Ans.*

(14)	(15)	(16)	(17)
19	4.5	.625	61.76
.125	4	64	.0071
95	18.0	2500	6176
38		3750	43232
19		40.000	.438496
2.375			

(18)	(24)	(25)
1.325	.1	100
.0716	.01	.0001
7950	.001	00.0100 $=$ .01, *Ans.*
1325		
9275		
.0948700		

(26)	(27)	(28)
.043	40000	.09375
.0021	.000001	1.064
43	.040000	37500
86		56250
.0000903		93750
		.09975000

Art. 150.

SUGGESTIONS TO TEACHERS.—The division of decimals is gener-
ally a troublesome subject to pupils; this arises from a want of
attention to the rule. Should the pupil be at a loss to understand
why, in some cases, when the divisor and dividend are both decimals,
the quotient should be a whole number, let him read the remarks on
the division of fractions, page 120. When the divisor contains more
decimal places than the dividend, it is best, before commencing the
division, to reduce them both to the same denomination, that is, to
make the number of decimal places the same in both; the quotient
will then be a whole number.

(7)
.03)1.125
    37.5, *Ans.*

(8)
27.5)86.075(3.13, *Ans.*
  825
  357
  275
  825
  825

(9)
3.44)24.73704(7.191, *Ans.*
2408
 657
 344
3130
3096
 344
 344

(10)
4.123)206.166492(50.004, *Ans.*
　20615
　────
　　16492
　　16492
　　─────

(13)
.5)21.0(42. *Ans.*
　20
　──
　10
　10
　──

(14)
.008)2.000
　────
　　250, *Ans.*

(15)
5)37.20
　────
7.44, *Ans.*

(16)
454)100.8788(.2222, *Ans.*
　908
　───
　1007
　　908
　　───
　　998
　　908
　　───
　　908
　　908
　　───

(18)
.108649)9811.004700(90300, *Ans.*
　977841
　──────
　325947
　325947
　──────
　　00

(19)
.19).21318(1.122, *Ans.*
19
──
　23
　19
　──
　41
　38
　──
　38
　38
　──

(20)
.3189)102048.0000(320000, *Ans.*
9567
────
6378
6378
────
0000

(21)
3189).102048(.000032, *Ans.*
9567
────
6378
6378

(22)
.0225)9.9000(440, *Ans.*
900
───
900
900
───
0

(26)	(27)	(28)
10).10	.1)1.0	.01)10.00
.01, *Ans.*	10, *Ans.*	1000, *Ans.*

(29.) $\dfrac{1.7}{64} = \dfrac{1.7000000}{64} = .0265625$, *Ans.*

(30)	(31)
80).080	7)1.5000000
.001, *Ans.*	.2142857+, *Ans.*

(32)

32.76)11.100000000(.3388278+ *Ans.*

```
        9828
        ‾‾‾‾‾‾
       12720
        9828
        ‾‾‾‾‾‾
       28920
       26208
        ‾‾‾‾‾‾
       27120
       26208
        ‾‾‾‾‾‾
        9120
        6552
        ‾‾‾‾‾‾
       25680
       22932
        ‾‾‾‾‾‾
       27480
       26208
        ‾‾‾‾‾‾
```

(33)

3.21).0123000000(.00383177+ *Ans.*

```
         963
         ‾‾‾‾
        2670
        2568
         ‾‾‾‾
        1020
         963
         ‾‾‾‾
         570
         321
         ‾‾‾‾
        2490
        2247
         ‾‾‾‾
        2430
        2247
         ‾‾‾‾
```

Art. 151.

(2.) .035 pk. × 8 = .280 qt.: .28 qt. × 2 = .56 pt., *Ans.*

(3.) .0075 bu. × 4 = .0300 pk.: .03 pk. × 8 = .24 qt., *Ans.*

(4.) .005 yd. × 3 = .015 ft., × 12 = 0.180 in. = .18 in., *Ans.*

(5.) .00546875 A. × 160 = 00.87500000 sq. rd. = .875 sq. rd., *Ans.*

Art. 152.

(2.) .75 yd. $\times$ 3 $=$ 2.25 ft.: .25 ft. $\times$ 12 $=$ 3.00 in. *Ans.* 2 ft. 3 in.

(3.) .3375 A. $\times$ 160 $=$ 54.0000 sq. rd. $=$ 54 sq. rd., *Ans.*

(4.) .7 lb. $\times$ 12 $=$ 8.4 oz.: .4 oz. $\times$ 20 $=$ 8.0 pwt. $=$ 8 pwt. *Ans.* 8 oz. 8 pwt.

(5.) .8125 bu. $\times$ 4 $=$ 3.2500 pk.: .25 pk. $\times$ 8 $=$ 2.00 qt. $=$ 2 qt. *Ans.* 3 pk. 2 qt.

(6.) .44 mi. $\times$ 320 $=$ 140.8 rd.: .8 rd. $\times$ 5$\frac{1}{2}$ $=$ 4.4 yd.: .4 yd. $\times$ 3 $=$ 1.2 ft.: .2 ft. $\times$ 12 $=$ 2.4 in. *Ans.* 140 rd. 4 yd. 1 ft. 2.4 in.

(7.) .33625 cwt. $\times$ 100 $=$ 33.625 lb.: .625 lb. $\times$ 16 $=$ 10.000 oz. $=$ 10 oz. *Ans.* 33 lb. 10 oz.

Art. 153.

(2.) .72 qt. $\div$ 8 $=$ .09 pk., $\div$ 4 $=$ .0225 bu., *Ans.*

(3.) .77 yd. $\div$ 5$\frac{1}{2}$ $=$ .14 rd., $\div$ 320 $=$ .0004375 mi., *Ans.*

(4.) .25 pt. $\div$ 2 $=$ .125 qt., $\div$ 4 $=$ .03125 gal., *Ans.*

(5.) .6 pt. $\div$ 2 $=$ .3 qt., $\div$ 8 $=$ .0375 pk. $\div$ 4 $=$ .009375 bu., *Ans.*

(6.) .7 rd. $\div$ 320 $=$ .0021875 mi., *Ans.*

Art. 154.

(1.) \$0.40 $\times$ 9 $=$ \$3.60: \$0.75 $\times$ 12 $=$ \$9.00: \$3.60 $+$ \$9.00 $=$ \$12.60, *Ans.*

(2.) \$0.45 $\times$ 2.3 $=$ \$1.035: \$0.375 $\times$ 1.5 $=$ \$0.5625: \$1.035 $+$ \$0.5625 $=$ \$1.5975, *Ans.*

(3.) \$2.6875 $\times$ 16$\frac{1}{4}$ $=$ \$43.671875, *Ans.*

(4.) 35.25 $\div$ .75 $=$ 47 bu., *Ans.*

(5.) $98.4 \div 2.5625 = 38.4$ yd., *Ans.*

(6.) 6 cwt. 50 lb. $= 6.5$ cwt.: $3.25 \times 6.5 = 21.125$, *Ans.*

(7.) 14 bu. 3 pk. 4 qt. $= 14.875$ bu.: $0.625 \times 14.857 = 9.296875$, *Ans.*

(8.) 13 A. 115 sq. rd. $= 13.71875$ A.: $17.28 \times 13.71875 = 237.06$, *Ans.*

(9.) $9.296875 \div 0.3125 = 29.75$ bu. $= 29$ bu. 3 pk., *Ans.*

(10.) $59.265 \div 4.32 = 13.71875$ A. $= 13$ A. 115 sq. rd., *Ans.*

(11.) 1 gal. would cost $\$\frac{49}{63} = \$\frac{7}{9} = \$0.77\frac{7}{9}$: $464 \times .77\frac{7}{9} = \$360.88$, *Ans.*

	ft.	.in
(12.) .34 yd. $\times 3 = 1.02$ ft.:	1	.24
.02 ft. $\times 12 = .24$ in.:	1	.84
1.07 ft.: .07 ft. $\times 12 = .84$ in.		8.92
Ans. 2	10.00

	qt.	pt.
(13.) .625 gal. $\times 4 = 2.500$ qt.:	2	1
.5 qt. $\times 2 = 1.0$ pt.:		
.75 qt. $\times 2 = 1.5$ pt.		1.5
Ans. 3	.5

	ft.	in.
(14.) 1.53 yd. $\times 3 = 4.59$ ft.:	4	7.08
.59 ft. $\times 12 = 7.08$ in.	2	3.08
Ans. 2	4

(15.) $365.25 \times .05 = 18.2625$ da.: $.2625$ da. $\times 24 = 6.3$ hr.: 6.3 hr. $- .5$ hr. $= 5.8$ hr.: .8 hr. $\times 60 = 48$ min. *Ans.* 18 da. 5 hr. 48 min.

(16.) $.41$ da. $= 9.84$ hr.: 9.84 hr. $- .16$ hr. $= 9.68$ hr.: .68 hr. $\times 60 = 40.8$ min.: .8 min. $\times 60 = 48$ sec. *Ans.* **9 hr.** 40 min. 48 sec.

(17.) 365.25 da. $\times$ .3 = 109.575 da.: .575 da. $\times$ 24 = 13.8 hr.: .8 hr. $\times$ 60 = 48 min. *Ans.* 109 da. 13 hr. 48 min.

(18.) 3 in. = $\frac{1}{4}$ ft.: $2\frac{1}{4}$ or $\frac{9}{4}$ ft. = $\frac{3}{4}$ yd.: $343\frac{3}{4} \times$ \$0.16 = \$55.00, *Ans.*

(19.) 17 mi. 135 rd. = 17.421875 mi.: \$690.35 $\times$ 17.421875 = \$12027.19140625, *Ans.*

THE METRIC SYSTEM.

Art. 160.

(3.) 20 Km. $\times$ .62137 = 12.42740 mi., *Ans.*

(4.) 160 acres $\div$ 2.471 = 64.75+ Ha., *Ans.*

(5.) 49 m. $\times$ 39.37 = 1929.13 in., $\div$ 12 = 160 ft. 9.13 in.: 160 ft. $\div$ 3 = 53 yd. 1 ft.: 53 yd. $\div$ 5$\frac{1}{2}$ = 9 rd. 3$\frac{1}{2}$ yd.: $\frac{1}{2}$ yd. = $\frac{3}{2}$ or 1$\frac{1}{2}$ ft.; $\frac{1}{2}$ ft. = 6 in.; 9.13 in. + 6 in. = 15.13 in. = 1 ft. 3.13 in.; 1 + 1 + 1 = 3 ft. = 1 yd.; 3 yd. + 1 yd. = 4 yd. *Ans.* 9 rd. 4 yd. 3.13 in.

(6.) 15 g. $\times$ 15.432 = 231.480 gr. T., $\div$ 24 = 9 pwt. 15.48 gr., *Ans.*

(7.) 42 bu. $\div$ 2.8375 = 14.8+ Hl., *Ans.*

(8.) 500 sters $\times$ .2759 = 137.95 C., *Ans.*

(9.) 9 m. $\times$ 5 m. = 4.5 m²., $\times$ 1.196 = 5.382 sq. yd., *Ans.*

(10.) 32 l. $\times$ 1.0567 = 33.8144 qt., $\div$ 4 = 8.4536 gal., *Ans.*

Art. 161.

(1.) 127 dl. + 234.5 dl. = 361.5 dl., $\div$ 10 = 36.15 l.: 1563 cl. $\div$ 100 = 15.63 l.: 4.87 l. + 36 15 l. + 15.63 l. = 56.65 l., *Ans.*

(2.) 45 Ha. = 4500 a., @ \$3.32 = \$14940, *Ans.*

(3.) $457.92 \div 3 = 152.64$ m., *Ans.*

(4.) $.72 \times .48 \times .5 = .1728:$ $\$.8640 \div .1728 = \$5$, *Ans.*

(5)	(6)	(7)
380)454.10(1.195	4685	346.75)194.1800(0.56
380 *Ans.* $1.195	1.6	173375
741	28110	208050
380	4685	208050
3610	7496.0	
3420		*Ans.* $0.56
1900	*Ans.* 7496 Hl.	
1900		

(8.) 1 M. $\times$ 100 = 100 cm.: $100 \div 2 = 50$, the number of coins: 50×5 g. $= 250$ g., *Ans.*

(9.) $1.25 \times 6.5 = 8.125, \div 1.85 = 4.39+$ m., *Ans.*

(10.) 60 mi. $\div .62137 = 96.56+$ Km., *Ans.*

(11.) 29 Mm. $\times$ 22.4 Mm. $= 649.6$ Mm^2, *Ans.*

(12.) 13.24 Km. $\times$ 1000 = 13240 m., $\div .715$ m. = 18517+, which would, of course, necessitate his taking 18518 steps, *Ans.*

NOTE.—The answer to the example given here is also 18517+ steps.

PERCENTAGE.

Art. 164.

(6)	
165	(7.) $240 \times .03\frac{3}{4} = 9$, *Ans.*
.03$\frac{1}{3}$	
495	(14.) $8\frac{1}{3}\% = \frac{1}{12}:$ $\frac{1}{12}$ of 384 = 32, *Ans.*
55	
5.50, *Ans.*	(16.) $12\frac{1}{2}\% = \frac{1}{8}:$ $\frac{1}{8}$ of 292 = 36.5, *Ans.*

(19.)
$$18\tfrac{3}{4} = \tfrac{3}{16}: \quad \frac{\overset{.7}{\cancel{11.2}}}{1} \times \frac{3}{\cancel{16}} = 2.1, \; \textit{Ans.}$$

(20.)
$$20\% = \tfrac{1}{5}: \quad \frac{\overset{1.97}{\cancel{9.85}}}{1} \times \frac{1}{\cancel{5}} = 1.97, \; \textit{Ans.}$$

(21.) $25\% = \tfrac{1}{4}: \quad \tfrac{1}{4}$ of $43 = 10.75, \; \textit{Ans.}$

(22.) $33\tfrac{1}{3}\% = \tfrac{1}{3}: \quad \tfrac{1}{3}$ of $6.93 = 2.31, \; \textit{Ans.}$

(23.) $45 \times 5.7 = 2.565, \; \textit{Ans.}$

(24.) $50\% = \tfrac{1}{2}: \quad \tfrac{1}{2}$ of $38.75 = 19.375, \; \textit{Ans.}$

(25.) $\tfrac{1}{2}\% = \tfrac{1}{200}: \quad \tfrac{1}{200}$ of $456 = 2.28, \; \textit{Ans.}$

(26.) $\tfrac{3}{8}\% = .00375: \quad 464 \times .00375 = 1.74, \; \textit{Ans.}$

(27.) $\tfrac{7}{16} = .4375: \quad 144 \times .4375 = 63, \; \textit{Ans.}$

(28.) $125\% = \tfrac{5}{4}: \quad \tfrac{5}{4}$ of $36 = 45, \; \textit{Ans.}$

(29.) 208% of $650 = 650 \times 2.08 = 1352, \; \textit{Ans.}$

(30.) $4\tfrac{1}{2}$ times $12 = 48 + 6 = 54, \; \textit{Ans.}$

(31.) 10 times $24.75 = 247.5, \; \textit{Ans.}$

Art. 165.

(3.) 3 is $\tfrac{1}{5}$ of 15: $\quad \tfrac{1}{5} = 20\%, \; \textit{Ans.}$

(4.) 6 is $\tfrac{3}{25}$ of 50: $\quad \tfrac{3}{25} = .12 = 12\%, \; \textit{Ans.}$

(5.) 4.5 is $\tfrac{4.5}{75}\%$ of 75 $= \tfrac{3}{5} = .6 = 6\%, \; \textit{Ans.}$

(11)

$243)8.505(.035 = 3\frac{1}{2}\%$, *Ans.*

$\underline{729}$

1215

$\underline{1215}$

(12.) $.002$ of $2 = .002 \div 2 = .001 = \frac{1}{10}$ of 1%, *Ans.*

(13.) $13.245 \div 3532 = .00375 = \frac{375}{100000} = \frac{3}{8}\%$, *Ans.*

(14.) $\dfrac{3}{\underset{5}{\cancel{25}}} \times \dfrac{\cancel{5}}{4} = \frac{3}{20} = 15\%$, *Ans.*

(15.) $\dfrac{\cancel{2}}{\underset{5}{\cancel{15}}} \times \dfrac{\cancel{3}}{\cancel{2}} = \frac{1}{5} = 20\%$, *Ans.*

(16.)

$\dfrac{\cancel{2}}{\cancel{7}} \times \dfrac{\overset{3}{\cancel{21}}}{\underset{8}{\cancel{16}}} = \frac{3}{8} = 37\frac{1}{2}\%$, *Ans.*

(17.) $\dfrac{\overset{3}{\cancel{21}}}{4} \times \dfrac{3}{\underset{5}{\cancel{35}}} = \frac{9}{20} = 45\%$, *Ans.*

(18.)

$\dfrac{\overset{}{\cancel{65}}}{\underset{2}{\cancel{6}}} \times \dfrac{\overset{3}{9}}{\underset{8}{\cancel{520}}} = \frac{3}{16} = 18\frac{3}{4}\%$, *Ans.*

Art. 166.

(3.) $20\% = \frac{1}{5}$: $60 \times 5 = 300$, *Ans.*

(4.) $75\% = \frac{3}{4}$. If 90 is $\frac{3}{4}$, $\frac{1}{4} = 30$, and $\frac{4}{4} = 120$, *Ans.*

(5.) $125\% = \frac{5}{4}$. If 85 is $\frac{5}{4}$, $\frac{1}{4} = 17$, and $\frac{4}{4} = 68$, *Ans.*

(6.) $7.13 \div .23 = 31$, *Ans.*

(7.) $20.23 \div .34 = 59.5$, *Ans.*

(8.) $23.5 \div .47 = 50$, *Ans.*

(9.) If 45 is $1\frac{1}{2}\%$, $\frac{1}{2}\%$ is $\frac{1}{3}$ of $45 = 15$: $1\%= 2$ times $15 = 30$: 100 times $30 = 3000$, the number.

(10.) $12\frac{1}{2}\% = \frac{1}{8}$: $2.25 \times 8 = 18$, *Ans.*

(11.) 1% is $\frac{1}{250}$ of $\frac{3}{4} = \frac{3}{1000}$: 100% is 100 times $\frac{3}{1000}$ $= \frac{300}{1000} = \frac{3}{10}$, *Ans.*

(12.) $14\frac{2}{7} = \frac{100}{7}$: $16\frac{2}{3}\% = \frac{1}{6}$. If $\frac{100}{7} = \frac{1}{6}$, $\frac{6}{6} = \frac{600}{7} = 85\frac{5}{7}$, *Ans.*

Art. 167.

(3.) $721 \div 1.03 = 700$, *Ans.*

(4.) $100\% - 66\% = 34\%$: $68 \div .34 = 200$, *Ans.*

(5.) If $2125 = \frac{5}{4}$, $\frac{1}{4} = 425$, and $\frac{4}{4} = 1700$, *Ans.*

(6.) If $7.52 = \frac{94}{100}$, $\frac{1}{100} = \frac{7.52}{94} = 8$, and the number $= 8$, *Ans.*

(7.) $37\frac{1}{2}\% = \frac{3}{8}$. If $8250 = \frac{11}{8}$, $\frac{1}{8} = 750$, and $\frac{8}{8} = 6000$, *Ans.*

(8.) $10\% = \frac{1}{10}$, then $\frac{9}{10}$ of the fraction $= \frac{3}{8}$: $\frac{3}{8} \times \frac{10}{9} = \frac{30}{72} = \frac{5}{12}$, *Ans.*

(9.) $20\% = \frac{1}{5}$. If $6.6 = \frac{6}{7}$, $\frac{1}{5} = 1.1$, and $\frac{5}{5} = 5.5$, *Ans.*

Art. 169.

(1.) $800 \times .36 = 288.00$: $\$800 - \$288 = \$512$, *Ans.*

(2.) $300 - 225 = 75 = \frac{1}{4}$ of $300 = 25\%$, *Ans.*

(3.) $100\% - 40\% = 60\% = \frac{6}{10}$. If $3000 = \frac{6}{10}$, $\frac{1}{10} =$ $500, and $\frac{4}{10}$ $(40\%) = \$2000$, *Ans.*

(4.) If 56 ct. $= 140\%$ of the cost, the cost $= 56 \div 1.40$ $= 40$ ct., *Ans.*

(5.) $12\frac{1}{2}\% = \frac{1}{8}$: $175 = \frac{7}{8}$, $\frac{1}{8} = 25$, and $\frac{8}{8} = \$200$, *Ans.*

(6.) $75 \times 4 = 300$: $\frac{1}{8}$ of 300 $= 37\frac{1}{2}$: $300 - 37\frac{1}{2} =$ $262\frac{1}{2}$, $\times 35$ ct. $= \$91.87\frac{1}{2}$, *Ans.*

(7.) $500 - \$425 = \$75$: $7500 \div 500 = 15\%$, *Ans.*

(8.) $100\% - 75\% = 25\%$: $5000 = 25\% = \frac{1}{4}$; then $\frac{4}{4}$ $= \$20000$, and $20000 - \$5000 = \$15000$, *Ans.*

(9.) $12\frac{1}{2}\% = \frac{1}{8}$: 250 A. 86 sq. rd. $= 40086$ sq. rd. $=$ $\frac{9}{8}$ of neighbor's: $\frac{1}{8} = 4454$, and $\frac{8}{8} = 35632$ sq. rd., $\div 160$ $= 222$ A. 112 sq. rd., *Ans.*

(10.) $160 \times .35 = 56.00$: $160 + 56 = 216$, *Ans.*

(11.) 5 bu. $\times 32 = 160$ qt.: $6.00 \div 160 = 3\frac{3}{4}\%$, *Ans.*

(12.) $60\% = \frac{6}{10}$: $\frac{6}{10}$ of $45\% = \frac{270}{10} = 27\%$: $540 \div .27$ $= 2000$ A., *Ans.*

(13.) $371.29 \div 1.07 = \$347$, *Ans.*

(14.) $18 + 15 + 23 + 12 = 68\%$: $100 - 68 = 32\%$: $800 \times .32 = \$256$, *Ans.*

(15.) $\frac{1}{20} = 5\%$: $\frac{17}{20} = 17 \times 5 = 85\%$, *Ans.*

(16.) $33\frac{1}{3}\% = \frac{1}{3}$: 2 bu. 3 pk. $= \frac{1}{3}$ of 6 bu. 9 pk. $= 8$ bu. 1 pk., *Ans.*

(17.) 100% less $7\frac{1}{2}\% = 92\frac{1}{2}\%$: $37 \div .925 = 40$, *Ans.*

(18.) $25.8 - 2.58$ $(10\%) = 23.22$ grains, *Ans.*

(19.) $1.25 = \frac{1}{4}$ of 5: $\frac{3}{4}$ remain $= 75\%$, *Ans.*

(20.) $25\% = \frac{1}{4}$. If $150 = \frac{5}{4}$, $\frac{1}{4} = 30$, and $\frac{4}{4} = \$120 =$ cost: $200 - \$120 = \$80$: $\frac{80}{120} = \frac{2}{3} = 66\frac{2}{3}\%$, *Ans.*

Art. 172.

(1.) $240 \times .05 = \$12$, *Ans.*

(2.) $11.50 \div 460 = .02\frac{1}{2} = 2\frac{1}{2}\%$, *Ans.*

(3.) $8.12\frac{1}{2} = 2\frac{1}{2}\%$ of the selling price: $8.12\frac{1}{2} \div .02\frac{1}{2} = \$325$, selling price: 1 barrel sold for $\frac{1}{25}$ of $325 = \$13$, *Ans.*

(4.) $210 \div 1.05 = \$200$, *Ans.*

(5.) $180 \times .04 = \$7.20$: $180 - \$7.20 = \$172.80$, *Ans.*

(6.) If $11.25 = \frac{1}{20}$ (5%), $\frac{20}{20} = \$225$, *Ans.*

(7.) $1323.54 \div 1.08 = \$1225.50$, cost of goods: $1323.54 - \$1225.50 = \$98.04$, commission, *Ans.*

(8.) $\left.\begin{array}{l} 250 \times \$15 = \$3750 \\ 175 \times \$7 = 1225 \\ 1456 \times \$0.25 = 364 \end{array}\right\} = \$5339$

3% of $5339 = \$160.17$: $5339 - \$160.17 = \$5178.83$, *Ans.*

Art. 173.

(1.) $20\% = \frac{1}{5}$: $\frac{1}{5}$ of $225.50 = \$45.10$: $225.50 - \$45.10 = \$180.40$, *Ans.*

(2.) $\frac{1}{3}$ of $725.16 = 241.72$: $725.16 - 241.72 = 483.44$, $\times .05 = 24.17+$: $483.44 - \$24.17 = \$459.27$, *Ans.*

(3.) $100\% - 3\% = 97\%$: $1430.75 \div .97 = \$1475$, *Ans.*

(4.) $100\% - 5\% = 95\%$: $390.45 \div .95 = \$411$: $100\% - 25\% = 75\%$: $411 \div .75 = \$548$, *Ans.*

(5.) $10\% = $ first discount; $100\% - 10\% = 90\%$: 10% of $90\% = 9\%$, second discount; $90\% - 9\% = 81\%$: 10% of $81\% = 8.1\%$, third discount: $10\% + 9\% + 8.1\% = 27.1\%$, sum of the three discounts: $325.20 \div .271 = \$1200$: 1 doz. cost $\frac{1}{20}$ of $1200 = \$60$, *Ans.*

(6.) 100 doz. @ 60 ct. $= \$60.00$, less $24 ($40\%$) $= \$36$, less $3.60 ($10\%$) $= \$32.40$, less $2.43 ($7\frac{1}{2}\%$) $= \$29.97$, *Ans.*

(7.) $50 less $50\% = \$25$, less $10\% = \$22.50$, less 10% $= \$20.25$, less $2\% = \$19.845$, $\div 10 = \$1.98+$, *Ans.*

Art. 174.

(1.) $\$40 + 10\% = \$44$, *Ans.*

(2.) 5 ct. $= \frac{5}{6}$ the cost; the loss, therefore, is $\frac{1}{6} = 16\frac{2}{3}\%$, *Ans.*

(3.) $12\frac{1}{2} = \frac{1}{8}$; then 27 ct. $= \frac{9}{8}$ of the cost, $\frac{1}{8} = 3$ ct., and $\frac{8}{8}$ or the cost $= 24$ ct., *Ans.*

(4.) $\$15.30 \div .04 = \$382.50$, *Ans.*

(5.) $37\frac{1}{2}\% = \frac{3}{8}$: $\$8 +$ its $\frac{3}{8} = \$11$, *Ans.*

(6.) $90 - 75 = 15 = \frac{1}{5}$ of $75 = 20\%$, *Ans.*

(7.) $6\frac{1}{4}\% = \frac{1}{16}$. If 5 ct. $= \frac{1}{16}$ of the cost, the cost $=$ 80 ct., *Ans.*

(8.) $18\frac{3}{4}\% = \frac{3}{16}$; then $\$4.75 = \frac{19}{16}$, $\frac{1}{16} = \$0.25$, and $\frac{16}{16}$ $= \$0.25 \times 16 = \$4$, *Ans.*

(9.) $\$1.35 = \frac{9}{10}$ of the cost, $\frac{1}{10} = \$0.15$, and $\frac{10}{10} = \$1.50$ $=$ cost: $16\frac{2}{3}\% = \frac{1}{6}$: $\frac{1}{6}$ of $1.50 = .25$: $\$1.50 + \$0.25 = \$1.75$, *Ans.*

(10.) $25\% = \frac{1}{4}$: $\frac{1}{4}$ of $\$874 = \$218.50$, *Ans.*

(11.) $\$1.75 - \$0.25 = \$1.50$: $25 = \frac{1}{6}$ of $150 = 16\frac{2}{3}\%$, *Ans.*

(12.) On the first horse $\$150 = \frac{5}{4}$ cost, $\frac{1}{4} = \$30$, and the cost $= \$120$: on the second horse $\$150 = \frac{3}{4}$ cost, $\frac{1}{4} = \$50$, and the cost $= \$200$: $\$200 + \$120 = \$320$, $- \$300 = \$20$, *Ans.*

(13.) 5 ct. $= 10\% - 8\% = 2\%$ of the cost per yd. If $2\% = 5$ ct., $1\% = 2\frac{1}{2}$ ct., and $100\% = \$2.50$, *Ans.*

(14.) 60 ct. $\times 10000 = \$6000$, cost of the corn: 65 ct. $\times 7000 = \$4550$: $10000 - 7000 = 3000$: 55 ct. $\times 3000 = \$1650$: $\$4550 + \$1650 = \$6200$, the selling price: $\$6200 - \$6000 = \$200$ gain: $\$200 = \frac{1}{30}$ of $\$6000 = 3\frac{1}{3}\%$, *Ans.*

(15.) $33\frac{1}{3}\% = \frac{1}{3}$; then $12000 = \frac{4}{3}$, $\frac{1}{3} = \$3000$, and $\frac{3}{3} = \$9000 =$ cost of house and lot. The profit was $3000. On the city lots he lost $\frac{1}{3}$. $\frac{1}{3}$ of 12000 $= 4000$: $4000 — \$3000 = \$1000$, *Ans.*

Art. 175.

(1.) $100\% — 20\% = 80\%$, cost price. If he sell at the list price, he will gain $\frac{20}{80} = \frac{1}{4} = 25\%$, *Ans.*

(2.) $74 \times 5 \times 45 = 166.50$, less 3.33 $(2\%) = \$163.17$: $12\frac{1}{3}\%$ of this amount $= \$20.12+$, *Ans.*

(3.) $45 less $5\% = \$42.75$, $\div 12 = \$3.56\frac{1}{4} =$ cost per pair: $4.25 — \$3.56\frac{1}{4} = \$0.68\frac{3}{4} =$ gain per pair: $5 \times 12 = 60 =$ number of pairs: $60 \times \$0.68\frac{3}{4} = \$41.25$, *Ans.*

(4.) The profit on 36 hats equals 36 times $37\frac{1}{2}$ ct., which is $13.50. If $13.50 $= \frac{1}{8}$ of the cost, $\frac{8}{8}$ are 8 times $13.50 = \$108$: $108 = \frac{9}{10}$ of the list price: $\frac{1}{10} = \$12$, $\frac{10}{10} = \$120$, *Ans.*

(5.) $1 \times 100 = \$100$: $100 less $60\% = \$40$: $40 less $5\% = \$38$: $38 less $5\% = \$36.10$: $36.10 + \$23.90 = \$60$: $60 \div (100 \times 12)$ or $1200 = 5$ ct., *Ans.*

(6.) 100 bbl. @ $9.50 = \$950$, less $2\frac{1}{2}\% = \$926.25$, less $17.25 = \$909$: $909 — (100 \times \$7.50)$ or $750 = \$159$, *Ans.*

(7.) $80 \times \$125 = \$10000$, $+ \$200 = \$10200$: $10450 — \$10200 = \$250 = 2\frac{1}{2}\%$ of $10000. *Ans.* $2\frac{1}{2}\%$.

(8.) 1500 lb. $\times 50 = 75000$ lb.: $10\frac{1}{2}$ ct. $\times 75000 = \$7875$: 2% of $7875 = \$157.50$, commission: $157.50 + \$22.50$, charges, $= \$180$: $7875 — \$180 = \$7695$, that the consignor receives: $7695 = 114\%$ of the cost price: $7695 \div 1.14 = \$6750$, cost: $6750 \div 75000 = 9$ ct., cost per pound.

(9.) 60×70 ct. $= \$42.00$: \$42 less 50% and 10% and 5% $= \$17.955$: \$42 less 20% and 10% and 5% $= \$28.728$: \$28.728 $-$ \$17.955 $= \$10.773$, *Ans.*

(10.) $\$35.91 = 112\%$ of the cost: $\$35.91 \div 1.12 = \$32.06\frac{1}{4}$, the cost: $\$32.06\frac{1}{4} \div .95 = \$33.75$: $\$33.75 \div .90 = \$37.50$: $\$37.50 \div .75 = \$50 =$ the list price: $\$50 \div 50 = \$1$, list price per gross, *Ans.*

Art. 177.

(1.) 1% of \$7500 is \$75, and $\frac{1}{4}\%$ is $\frac{1}{4}$ of \$75 $= \$18.75$, *Ans.*

(2.) 50 shares $= \$5000$: $\$6.25 \div \$5000 = .00125 = \frac{1}{8}\%$, *Ans.*

(3.) $\$10 = \frac{1}{4}\%$ of the investment: $1\% = 4$ times \$10 $= \$40$: $100\% = 100$ times \$40 $= \$4000 = 40$ shares, *Ans.*

(4.) 1% on \$1700 $= \$17.00$, and $\frac{1}{4}\% = \$4.25$, *Ans.*

(5.) 95 shares $= \$9500$: $\$11.875 \div \$9500 = .00125 = \frac{1}{8}\%$, *Ans.*

(6.) If $\$9.50 = \frac{1}{4}\%$, $1\% = \$38$, and $100\% = \$3800 = 38$ shares, *Ans.*

Art. 178.

(1.) The dividend will be 3500 times 4 ct. or ($\$0.04$) $= \$140$, *Ans.*

(2.) If \$300 is $7\frac{1}{2}\% = \frac{15}{2}\%$, $\frac{1}{2}\%$ is \$20, and 1% is \$40. If $\$40 = 1\%$, then 100% is $\$4000 = 40$ shares, *Ans.*

(3.) 15% on \$8000 $= \$1200$, *Ans.*

(4.) $5\% = \frac{1}{20}$: $\frac{1}{20}$ of $60 = 3$: $60 + 3 = 63$ shares, *Ans.*

(5.) $\$15700 - \$4500 = \$11200$: $11200 \div 160000 = .07 = 7\%$, *Ans.*

Art. 179.

(1.) 150 shares of $50 each are equivalent to 75 shares of $100. $139\frac{3}{4} \times 75 = \$10481.25$
$\frac{1}{4}\%$ brokerage on $7500 = \underline{\hspace{1cm} 18.75}$
$\overline{\hspace{1.5cm}\$10500.00}$, *Ans.*

(2.) $\$8000 \times 1.10 = \$8800$
$\frac{1}{8}\%$ brokerage on $8000 = \underline{\hspace{1cm} 10}$
$\overline{\hspace{1cm}\$8810}$, *Ans.*

(3.) $\frac{1}{4}\%$ brokerage on 50 shares $= \$12.50$: $\$2475 +$ $\$12.50 = \$2487.50$: $2487.50 \div 50 = 49\frac{3}{4}\%$, *Ans.*

(4.) $\$25000 \times 1.14\frac{1}{4} = \$28562.50$
$\frac{1}{8}\%$ brokerage on $25000 = \underline{\hspace{1cm} 31.25}$
$\overline{\hspace{1.5cm}\$28593.75}$, *Ans.*

(5.) $19\frac{1}{4} + \frac{1}{4} = 19\frac{1}{2}$ or 19.5: $\$1560 \div 19.5 = 80$, *Ans.*

(6.) $100 \div 1.05 = 95\frac{5}{21}$ ct., *Ans.*

(7.) $1.12\frac{1}{2} = 1\frac{1}{8} = \frac{9}{8}$: $100 \times \frac{8}{9} = \frac{800}{9} = 88\frac{8}{9}$ ct., *Ans.*

(8.) $35\frac{5}{7} = \frac{250}{7}$: $100 \times \frac{7}{250} = 2.80 = 280$, *Ans.*

(9.) $\$8946.25 \div 1.0525 = \$8500$, *Ans.*

(10.) If $\$15.62\frac{1}{2} = \frac{1}{16}\%$, $1\% = \$250$, and $100\% = \$25000$: $\$25734.37\frac{1}{2} - \$25000 = \$734.375$; adding the brokerage to this $= \$750$: $\$750 \div 25000 = .03 =$ gold premium: $103 = Ans.$

Art. 180.

(1.) $\$39900 \times .06 = \$2394$, *Ans.*

(2.) $\$39900 \div 1.05 = \$38000$: $\$38000 \times .06 = \$2280$, *Ans.*

(3.) $\$39900 \div .95 = \$42000$: $42000 \times .06 = \$2520$, *Ans.*

(4.) If gold was *at par*, 6% interest on $20000 would be $1200; at 7% premium it would yield an income 7% greater = $1284, *Ans.*

(5.) $5220 ÷ 1.16 = $4500 = amount in bonds; $4500 × .06 (%) = $270. Gold being at 5% premium, add to $270 its 5% = $13.50; $270 + $13.50 = $283.50. *Ans.*

(6.) 4½ per cents, when gold is at 105, would yield an income $\frac{1}{20}$ greater than when at par. 4.5 + ($\frac{1}{20}$ of 4.5) or .225 = 4.725 : 4.725 ÷ 1.08 = 4⅜%, *Ans.*

(7.)
$$37\tfrac{1}{2}\% = \tfrac{3}{8} : \frac{\overset{2}{\cancel{6}}\%}{1} \times \frac{8}{\underset{3}{\cancel{3}}} = 16\%, \; Ans.$$

(8.) $1921 ÷ 1.13 = $1700 = annual income in gold. $1700 ÷ .05 = $34000 : $34000 × 1.18 = $40120, *Ans.*

(9.) 95¼ + ¼ = 95½ : 105 − ¼ = 104¾ : 104¾ − 95½ = 9¼% = .0925 : $925 ÷ .0925 = $10000 = 100 shares, *Ans.*

(10.) 6 = ¾ of 8 : ¾ = 75%, *Ans.*

(11.) $4982 ÷ 1.06 = $4700 = amount of bonds that can be bought : 4% on $4700 = $188, *Ans.*

(12.) 7 ÷ .87½ = .08 = 8%, *Ans.*

(13.) .07 ÷ .06 = 116⅔, *Ans.*

INTEREST.

Simple Interest.

Art. 183.

1*st. When the time is one year.*

(7.) 6¼% = $\frac{1}{16}$: $7200 ÷ 16 = $450, *Ans.*

(8.) 8⅓% = $\frac{1}{12}$: $28.20 ÷ 12 = $2.35 : $28.20 + $2.35 = $30.55, *Ans.*

(9.) $10\% = \frac{1}{10}$: $\frac{1}{10}$ of $45.50 = 4.55$: $45.50 + $4.55 = $50.05, *Ans.*

(10.) $420 × .05\frac{1}{3} = $22.40, + $420 = $442.40, *Ans.*

(11.) $857 × .09 = $77.13, + $857 = $934.13, *Ans.*

(12.) $96 × .08\frac{1}{2} = $8.16, + $96 = $104.16, *Ans.*

(13.) $2000 × .04\frac{1}{2} = $90, + $2000 = $2090, *Ans.*

(14.) $12\frac{1}{2}\% = \frac{1}{8}$: $164 ÷ 8 = $20.50, + $164 = $184.50, *Ans.*

2d. When the time is two or more years.

(8.) $45 × .08 = $3.60: $3.60 × 2 = $7.20: $7.20 + $45 = $52.20, *Ans.*

(9.) $80 × .07 = $5.60: $5.60 × 4 = $22.40: $80 + $22.40 = $102.40, *Ans.*

(10.) $3\frac{3}{4}\% × 2 = 7\frac{1}{2}\%$: $237.16 × .07\frac{1}{2} = $17.79: $237.16 + $17.79 = $254.95, *Ans.*

(11.) $4\% × 5 = 20\% = \frac{1}{5}$: $74.75 ÷ 5 = $14.95: $74.75 + $14.95 = $89.70, *Ans.*

(12.) $85.45 × .06 = $5.127: $5.127 × 4 = $20.51: $20.51 + $85.45 = $105.96, *Ans.*

(13.) $325 × .05\frac{2}{5} = $17.55: $17.55 × 3 = $52.65: $52.65 + $325 = $377.65, *Ans.*

(14.) $129.36 × .04\frac{3}{8} = $5.6595: $5.6595 × 4 = $22.638: $22.64 + $129.36 = $152, *Ans.*

(15.) $8745 × .16 = $1399.20, + $8745 = $10144.20, *Ans.*

3d. When the time is any number of months.

(2.) $300 @ 6\%, 1 yr. = $18: 1 mo. = $\frac{1}{12}$ yr.: $18 ÷ 12 = $1.50, *Ans.*

(3.) $240 \times .08 = \$19.20$: 2 mo. $= \frac{1}{6}$ yr.: $19.20 \div$ 6 = **\$3.20**, *Ans.*

(4.) $50 \times .06 = \$3.00$: 4 mo. $= \frac{1}{3}$ yr.: $\frac{1}{3}$ of $3.00 = 1.00$
 1 mo. $= \frac{1}{4}$ of 4 mo.: $\frac{1}{4}$ of $1.00 = .25$
 Interest 5 mo. $= \overline{\$1.25}$

(5.) $86 \times .06 = \$5.16$: 3 mo. $= \frac{1}{4}$ yr.: $\frac{1}{4}$ of $5.16 =$ **\$1.29**, *Ans.*

(6.) $50 \times .08 = \$4.00$: 4 mo. $= \frac{1}{3}$ yr.: $\frac{1}{3}$ of $4.00 =$ **\$1.33+**, *Ans.*

(7.) $150.25 \times .08 = \$12.0200$: 6 mo. $= \frac{1}{2}$ yr.: $\frac{1}{2}$ of $12.02 = \$6.01$: $150.25 + \$6.01 = \$156.26$, *Ans.*

(8.) $360 \times .05 = \$18$: 6 mo. $= \frac{1}{2}$ yr.: $\frac{1}{2}$ of $18 = \$9$: 1 mo. $= \frac{1}{6}$ of 6 mo.: $\frac{1}{6}$ of $9 = \$1.50$: $9 + \$1.50 = \$10.50 =$ int. 7 mo.: $360 + \$10.50 = \$370.50$, *Ans.*

(9.) $204 \times .07 = \$14.28 $ 10 mo. $= \frac{10}{12}$ yr.
$\frac{10}{12}$ of $14.28 = 11.90 $ 1 mo. $= \frac{1}{10}$ of 10 mo.
$\frac{1}{10}$ of $11.90 = 1.19$
Int. 11 mo. $= \overline{\$13.09}$, $+ \$204 = \$217.09$. *Ans.*

(10.) $228 \times .06 = \$13.68 $ 6 mo. $= \frac{1}{2}$ yr.
$\frac{1}{2}$ of $13.68 = 6.84 $ 3 mo. $= \frac{1}{2}$ of 6 mo.
$\frac{1}{2}$ of $6.84 = 3.42$
Int. 9 mo. $= \overline{\$10.26}$, $+ \$228 = \$238.26$, *Ans.*

(11.) $137.50 \times .06 = \$8.25$: 8 mo. $= \frac{2}{3}$ yr.: $\frac{1}{3}$ of $8.25 = \$2.75$, $\frac{2}{3} = \$5.50$: $137.50 + \$5.50 = \$143$, *Ans.*

(12.) $7596 \times .08 = \$607.68$: 10 mo. $= \frac{5}{6}$ yr.: $\frac{5}{6}$ of $607.68 = \$506.40$: $7596 + \$506.40 = \$8102.40$, *Ans.*

4th. When the time is any number of days.

(2.) $360 \times .06 = 21.60$: $\frac{1}{12}$ (1 mo.) of $21.60 = \$1.80$: 20 da. $= \frac{2}{3}$ mo.: $\frac{2}{3}$ of $1.80 = \$1.20$, *Ans.*

(3.) $726 × .06 = $43.56: $\frac{1}{12}$ (1 mo.) of $43.56 = $3.63:
10 da. = $\frac{1}{3}$ mo.: $\frac{1}{3}$ of $3.63 = $1.21, *Ans.*

(4.) $1200 × .06 = $72: $\frac{1}{12}$ of $72 = $6 = int. 1 mo.:
15 da. = $\frac{1}{2}$ mo.: $\frac{1}{2}$ of $6 = $3, *Ans.*

(5.) $180 × .08 = $14.40: $\frac{1}{12}$ of $14.40 = $1.20 (1 mo.).
$\qquad$ 15 da. = $\frac{1}{2}$ mo.   = $0.60
$\qquad$ 3 da. = $\frac{1}{5}$ 15 da. =   .12
$\qquad$ 1 da. = $\frac{1}{3}$ 3 da. =   .04
$\qquad$ Int. for 19 da. = $\overline{\$0.76}$, *Ans.*

(6.) $240 × .07, ÷ 12 = $1.40 = int. 1 mo.
$\qquad$ 24 da. = $\frac{4}{5}$ mo.   = $1.12
$\qquad$ 3 da. = $\frac{1}{8}$ 24 da. =   .14
$\qquad$ Int. 27 da. = $\overline{\$1.26}$, *Ans.*

(7.) $320 × .05, ÷ 12 = 1.33\frac{1}{3}$ = int. 1 mo.
$\qquad$ 20 da. = $\frac{2}{3}$ mo.   = $0.888+
$\qquad$ 1 da. = $\frac{1}{20}$ 20 da. =   .044+
$\qquad$ Int. 21 da. = $\overline{\$0.93}$, *Ans.*

(8.) $450 × .10, ÷ 12 = $3.75 = int. 1 mo.:   25 da. =
$\frac{5}{6}$ mo.: $\frac{5}{6}$ of $3.75 = $3.125.   *Ans.* $3.13.

(9.) $100.80 × .05, ÷ 12 = $0.42 = int. 1 mo.
$\qquad$ 25 da. = $\frac{5}{6}$ mo. = $0.35
$\qquad$ 3 da. = $\frac{1}{10}$ mo. =   .042
$\qquad$ Int. 28 da. = $\overline{\$0.39}$, + $100.80 = $101.19, *Ans.*

(10.) $150 × .05, ÷ 12 = 0.62\frac{1}{2}$: 18 da. = $\frac{3}{5}$ mo.: $\frac{3}{5}$ of
$0.625 = $0.375: $150 + $0.375 = $150.38, *Ans.*

(11.) $360 × .06, ÷ 12 = $1.80 = int. 1 mo.
  10 da. = $\frac{1}{3}$ mo.   = $0.60
  1 da. = $\frac{1}{10}$ 10 da. =   .06
   Int. for 11 da. = $0.66, + $360 = $360.66, *Ans.*

(12.) $264 × .06, ÷ 12 = $1.32 = int. 1 mo.
  6 da. = $\frac{1}{5}$ mo.   = $0.264
  3 da. = $\frac{1}{2}$ 6 da. =   .132
   Int. 9 da. = $0.40, + $264 = $264.40, *Ans.*

(13.) $900 × .07 = $63, ÷ 12 = $5.25 = int. 1 mo.
  10 da. = $\frac{1}{3}$ mo.   = $1.75
  3 da. = $\frac{1}{10}$ mo.   =   .525
  1 da. = $\frac{1}{3}$ 3 da. =   .175
   Int. 14 da. = $2.45, + $900 = $902.45, *Ans.*

(14.) $430 × .04$\frac{1}{2}$, ÷ 12 = 1.61\frac{1}{4}$ = int. 1 mo.
  15 da. = $\frac{1}{2}$ mo.   = $0.806
  3 da. = $\frac{1}{5}$ 15 da. =   .161
  1 da. = $\frac{1}{3}$ 3 da. =   .053
   Int. 19 da. = $1.02, + $430 = $431.02, *Ans.*

5th. When the time is years, months, and days, or any two of these periods.

(3.) $150 × .06 = $9, × 4 (yr.) = $36.00 : 2 mo. = $\frac{1}{6}$ yr.: $\frac{1}{6}$ of $9 = $1.50 : $36 + $1.50 = $37.50, *Ans.*

(4.) $375.40 × .06 = $22.524   8 mos. = $\frac{2}{3}$ yr.
  $\frac{2}{3}$ of $22.524 =   15.016
        $37.54, *Ans.*

(5.) $92.75 × .06 = $5.565, × 3 (yr.) = $16.695
  4 mo. = $\frac{1}{3}$ yr. $\frac{1}{3}$ of 5.565 =   1.855
  1 mo. = $\frac{1}{4}$ 4 mo. $\frac{1}{4}$ of 1.855 =   .46375
          $19.01, *Ans.*

(6.) $\$500 \times .06 = \$30.00 = $ int. 1 yr.

$\frac{1}{12}$ of $\$30.00 = \quad 2.50 = $ int. 1 mo.

$\frac{1}{2}$ of $\quad 2.50 = \quad 1.25 = $ int. 15 da.

$\frac{1}{5}$ of $\quad 1.25 = \quad\quad .25 = $ int. 3 da.

$\quad\quad\quad\quad\quad\quad\quad \overline{\$34.00}$, *Ans.*

(7) $\$560 \times .08 = \$44.80, \times 2 = \$89.60 = $ int. 2 yr.

$\frac{1}{3}$ of $44.80 = \quad 14.933+ = $ int. 4 mo.

$\frac{1}{8}$ of $14.933 = \quad 1.866 = $ int. 15 da.

$\quad\quad\quad\quad\quad\quad \overline{\$106.40}$, *Ans.*

(8.) $\$750 \times .06 = \$45, \times 4 = \$180.00 = $ int. 4 yr.

3 mo. $= \frac{1}{4}$ yr. $\quad \frac{1}{4}$ of $\$45.00 = \quad 11.25 = $ int. 3 mo.

Int. 1 mo. $= \frac{1}{3}$ of $11.25 = 3.75 :$

$\frac{1}{5}$ of $3.75 = \quad\quad .75 = $ int. 6 da.

$\quad\quad\quad\quad\quad \overline{\$192}$, *Ans.*

(9.) $\$456 \times .05 = \$22.80, \times 3 = \$68.40 = $ int. 3 yr.

$\frac{1}{12}$ of $\$22.80 = \$1.90, \frac{5}{12} = \quad 9.50 = $ int. 5 mo.

$\frac{1}{2}$ of $1.90 = \quad\quad .95 = $ int. 15 da.

$\frac{1}{5}$ of $\quad .95 = \quad\quad .19 = $ int. 3 da.

$\quad\quad\quad\quad\quad\quad \overline{\$79.04}$, *Ans.*

(10.) $\$216 \times .10 = \$21.60, \times 5 = \$108.00 = $ int. 5 yr.

$\frac{1}{12}$ of $\$21.60 = 1.80$ (1 mo.),

$\frac{7}{12}$ of $21.60 = \quad 12.60 = $ int. 7 mo.

27 da. $= 3$ da., or $\frac{1}{10}$ less than 1

mo.: $\frac{1}{10}$ of $1.80 = .18 : 1.80 - .18 = \quad 1.62 = $ int. 27 da.

$\quad\quad\quad\quad\quad\quad \overline{\$122.22}$, *Ans.*

(11.) $\$380 \times .15 = \$57.00, \times 3 = \$171.00 \quad = $ int. 3 yr.

9 mo. $= \frac{3}{4}$ yr.: $\quad\quad \frac{3}{4}$ of $\$57 = \quad 42.75 \quad = $ int. 9 mo.

$\frac{1}{12}$ of $\$57 = \$4.75$ (1 mo.): 9 da.

$= \frac{3}{10}$ mo.: $\frac{3}{10}$ of $\$4.75 = \quad\quad 1.425 = $ int. 9 da.

$\quad\quad\quad\quad\quad\quad \overline{\$215.18}$, *Ans.*

(12.) $300 \times .06 = \$18, \times 3 = \$54.00 = $ int. 3 **yr.**
$\frac{1}{2}$ of $18 = \quad 9.00 = $ int. 6 mo.
$\frac{1}{3}$ of $\quad 9 = \quad 3.00 = $ int. 2 mo.
Int. 3 yr. 8 mo. $= \$66.$
$\qquad \qquad \underline{300.}$
$\qquad \qquad \$366, \textit{Ans.}$

(13.) $250 \times .06 = \$15.00 = $ int. 1 **yr.**
$\frac{1}{2}$ of $15.00 = \quad 7.50 = $ int. 6 mo.
$\frac{1}{6}$ of $\quad 7.50 = \quad 1.25 = $ int. 1 mo.
$\qquad \qquad \underline{\$23.75}$
$\qquad \qquad \underline{250.00}$
$\qquad \qquad \$273.75, \textit{Ans.}$

(14.) $205.25 \times .06 = \$12.315, \times 2 = \$24.63$ (2 **yr.**)
Int. 6 mo. $= \frac{1}{2}$ of $12.315 = \quad 6.1575$
Int. 2 mo. $= \frac{1}{3}$ of $\quad 6.1575 = \quad 2.0525$
Int. 15 da. $= \frac{1}{4}$ of $\quad 2.0525 = \quad \underline{.5131}$
$\qquad \qquad \qquad \$33.3531$
$\qquad \qquad \qquad \underline{205.25}$
$\qquad \qquad \qquad \$238.60, \textit{Ans.}$

(15.) $150.62 \times .05 = \$7.5310, \times 3 = \$22.5930$ (3 **yr.**)
Int. 4 mo. $= \frac{1}{3}$ of $7.5310 = \quad 2.5103$
Int. 1 mo. $= \frac{1}{4}$ of $\quad 2.5103 = \quad .6275$
Int. 12 da. $= \frac{2}{5}$ of $\quad .6275 = \quad \underline{.2510}$
$\qquad \qquad \qquad \$25.9818$
$\qquad \qquad \qquad \underline{150.62}$
$\qquad \qquad \qquad \$176.60, \textit{Ans.}$

(16.) $210.25 × .07 = $14.7175, × 2 = $29.4350 (2 yr.)
     Int. 6 mo. $= \frac{1}{2}$ of $14.7175 =   7.3587
     Int. 1 mo. $= \frac{1}{6}$ of   7.3587 =   1.2264
     Int. 20 da. $= \frac{2}{3}$ of   1.2264 =   .8176
                                $38.8377
                                210.25
                            $249.09, *Ans.*

(17.) $57.85 × .05 = $2.8925, × 2 = $5.7850 (2 yr.)
       Int. 3 mo. $= \frac{1}{4}$ of $2.8925 =   .7231
  Int. 20 da. $= \frac{2}{3}$ of $\frac{1}{3}$ of   .7231 =   .1606
     Int. 2 da. $= \frac{1}{10}$ of   .1606 =   .0160
     Int. 1 da. $= \frac{1}{2}$ of   .0160 =   .0080
                              $6.6927
                            57.85
                            $64.54, *Ans.*

(18.)

yr.	mo.	da.
1849	4	19
1847	1	9
2	3	10

$150 × .06 = $9.00, × 2 = $18.00 = int. 2 yr.
     Int. 3 mo. $= \frac{1}{4}$ of $9.00 =   2.25
Int. 10 da. $= \frac{1}{3}$ of $\frac{1}{3}$ of   2.25 =   .25
                            $20.50, *Ans.*

(19.)

yr.	mo.	da.
1849	4	27
1848	2	15
1	2	12

$240 × .08 = $19.20 = int. 1 yr.
  $\frac{1}{6}$ of $19.20 =   3.20 = int. 2 mo.
$\frac{2}{5}$ of $\frac{1}{2}$ of   3.20 =   .64 = int. 12 da.
                          $23.04, *Ans.*

(20.)   yr.   mo.   da.

	yr.	mo.	da.
	1845	8	28
	1843	5	14
	2	3	14

$180 × .07 = $12.60, × 2 = $25.20 = int. 2 yr.

$\frac{1}{4}$ of $12.60 =   3.15 = int. 3 mo.

$\frac{2}{5}$ of $\frac{1}{3}$ of   3.15 =   .42 = int. 12 da.

$\frac{1}{6}$ of   .42 =   .07 = int. 2 da.

          $28.84, *Ans.*

(21.) mo.   da.

mo.	da.
11	27
7	3
	24

$137.50 × .09 = $12.3750 = int. 1 yr.

$\frac{1}{3}$ of $12.3750 = $4.125 = int. 4 mo.

$\frac{4}{5}$ of $\frac{1}{4}$ (= $\frac{1}{5}$) of   4.125 =   .825 = int. 24 da.

          $4.95, *Ans.*

(22.) mo.   da.

mo.	da.
8	28
3	1
5	27

$125.40 × .08$\frac{1}{2}$ = $10.659 = int. 1 yr.

$\frac{5}{12}$ of $10.659 = $4.44 + = int. 5 mo.

$\frac{9}{10}$ of $\frac{1}{5}$ of   4.44 =   .799+ = int. 27 da.

          $5.24

         125.40

        $130.64, *Ans.*

(23.)   yr.   mo.   da.

        1848   3   9

        1847   8   2

               7   7

$\$234.60 \times .05\frac{1}{4} = \$12.3165 = $ int. 1 yr.

$\frac{7}{12}$ of $\$12.3165 = \$7.1848 = $ int. 7 mo.

$\frac{1}{5}$ of $\frac{1}{12}$ of $12.3165 = \quad .2052 = $ int. 6 da.

$\frac{1}{6}$ of $\quad .2052 = \quad .0342 = $ int. 1 da.

$$\$7.4242$$
$$234.60$$
$$\overline{\$242.02, \textit{Ans.}}$$

(24.)   yr.   mo.   da.

        1847   7   24

        1846   10   25

               8   29

$\$153.80 \times .05 = \$7.69 = $ int. 1 yr.

$\frac{2}{3}$ of $\$7.69 = \$5.126 = $ int. 8 mo.

Int. 1 mo. $= \frac{1}{8}$ of $\$5.126 = .64$

Int. 29 da. $= .64$ less $\frac{1}{30} = \quad .62$

$$\overline{\quad\quad\$5.75}$$
$$153.80$$
$$\overline{\$159.55, \textit{Ans.}}$$

Art. 184. 1st Process.

(5.) 1 yr. 4 mo. $= 16$ mo.   *Ans.* 16 ct.

(6.) 1 yr. 5 mo. $= 17$ mo.: $\frac{1}{3}$ of 27 da. $= 9.$ *Ans.* $0.179

(7.) 2 yr. 3 mo. $= 27$ mo.: $\frac{1}{3}$ of 21 da. $= 7.$ *Ans.* $0.277

(8.) 3 yr. 7 mo. $= 43$ mo.: $\frac{1}{3}$ of 12 da. $= 4.$ *Ans.* $0.434

(9.) 4 yr. 2 mo. = 50 mo.: $\frac{1}{3}$ of 15 da. = 5 da. *Ans.* $0.505

(10.) 2 ct. for the 2 mo., and $\frac{1}{3}$ mill for the 1 da. *Ans.* 0.020\frac{1}{3}$

(11.) $\frac{1}{3}$ of 17 = 5$\frac{2}{3}$ (apply rule). *Ans.* 0.055\frac{2}{3}$

(12.) $\frac{1}{3}$ of 13 = 4$\frac{1}{3}$ (apply rule). *Ans.* 0.104\frac{1}{3}$

(13.) 1 yr. 2 mo. = 14 mo.: $\frac{1}{3}$ of 4 = 1$\frac{1}{3}$. *Ans.* 0.141\frac{1}{3}$

(14.) 2 yr. 9 mo. = 33 mo.: $\frac{1}{3}$ of 20 = 6$\frac{2}{3}$. *Ans.* 0.336\frac{2}{3}$

(15.) 3 yr. 5 mo. = 41 mo.: $\frac{1}{3}$ of 29 = 9$\frac{2}{3}$. *Ans.* 0.419\frac{2}{3}$

2D PROCESS.

(3.) Int. on $1 for 7 mo. 24 da. @ 12% = $0.078: int. for 7 mo. 24 da. @ 6% = $\frac{1}{2}$ of $0.078 = $0.039, *Ans.*

(4.) Int. at 12% = $0.105

Int. at 4% = $\frac{1}{3}$ of $0.105 = $0.035
Int. at 1% = $\frac{1}{4}$ of   .035 =   .00875
                                      0.043\frac{3}{4}$, *Ans.*

(5.) Int. at 12% = $0.116: int. at 9% = $\frac{3}{4}$ of $0.116 = $0.087, *Ans.*

(6.) 1 yr. 2 mo. = 14 mo.: int. 14 mo. 9 da. @ 12% = $0.143: int. @ 6% = $\frac{1}{2}$ of $0.143 = 0.071\frac{1}{2}$, *Ans.*

(7.) 2 yr. 5 mo. = 29 mo.: int. 29 mo. 12 da. @ 12% = $0.294: int. @ 8% = $\frac{2}{3}$ of $0.294 = $0.196, *Ans.*

(8.) 3 yr. 10 mo. = 46 mo.: int. 46 mo. 17 da. @ 12% = 0.465\frac{2}{3}$: int. @ 10% = $\frac{5}{6}$ of 0.465\frac{2}{3}$ = 0.388\frac{1}{18}$, *Ans.*

(9.) 4 yr. 3 mo. = 51 mo.: int. 51 mo. 11 da. @ 12% = 0.513\frac{2}{3}$

Int. @ 6% = $\frac{1}{2}$ of 0.513\frac{2}{3}$ = 0.256\frac{5}{6}$
Int. @ 1% = $\frac{1}{6}$ of   .256$\frac{5}{6}$ =   .042$\frac{29}{36}$
                                        0.299\frac{23}{36}$, *Ans.*

(10.) 5 yr. 7 mo. $=$ 67 mo.: int. 67 mo. 24 da. @ 12% $=$ \$0.678: int. @ $4\% = \frac{1}{3}$ of \$0.678 $=$ \$0.225, *Ans.*

3d Process.

(3.) Int. \$1 for 6 mo. 21 da. @ 12% $=$ \$0.067: @ 6% $= \frac{1}{2}$ of \$0.067 $=$ \$0.0335, $\times$ 40 $=$ \$1.34, *Ans.*

(4.) Int. \$1 for 8 mo. 24 da. @ 12% $=$ \$0.088: int. \$1 for 8 mo. 24 da. @ $9\% = \frac{3}{4}$ of \$0.088 $=$ \$0.066: \$0.066 $\times$ 50 $=$ \$3.30, *Ans.*

(5.) Int. \$1 for 10 mo. 12 da. @ 12% $=$ \$0.104
Int. \$1 for 10 mo. 12 da. @ $6\% = \frac{1}{2}$ of \$0.104 $=$ \$0.052
Int. \$1 for 10 mo. 12 da. @ $1\% = \frac{1}{6}$ of .052 $=$ .008$\frac{2}{3}$
\qquad\qquad \$0.060$\frac{2}{3}$ $\times$ 120 $=$ \$7.28, *Ans.* \qquad \$0.060$\frac{2}{3}$

(6.) Int. \$1 for 11 mo. 15 da. @ 12% $=$ \$0.115: int. \$1 for 11 mo. 15 da. @ $6\% = \frac{1}{2}$ of \$0.115 $=$ \$0.0575: \$0.0575 $\times$ 200 $=$ \$11.50, *Ans.*

(7.) 1 yr. 3 mo. $=$ 15 mo.: int. \$1 for 15 mo. 6 da. @ 12% $=$ \$0.152: at $3\% = \frac{1}{4}$ of \$0.152 $=$ \$0.038: \$0.038 $\times$ 500 $=$ \$19, *Ans.*

(8.) 1 yr. 5 mo. $=$ 17 mo.: int. \$1 for 17 mo. 27 da. @ 12% $=$ \$0.179: at $8\% = \frac{2}{3}$ of \$0.179 $=$ \$0.119$\frac{1}{3}$: \$0.119$\frac{1}{3}$ $\times$ 750 $=$ \$89.50, *Ans.*

(9.) 1 yr. 9 mo. $=$ 21 mo.: int. \$1 for 21 mo. 3 da. @ 12% $=$ \$0.211: @ $6\% = \frac{1}{2}$ of \$0.211 $=$ \$0.105$\frac{1}{2}$, $\times$ 48.75 $=$ \$5.14, *Ans.*

(10.) 1 yr. 10 mo. $=$ 22 mo.: Int. \$1 for 22 mo. 25 da. @ 12% $=$ \$0.228$\frac{1}{3}$: at $4\% = \frac{1}{3}$ of \$0.228$\frac{1}{3}$ $=$ \$0.076$\frac{1}{9}$: \$0.076$\frac{1}{9}$ $\times$ 76.32 $=$ \$5.81, *Ans.*

(11.) 2 yr. 1 mo. $=$ 25 mo.: int. \$1 for 25 mo. 9 da. @ 12% $=$ \$0.253: at $4\% = \frac{1}{3}$ of \$0.253 $=$ \$0.084$\frac{1}{3}$: $1\% = \frac{1}{4}$

of $0.084\frac{1}{3} = \$0.021\frac{1}{12}$: $0.084\frac{1}{3} + \$0.021\frac{1}{12} = \$0.105\frac{5}{12}$, $\times$ 600 = $63.25: $600 + $63.25 = $663.25, *Ans.*

(12.) 2 yr. 4 mo. = 28 mo.: int. $1 @ 12% for 28 mo. 10 da. = $0.283\frac{1}{3}$: @ 6% = \frac{1}{2} of $0.283\frac{1}{3} = \$0.141\frac{2}{3}$, $\times$ 900 = $127.50: $900 + $127.50 = $1027.50, *Ans.*

(13.) 2 yr. 7 mo. = 31 mo.: int. $1 @ 12% for 31 mo. 17 da. = $0.315\frac{2}{3}$: 9% = \frac{3}{4} of 12% = $0.236\frac{3}{4}$: $0.236\frac{3}{4} \times 86.25 = $20.419+: $86.25 + $20.42 = $106.67, *Ans.*

(14.) 3 yr. 2 mo. = 38 mo.: int. $1 for 38 mo. 13 da. @ 12% = $0.384\frac{1}{3}$: 8% = \frac{2}{3} of 12% = $0.256\frac{2}{3}$, $\times$ 450 = $115.30: $450 + $115.30 = $565.30, *Ans.*

(15.) 3 yr. 5 mo. = 41 mo.: int. $1 for 41 mo. 22 da. @ 12% = $0.417\frac{1}{3}$: 4% = \frac{1}{3} of 12% = $0.139\frac{1}{9}$: $0.139\frac{1}{9} \times 534.78 = $74.39+: $534.78 + $74.39 = $609.17, *Ans.*

(16.) 3 yr. 11 mo. = 47 mo.: int. $1 @ 12% for 47 mo. 15 da. = $0.475: int. @ 10% = \frac{5}{6} of 12% = $0.395\frac{5}{6}$: $0.395\frac{5}{6} \times 1200 = $475, + $1200 = $1675, *Ans.*

Art. 185.

(4.) Int. on $200 for 1 yr. @ 6% = $12.00: 36 ÷ 12 = 3. *Ans.* 3 yr.

(5.) Int. on $60 for 1 yr. @ 5% = $3.00: $72 — $60 = $12: 12 ÷ 3 = 4. *Ans.* 4 yr.

(6.) If the principal is doubled, the int. will equal 100%. 100% ÷ 6% = 16\frac{2}{3}: \frac{2}{3} yr. = 8 mo. *Ans.* 16 yr 8 mo.

(7.) Int. on $375 for 1 yr. @ 8% = $30: 90 ÷ 30 = 3. *Ans.* 3 yr.

(8.) Int. on $600 @ 9% for 1 yr. = $54: $798 — $600 = $198: 198 ÷ 54 = 3\frac{2}{3} = 3 yr. 8 mo., *Ans.*

(9.) $100(\%) \div 10(\%) = 10$. *Ans.* 10 yr.

(10.) Int. on \$250 for 1 yr. @ $6\% = \$15$: $34.50 \div 15 = 2.30$ or $2\frac{3}{10}$ yr.: $\frac{3}{10}$ yr. $= 3\frac{3}{5}$ mo.: $\frac{3}{5}$ mo. $= 18$ da. *Ans.* 2 yr. 3 mo. 18 da.

(11.) The int. on \$60 for 1 yr. @ $6\% = \$3.60$: \$73.77 — \$60 = \$13.77: $13.77 \div 3.60 = 3.825$ or $3\frac{33}{40}$ yr.: $\frac{33}{40}$ yr. $= 9\frac{9}{10}$ mo.: $\frac{9}{10}$ mo. $= 27$ da. *Ans.* 3 yr. 9 mo. 27 da.

(12.) If the principal is trebled, the int. will equal 200%. $200(\%) \div 6(\%) = 33\frac{1}{3}$: $\frac{1}{3}$ yr. $= 4$ mo. *Ans.* 33 yr. 4 mo.

(13.) Int. on \$400 for 1 yr. @ $7\% = \$28$: $68.60 \div 28 = 2.45$ or $2\frac{9}{20}$ yr.: $\frac{9}{20}$ yr. $= 5\frac{4}{10}$ mo.: $\frac{4}{10}$ mo. $= 12$ da. *Ans.* 2 yr. 5 mo. 12 da.

(14.) Int. on \$700 for 1 yr. @ $9\% = \$63$: \$924.70 — \$700 = \$224.70: $224.70 \div 63 = 3.566+$ or $3\frac{57}{100}$ yr.: $\frac{57}{100}$ yr. $= 6\frac{79}{100}$ mo.: $\frac{79}{100}$ mo. $= 23\frac{9}{10}$ da. *Ans.* 3 yr. 6 mo. 24 da.

(15.) If the principal is increased one half, the int. will equal 50%. $50(\%) \div 8(\%) = 6\frac{1}{4}$: $\frac{1}{4}$ yr. $= 3$ mo. *Ans.* 6 yr. 3 mo.

(16.) Int. on \$1200 for 1 yr. @ $10\% = \$120$: \$1675 — \$1200 = \$475: $475 \div 120 = 3.959+$ or $3\frac{96}{100}$ yr.: $\frac{96}{100}$ yr. $= 11\frac{52}{100}$ mo.: $\frac{52}{100}$ mo. $= 15+$ da. *Ans.* 3 yr. 11 mo. 15 da.

Art. 186.

(3.) $\$48 \div 2 = \$24 = $ int. 1 yr.: $24 \div 600 = .04 = 4\%$, *Ans.*

(4.) 2 yr. 6 mo. $= 2\frac{1}{2}$ or $\frac{5}{2}$ yr. If int. for $\frac{5}{2}$ yr. $= \$200$, for $\frac{1}{2}$ yr. $= \$40$, and for 1 yr. $= \$80$: $80 \div 1000 = .08 = 8\%$, *Ans.*

(5.) 2 yr. 4 mo. 24 da. $= 2\frac{2}{5}$ or $\frac{12}{5}$ yr.: $310 — $250 $= 60. If int. for $\frac{12}{5}$ yr. $= 60, for $\frac{1}{5}$ yr. $= 5, and for 1 yr. $= 25: $25 \div 250 = .10 = 10\%$, *Ans.*

(6.) $23.40 \div 2 = $11.70 = $ int. 1 yr.: $11.70 \div 260 = .04\frac{1}{2} = 4\frac{1}{2}\%$, *Ans.*

(7.) Since the int. for $12\frac{1}{2}$ or $\frac{25}{2}$ yr. is 100%, for $\frac{1}{2}$ yr. it is $\frac{100}{25}$ or 4   and for 1 yr. $= 8\%$, *Ans.*

(8.) $250.25 — $175 = 75.25: 3 yr. 7 mo. $= 3\frac{7}{12}$ or $\frac{43}{12}$ yr. Since $75.25 = $ int. for $\frac{43}{12}$ yr., for $\frac{1}{12}$ yr. $= $75.25 \div 43 = $1;75$, and for 1 yr. $= $1.75 \times 12 = 21: $21 \div 175 = .12 = 12\%$, *Ans.*

(9.) 1 yr. 8 mo. 12 da. $= 1\frac{7}{10}$ or $\frac{17}{10}$ yr.: $61.20 \div 17 = $3.60, \times 10 = $36 = $ int. 1 yr.: $36 \div 450 = 0.08 = 8\%$, *Ans.*

(10.) 11 yr. 1 mo. 10 da. $= 11\frac{1}{9}$ or $\frac{100}{9}$ yr. Since the int. for $\frac{100}{9}$ yr. $= 100\%$, for $\frac{1}{9}$ yr. $= 1\%$, and for 1 yr. $= 9\%$, *Ans.*

(11.) $746.20 — $650 = 96.20: 2 yr. 5 mo. 18 da. $= 2\frac{7}{15}$ or $\frac{37}{15}$ yr.: $96.20 \div 37 = $2.60, \times 15 = $39 = $ int. 1 yr.: $39 \div 650 = .06 = 6\%$, *Ans.*

(12.) $110.40 \div 6 = $18.40 = $ int. 1 yr.: $18.40 \div 640 = .02\frac{7}{8} = 2\frac{7}{8}\%$, *Ans.*

Art. 187.

(3.) The int. of $1 for 3 yr. at 5% is 15 ct. It will take as many dollars to gain $8.25 int. as 15 ct. are contained times in $8.25 = 55$ times. *Ans.* $55.

(4.) Int. of $1 for 3 yr. at $5\% = 15$ ct.: $341.25 \div .15 = 2275, *Ans.*

(5.) 1 yr. 4 mo. $= 1\frac{1}{3}$ yr.: 6% for 1 yr. $= .06$, and for $1\frac{1}{3}$ yr. $= .08$: $226 \div .08 = 28.25, *Ans.*

(6.) Int. of $1 = 5 ct.: $1023.75 ÷ .05 = $20475, *Ans.*

(7.) The int. of $1 for 1 yr. 6 mo. 27 da. at 12% = $0.189: at 8% the int. is $\frac{2}{3}$ of $0.189 = $0.126: $30.24 ÷ .126 = $240, *Ans.*

(8.) Int. of $1 for 12 yr. 3 mo. 20 da. at 12% = 1.476\frac{2}{3}$: at 9% = $\frac{3}{4}$ of 1.476\frac{2}{3}$ = $1.1075: $525.40 ÷ 1.1075 = $474.40, *Ans.*

(9.) Int. at 12% on $1 for 2 yr. 7 mo. 11 da. is 0.313\frac{2}{3}$: at 4% it is $\frac{1}{3}$ of 0.313\frac{2}{3}$ = 0.104\frac{5}{9}$: $9.41 ÷ .104$\frac{5}{9}$ = $90, *Ans.*

(10.) The int. of $1 for 5 yr. 8 mo. 24 da. at 12% is $0.688: at 6% it is $\frac{1}{2}$ of $0.688 = $0.344: $28.38 ÷ .344 = $82.50, *Ans.*

Art. 188.

(2.) 9 yr. × .05 = .45: $435 ÷ 1.45 = $300, *Ans.*

(3.) 4 yr. × .05 = .20: $571.20 ÷ 1.20 = $476 = principal: $571.20 — $476 = $95.20, *Ans.*

(4.) 6 yr. × .07 = 0.42: $532.50 ÷ 1.42 = $375: $532.50 — $375 = $157.50, *Ans.*

(5.) 2 yr. 9 mo. = 2$\frac{3}{4}$ yr.: 2$\frac{3}{4}$ × .08 = 0.22: $285.48 ÷ 1.22 = $234, *Ans.*

(6.) 2$\frac{1}{2}$ yr. × .06 = 0.15: $690 ÷ 1.15 = $600: $690 — $600 = $90, *Ans.*

(7.) 3 yr. 4 mo. 24 da. = 3$\frac{2}{5}$ yr.: 3$\frac{2}{5}$ × .07 = 0.238: $643.760 ÷ 1.238 = $520, *Ans.*

(8.) 4 yr. 3 mo. 27 da. = $\frac{519}{120}$ yr.: $\frac{519}{120}$ × .04 = 0.173: $914.940 ÷ 1.173 = $780 = principal: $914.94 — $780 = $134.94, *Ans.*

COMPOUND INTEREST.

Art. 190.

(2)	$500		530		561.80
	.06		.06		.06
	30.00		31.80		33.7080
	500		530		561.80
	$530, 1st yr.		$561.80, 2d yr.		Ans. $595.51

(3)	$800	848	898.88	952.81
	.06	.06	.06	.06
	48.00	50.88	53.9328	57.1686
	800	848	898.88	952.81

$848, 1st yr. $898.88, 2d yr. $952.81, 3d yr. $1009.98, *Ans.*

(4)

	$250		15.90
	.06		265
	$15.00 = 1st yr.		$280.90
	250		.06
	265		$16.8540 = 3d yr.
	.06		
	$15.90 = 2d yr.		$15+$15.90+$16.85=$47.75, *Ans.*

(5)

	$300		330.75
	.05		.05
	$15.00 = 1st yr.		$16.5375 = 3d yr.
	300		330.75
	315		347.29
	.05		.05
	$15.75 = 2d yr.		$17.3645 = 4th yr.
	315		
	$330.75		$15+$15.75+$16.54+$17.36=$64.65, *Ans.*

(5) $200   212.18
          .03   .03
       ――――   ―――――
       $6.00 = 1st hf.-yr. $6.3654 = 3d hf.-yr.
        200   212.18
       ―――   ―――――
        206   218.55
        .03   .03
       ―――   ―――――
       $6.18 = 2d hf.-yr. $6.5565 = 4th hf.-yr.
        206
       ――――
       $212.18 $6 + $6.18 + $6.36 + $6.56 = $25.10, *Ans.*

(7.) 20% annually = 5% quarterly.
1st qr., $500 × .05 = $25, + $500 = $525 :
2d qr., $525 × .05 = $26.25, + $525 = $551.25 :
3d qr., $551.25 × .05 = $27.56, + $551.25 = $578.81 :
4th qr., $578.81 × .05 = $28.94, + $578.81 = $607.75 :
5th qr., $607.75 × .05 = $30.39, + $607.75 = $638.14 :
6th qr., $638.14 × .05 = $31.91, + $638.14 = $670.05 :
7th qr., $670.05 × .05 = $33.50, + $670.05 = $703.55 :
8th qr., $703.55 × .05 = $35.18, + $703.55 = $738.73, *Ans.*

(8.) Int. on $300, 1 yr. @ 6% = $18, + $300 = $318 :
int. on $318 for 1 yr. @ 6% = $19.08, + $318 = $337.08 :
int. on $337.08, ½ yr. @ 6% = $10.11, + $337.08 = $347.19 :
$347.19 — $300 = $47.19, *Ans.*

(9.) Int. on $1000, 1 yr. @ 6% = $60, + $1000 = $1060 :
int. on $1060, 1 yr. @ 6% = $63.60, + $1060 = $1123.60 :
int. on $1123.60 for 8½ mo. @ 6% = $47.75, + $1123.60 =
$1171.35 : $1171.35 — $1000 = $171.35, *Ans.*

(10.) 6% int. annually = 3% semi-annually.
Int. 6 mo. on $620 @ 3% = $18.60, + $620 = $638.60 :
int. 6 mo. on $638.60 @ 3% = $19.16, + $638.60 = $657.76 :
int. 6 mo. on $657.76 @ 3% = $19.73, + $657.76 = $677.49 :
int. 6 mo. on $677.49 @ 3% = $20.32, + $677.49 = $697.81 :

int. 6 mo. on $697.81 @ 3% = $20.93, + $697.81 = $718 74;
int. 6 mo. on $718.74 @ 3% = $21.56, + $718.74 = $740.31:
int. 6 mo. on $740.31 @ 3% = $22.21, + $740.30 = $762.52,
Ans.

(1st.—Compound Interest.)

(11.) 1st yr., int. on $500 @ 6% = $30, + $500 = $530 :
2d yr., int. on $530 @ 6% = $31.80, + $530 = $561.80 :
3d yr., int. on $561.80 @ 6% = $33.71, + $561.80 =
$595.51 : 4th yr., int. on $595.51 @ 6% = $35.73, + $595.51
= $631.24 : 8 mo. = $\frac{2}{3}$ yr., int. on $631.24 @ 6% = $25.25,
+ $631.24 = $656.49 : $656.49 — $500 = $156.49

(2d.—Simple Interest.)

Int. on $500 for 1 yr. @ 6% = $30 : int. on $500 for $4\frac{2}{3}$
yr. = $140. $156.49 — $140 = $16.49, *Ans.*

ANNUAL INTEREST.

Art. 191.

(2.) Int. @ 8% on $800 for 3 yr. = $192.00
Int. @ 8% on $800 for 1 yr. = $64
  Int. on annual int. 1 yr. = $5.12
  Int. on annual int. 3 yr. = $15.36 . .   15.36
              Total interest, $207.36
              Add principal,   800.00
                    Ans. $1007.36

(3.) Int. on $750 for 3 yr. @ 10% = $225.00
          Annual int. = $75.00
        Int. on annual int. =   7.50
    Int. on an. int. 2 + 1, or 3, yr. =   22.50
                    $247.50
              Add principal,   750.00
                    Ans. $997.50

(4.) Int. on $10000 for 4 yr. @ 5% = $2000.

Annual int. = $500

Int. on annual int. = 25

Int. on an. int. 3 + 2 + 1, or 6, yr. = 150.

Ans. $2150.

(5.)

yr.	mo.	da.
1877	9	1
1875	6	1
2	3	$= 2\frac{1}{4}$ yr.

Int. on $500 for 1 yr. @ 6% = $30.00

Int. on $500 for $2\frac{1}{4}$ yr. @ 6% = 67.50 .. $67.50

Each semi-annual int. = 15.00

Interest on int. each half-yr. = .45

Interest on int. $3\frac{1}{2} + 2\frac{1}{2} + 1\frac{1}{2} + \frac{1}{2}$, or 8, half-yr. ... 3.60

Total interest, $71.10

Add principal, 500.00

Ans. $571.10

(6.)

yr.	mo.	da.
1877	9	20
1873	5	12
4	4	$8 = 4\frac{16}{45}$ yr.

Int. on $1200 for 1 yr. @ 6% = $72.00

Int. on $1200 for $4\frac{16}{45}$ yr. @ 6% = 313.60 .. $313.60

Int. on annual int. 1 yr. = 4.32

Int. on an. int. $3\frac{16}{45} + 2\frac{16}{45} + 1\frac{16}{45} + \frac{16}{45}$, or $7\frac{19}{45}$, yr. = 32.06

Total interest, $345.66

Add principal, 1200.00

Ans. $1545.66

(7.)

yr.	mo.	da.
1877	5	1
1872	10	10
4	6	$21 = 4\frac{67}{120}$ yr.

Int. on \$1500 for 1   yr. @ $5\% = \$75.00$
Int. on \$1500 for $4\frac{67}{120}$ yr. @ $5\% = 341.88 . . \$341.88$
Int. on an. int. 1 yr. $=$ 3.75
Int. on an. int. $3\frac{67}{120} + 2\frac{67}{120} + 1\frac{67}{120} + \frac{67}{120}$, or
$8\frac{7}{30}$, yr. $=$ 30.87

Total interest, \$372.75
Add principal, 1500.00
Ans. \$1872.75

(8.) Simple int. 1 yr. on \$1000 @ $6\% = \$60$: 5 yr. $=$
\$300: int. on int. 1 yr. $= \$3.60$: for $4 + 3 + 2 + 1$, or
10, yr. $= \$36.00$: annual int. $= \$336$; simple int. $= \$300$;
difference $= \$36$, *Ans.*

(9.) \$500 $\times$ 6 $=$ \$3000
Int. on \$3000 for 1 yr. @ $6\% = \$180.00$
Int. on \$3000 for 3 yr. @ $6\% =$ 540.00 . . \$540.00
Int. on int. $\frac{1}{2}$ yr. $=$ 2.70
Int. on int. $5 + 4 + 3 + 2 + 1$, or 15, half-yr. $=$ 40.50

Total interest, \$580.50
Add principal, 3000.00
Ans. \$3580.50

(10.)   Int. on \$20000 for 5 yr. @ $4\% = \$4000.00$
Int. on \$20000 for 1 yr. $= \$800.00$
Int. on \$20000 for $\frac{1}{4}$ yr. $=$ 200.00
Int. on $\frac{1}{4}$ an. int. @ $1\frac{1}{2}\%$ ($\frac{1}{4}$ of 6%) $=$ 3.00
Int. on $\frac{1}{4}$ an. int. $19 + 18 + 17 + 16 + 15 + 14 +$
$13 + 12 + 11 + 10 + 9 + 8 + 7 + 6$
$+ 5 + 4 + 3 + 2 + 1$, or 190, qrs. $=$ 570.00

Total interest, \$4570.00
Add to this the premium on gold, $5\%, = \frac{1}{20}$,   228.50
Ans. \$4798.50

Art. 192.

yr.	mo.	da.	
1876	3	1 . . $44
1875	7	1
	8 mo.	
1876	10	1 . . $10
1876	3	1
	7 mo.	
1877	1	1 . . $26
1876	10	1 $36 . .
	3 mo.	
1877	12	1 . . $15
1877	1	1
	11 mo.	
1878	3	16
1877	12	1
	3	15=3½ mo.

(2)

$350
  14=int. 8 mo.
$364
  44
$320
  16=int. 7+3=10 mo.
$336
  36
$300
  21.75=int. 11+3½=14½ mo.
$321.75
  15.00
$306.75, *Ans.*

(3.) Amt. of $200, 1 yr. @ 6% = $212: $212 — $70 = $142: amt. of $142, 1 yr. @ 6% = $150.52, *Ans.*

(4)

1874	1	1 . . $109
1873	7	1
	6 mo.	
1874	7	1
1874	1	1
	6 mo.	
1875	1	1
1874	7	1
	6 mo.	

6% per yr. = 3% per ½ yr.

$300	$6.00
.03	200
9.00	206
300	100
309	106
109	.03
200	3.18
.03	106
6.00	$109.18, *Ans*

(5)

1871	9	10	. . $32
1870	5	10	

1 yr. 4 mo.

1872	9	10	. . $6.80
1871	9	10	

1 yr.

1872	11	10
1872	9	10

2 mo.

$150
   12 = int. for 1 yr. 4 mo.
 162
  32
 130
  9.10 = int. 1 **yr.** 2 mo.
139.10
  6.80
$132.30, *Ans.*

(6)

1872	6	5	. . $20
1871	3	5	

1 yr. 3 mo.

1872	12	5	. . $50.50
1872	6	5	$70.50

6 mo.

1874	6	5
1872	12	5

1 yr. 6 mo.

$200
  35 = int. 1 yr. 9 mo.
235
 70.50
164.60
 24.68 = int. 1 yr. 6 mo.
$189.18, *Ans.*

(7)

1875	6	1	. . $6
1875	1	1	

5 mo.

1876	1	1	. . $21.50
1875	6	1	$27.50

7 mo.

1876	7	1
1876	1	1

6 mo.

$250
 17.50 = int. 12 mo.
267.50
 27.50
240
  8.40 = int. 6 mo.
$248.40, *Ans.*

(8)

1875	2	1	. .	$25.40
1874	8	1		

6 mo.

$180

    5.40 = int. 6 mo.

185.40

 25.40

160

1875	8	1	. .	$4.30
1875	2	1		

6 mo.

    8.80 = int. 11 mo.

168.80

 34.30

134.50

1876	1	1	. .	$30
1875	8	1		$34.30

5 mo.

   4.035 = int. 6 mo.

$138.54, *Ans.*

1876	7	1
1876	1	1

6 mo.

(9)

1875	9	1	. .	$10
1875	3	1		

6 mo.

1877	3	1
1876	9	1

6 mo.

1876	1	1	. .	$30
1875	9	1		$40.

4 mo.

$400

  20 = int. 10 mo. (6+4.)

420

 40

380

1876	7	1	. .	$11
1876	1	1		

6 mo.

  15.10 = int. 8 mo. (6+2.)

395.20

 91

1876	9	1	. .	$80
1876	7	1		$91.

2 mo.

304.20

  9.126 = int. 6 mo.

$313.33, *Ans.*

(10)

1877	1	1	.. $20
1876	4	16	

8 mo. 15 da.

1877	4	1	.. $14
1877	1	1	

3 mo.

1877	7	16	.. $31
1877	4	1	$65

3 mo. 15 da.

1877	12	25	.. $10
1877	7	16	

5 mo. 9 da.

1878	7	4	.. $18
1877	12	25	$28

6 mo. 9 da.

1879	6	1	
1878	7	4	

10 mo. 27 da.

$450 + $45 (int. 8 mo. 15 da. + 3 mo. + 3 mo. 15 da.) = $495: $495 — $65 = $430: $430 + $64.50 (int. 5 mo. 9 da. + 6 mo. 9 da. + 10 mo. 27 da.) = $494.50: $494.50 — $28 = $466.50, *Ans.*

(11)

1870	5	1	.. $18
1870	1	1	

4 mo.

1870	9	4	.. $20
1870	5	1	

4 mo. 3 da.

1870	12	16	.. $15
1870	9	4	

3 mo. 12 da.

1871	4	10	.. $21
1870	12	16	

3 mo. 24 da.

1871	7	13	.. $118
1871	4	10	$192

3 mo. 3 da.

1871	12	23	.. $324
1871	7	13	

5 mo. 10 da.

1873	10	1	
1871	12	23	

1 yr. 9 mo. 8 da.

$1000

92 = int. 18 mo. 12 da.

1092

192

900

24 = int. 5 mo. 10 da.

924

324

600

63.80 = int. 1 yr. 9 mo. 8 da.

$663.80, *Ans.*

Art. 193.

(1.) Int. $320, 1 yr. @ 6% = $19.20

Amount = $339.20

Amt. of $50, 8 mo. @ 6% = $52.00

Amt. of $100, 1½ mo. @ 6% = 100.75   152.75

Balance due, $186.45, *Ans.*

(2.) Time from March 1, 1877, to Jan. 1, 1878, = 10 mo.

Amt. of $540, 10 mo. @ 8% = $576.00

Amt. of $90, 8 mo.   = $94.80

Amt. of $100, 6 mo.   = 104.00

Amt. of $150, 5 mo.   = 155.00

Amt. of $180, 2 mo. 20 da. = 183.20   537.00

Balance due, $39.00, *Ans.*

DISCOUNT.

Case I.

Art. 196.

1st. *When the note does not bear interest.*

(2.) Days in June, 10   Int. of $1 for 63 da. @

Days in July, 31   6% = $0.0105.

Days in Aug., 19 $100 × .0105 = $1.05

60    $100 − $1.05 = $98.95

To 19th Aug. add 3 da. grace.

Ans. Aug. $^{19}/_{22}$. $1.05, $98.95

(3.) Remaining days in Oct., 19: 30 − 19 = Nov. $^{11}/_{14}$:

int. on $1 33, da. @ 8% = $0.0073+: $120 × .0073+ =

$0.88: $120 − $0.88 = $119.12

Ans. Nov. $^{11}/_{14}$, $0.88, $119.12

(4.) Int. of \$1, 4 mo. 3 da. @ 6% = \$0.0205 : \$140 × .0205 = \$2.87 : \$140 — \$2.87 = \$137.13.

Ans. May $^{15}/_{18}$, \$2.87, \$137.13

(5.) Int. of \$180, 1 yr. @ 4% = \$7.20 : int. of \$180, 6 mo. @ 4% = \$3.60 : int. of \$180, 3 da. @ 4% = \$0.06 : \$3.60 + \$0.06 = \$3.66 : \$180 — \$3.66 = \$176.34

Ans. Oct. $^{10}/_{13}$, \$3.66, \$176.34

(6.) Int. of \$250, 1 yr. @ 8% = \$20.00 : int. of \$250, 5 mo. 3 da. = \$8.50 : \$250 — \$8.50 = \$241.50

Ans. May $^{1}/_{4}$, \$8.50, \$241.50

(7.) Days remaining in Aug., 27, + 3 = Sept. $^{3}/_{6}$: 6% on \$1 for 33 da. = \$0.0055 : \$375 × .0055 = \$2.06 : \$375 — \$2.06 = \$372.94   *Ans.* Sept. $^{3}/_{6}$, \$2.06, \$372.94

(8.) Int. on \$600 for 2 mo. 3 da. = \$9.45 : \$600 — \$9.45 = \$590.55   *Ans.* Apr. $^{12}/_{15}$, \$9.45, \$590.55

(9.) Remaining days in Feb., 8, March, 31, April, 30 = 69 da.: 90 — 69 = May $^{21}/_{24}$. Int. on \$1200, 1 mo. @ 10% = \$10 : for $3\frac{1}{10}$ mo. = \$31 : \$1200 — \$31 = \$1169.

Ans. May $^{21}/_{24}$, \$31, \$1169.

(10.) Int. on \$1, 93 da. @ 6% = \$0.0155 : \$1780 × .0155 = \$27.59 : days remaining in Jan., 20, + 29 (Feb., leap yr.) + 31 (Mar.) = 80 : 90 — 80 = Apr. $^{10}/_{13}$. \$1780 — \$27.59 = \$1752.41   *Ans.* Apr. $^{10}/_{13}$, \$27.59, \$1752.41

(11.) Due Sept. $^{15}/_{18}$, 1877: number of days from May 21 to Sept. 18 = May, 10, June, 30, July, 31, Aug., 31, Sept., 18 = 120: int. on $600 for 120 da. (4 mo.) at 10% = $20: $600 — $20 = $580.

Ans. Sept. $^{15}/_{18}$, 1877, 120 da., $20, $580.

(12.) In May, 23 da., June, 30, July, 31 = 84: 90 — 84 = $^{6}/_{9}$ Aug.: June 8 to Aug. 9 = 48 da. = 1$\frac{3}{5}$ mo.: int. on $1000, 1$\frac{3}{5}$ mo. @ 6% = $8: $1000 — $8 = $992. *Ans.* Aug. $^{6}/_{9}$, 48 da., $8, $992.

(13.) 6 mo. after July 10, 1877, = Jan. $^{10}/_{13}$, 1878: days in Oct., 7*, Nov., 30, Dec., 31, Jan., 13 = 81: 81 da. = 2 mo. 21 da.: int. on $1500 for this time @ 6% = $20.25: $1500 — $20.25 = $1479.75

Ans. Jan. $^{10}/_{13}$, 1878, 81 da., $20.25, $1479.75

2D. *When the note bears interest.*

(2.) 6 mo. from May 20, 1875, = Nov. $^{20}/_{23}$: amt. of $150 @ 6% int. 6, mo. 3 da. = $154.58: Sept. 9 to Nov. 23 = 75 da. or 2$\frac{1}{2}$ mo.: discount on $154.58, 2$\frac{1}{2}$ mo. @ 8% = $2.58: $154.58 — $2.58 = $152.

Ans. Nov. $^{20}/_{23}$, 1875, 75 da., $2.58, $152.

---

* See Rem. 3, page 249, Ray's New Practical Arithmetic.

(3.) 1 yr. from Aug. 5, 1876, = Aug. $^5/_8$, 1877: amt. of $300, 1 yr. 3 da. @ 8% int. = $324.20: Apr. 16 to Aug. 8 = 114 da. or $3\frac{4}{5}$ mo.: discount on $324.20, $3\frac{4}{5}$ mo. at 6% = $6.16: $324.20 — $6.16 = $318.04 = proceeds.

Ans. Aug. $^5/_8$, 1877, 114 da., $6.16, $318.04

(4.)

1878	1	4
1877	3	4
	10 mo.	

$450, 10 mo. @ 6% amounts to $472.50: Aug. 13, 1877, to Jan. 4, 1878, = 144 da. or $4\frac{4}{5}$ mo.: discount on $472.50, $4\frac{4}{5}$ mo. @ 10% = $18.90: $472.50 — $18.90 = $453.60

Ans. Jan. $^1/_4$, 1878, 144 da., $18.90, $453.60

(5.)

1878	9	4
1876	5	16
2	3	18

$650, 2 yr. 3 mo. 18 da. @ 9% = $784.55: Apr. 25, 1878, to Sept. 4, 1878, = 132 da. or $4\frac{2}{5}$ mo.: discount @ 6% on $784.55 for $4\frac{2}{5}$ mo. = $17.26: $784.55 — $17.26 = $767.29 = proceeds.

Ans. Sept. $^1/_4$, 1878, 132 da., $17.26, $767.29

(6.) Amt. of $840, 6 mo. 3 da. @ 10% = $882.70: Dec. 20, 1875, to Mar. 4, 1876 = 75 da. or $2\frac{1}{2}$ mo.: discount on $882.70, $2\frac{1}{2}$ mo. @ 8% = $14.71: $882.70 — $14.71 = $867.99 = proceeds.

Ans. Mar. $^1/_4$, 1876, 75 da., $14.71, $867.99

(7.) 1876   5   4   Amt. of $1400, 9½ mo. @
     1875   7   19   6% = $1466.50 :   Jan. 17,
           9 mo. 15 da.   1876, to May 4, 1876, = 108
                              da. or $3\frac{3}{5}$ mo. : discount on

$1466.50, $3\frac{3}{5}$ mo. @ 10% = $44.00 : $1466.50 — $44.00 =
$1422.50 = proceeds.

Ans. May $^{1}/_{4}$, 1876, 108 da., $44, $1422.50

(8.) 1878   1   4   Amt. of $2400, 1 yr. 2 mo.
     1876   10   16   18 da. @ 8% = $2633.60 :
       1 yr. 2 mo. 18 da.   July 26, 1877, to Jan. 4,
                           1878 = 162 da. or $5\frac{2}{5}$ mo. :

discount on $2633.60, $5\frac{2}{5}$ mo. @ 10% = $118.51 : $2633.60
— $118.51 = $2515.09 = proceeds.

Ans. Jan. $^{1}/_{4}$, 1878, 162 da., $118.51, $2515.09

(9.) Amt. of $3500 @ 6%, 1 yr. 3 da. = $3711.75 :
May 15 to Oct. 18, 1878, = 156 da. or $5\frac{1}{5}$ mo. : discount
on $3711.75, $5\frac{1}{5}$ mo. @ 9% = $144.76 : $3711.75 — $144.76
= $3566.99 = proceeds.

Ans. Oct. $^{15}/_{18}$, 1878, 156 da., $144.76, $3566.99

(10.) Amt. of $6000, 1 yr. 3 da. @ 8% = $6484.00 : Nov.
21, 1875, to May 13, 1876, = 174 da. or $5\frac{4}{5}$ mo. : discount
on $6484, $5\frac{4}{5}$ mo. @ 10% = $313.39 : $6484.00 — $313.39
= $6170.61 = proceeds.

Ans. May $^{10}/_{13}$, 1876, 174 da., $313.39, $6170.61

Art. 197.

(2.) Bank discount on $1, 63 da. @ 6% = $0.0105 :
$1 — $0.0105 = $0.9895 : $197.90 ÷ .9895 = $200, *Ans.*

(3.) Discount on $1, 93 da. @ 6% = $0.0155 : $1 —
$0.0155 = $0.9845 : $393.80 ÷ .9845 = $400, *Ans.*

(4.) Discount on \$1, 5 mo. 3 da. @ 8% = \$0.034: \$1 — \$0.034 = \$0.966: \$217.35 ÷ .966 = \$225, *Ans.*

(5.) Discount on \$1, 4 mo. 3 da. @ 6% = \$0.0205: \$1 — \$0.0205 = \$0.9795: \$352.62 ÷ .9795 = \$360, *Ans.*

(6.) Discount on \$1, 33 da. @ 6% = \$0.0055: \$1 — \$0.0055 = \$0.9945: \$400 ÷ .9945 = \$402.21+, *Ans.*

(7.) Discount on \$1, 2 mo. 3 da. @ 8% = \$0.014: \$1 — \$0.014 = \$0.986: \$500 ÷ .986 = \$507.10 (nearly), *Ans.*

(8.) Discount on \$1, 6 mo. 3 da. @ 10% = \$0.050833+: \$1 — \$0.050833 = \$0.949166: \$1500 ÷ .949166 = \$1580.33+, *Ans.*

(9.) Oct. 12, 1876, to Jan. 4, 1877, = 2 mo. 24 da., or 2⅘ mo.: discount on \$1, 2⅘ mo. @ 6% = \$0.014: \$1 — \$0.014 = \$0.986: \$1055.02 ÷ .986 = \$1070.

1877	1	4	\$1 @ 8% for 10 mo. 15 da. =
1876	2	19	\$0.07: \$1 + \$0.07 = \$1.07: \$1070
	10 mo. 15 da.		÷ 1.07 = \$1000, *Ans.*

Art. 199.

(3.) Amt. of \$1, 2 yr. @ 6% = \$1.12: \$224 ÷ 1.12 = \$200 = present worth: \$224 — \$200 = \$24 = discount.

(4.) Amt. of \$300 for 2 yr. @ 8% = \$348: amt. of \$1 for 2 yr. @ 6% = \$1.12: \$348 ÷ 1.12 = \$310.71 = present worth: \$348 — \$310.71 = \$37.29 = discount.

(5.) Amt. of \$1, 5 yr. 10 mo. @ 6% = \$1.35: \$675 ÷ 1.35 = \$500 = present worth: \$675 — \$500 = \$175 = discount.

(6.) Amt. of \$1, 5 mo. @ 10% = \$1.04166+: \$368.75 ÷ 1.04166 = \$354 = present worth: \$368.75 — \$354 = \$14.75 = discount.

(7.) 1878   1   1   Amt. of $800, 1 yr. 3 mo.
      1876   9   10   21 da. @ 6% = $862.80 :
      ‾‾‾‾‾‾‾‾‾‾‾‾‾   July 19, 1877, to Jan. 1,
         1   3   21   1878 = 5 mo. 12 da. : amt.

of $1, 5 mo. 12 da. @ 10% = $1.045 : $862.80 ÷ 1.045 =
$825.65 = present worth : $862.80 — $825.65 = $37.15 =
discount.

(8.) Amt. of $1, 4 mo. @ 10% = $1.03⅓ : $775 ÷ 1.03⅓
= $750, *Ans.*

(9.) Amt. of $1, 8 mo. @ 6% = $1.04 : $260 ÷ 1.04 =
$250, *Ans.*

(10.) $2480 — its 5% ($124) = $2356 = cash cost. **Amt.**
of $1, 4 mo. @ 10% = $1.03⅓ : $2480 ÷ 1.03⅓ = $2400
present worth. $2400 — $2356 = $44, *Ans.*

(11.) ⅓ of $956.34 = $318.78
Amt. of $1, 1 yr. @ 5% = $1.05 : $318.78 ÷ 1.05 = $303.60
Amt. of $1, 2 yr. @ 5% = $1.10 : $318.78 ÷ 1.10 = 289.80
Amt. of $1, 3 yr. @ 5% = $1.15 : $318.78 ÷ 1.15 = 277.20
                                                 ‾‾‾‾‾‾‾‾
                                        Ans. $870.60

(12.) $535 × .07 = $37.45 = bank discount : $535 ÷ 1.07
= $500 : $535 — $500 = $35 : $37.45 — $35 = $2.45, *Ans.*

(13.) $750—($750 × .04) = $720, cash cost. Amt. of $1
for 3 mo. @ 8% = $1.02 : $750 ÷ $1.02 = $735.29, present
worth : $735.29 — $720 = $15.29, *Ans.*

(14.) ⅓ of $10296 = $3432. Amt. of $1, 1 yr. @ 10%
= $1.10 : amt. of $1, 2 yr. @ 10% = $1.20 : amt. of $1,
3 yr. @ 10% = $1.30.

              $3432 ÷ 1.10 = $3120
              $3432 ÷ 1.20 = 2860
              $3432 ÷ 1.30 = 2640 $8620
              $8620 — $8000 = $620, *Ans.*

(15.) July 4, 1876, to May 1, 1878, $= 1$ yr. 9 mo. 27 da. Amt. of $2000, 1 yr. 9 mo. 27 da. @ $8\% = \$2292$: Oct. 25, 1877, to May 1, 1878, $= 6$ mo. 6 da.: Amt. of $1, 6 mo. 6 da. @ $6\% = \$1.031$: $\$2292 \div 1.031 = \$2223.08 =$ present worth: $\$2292 - \$2223.08 = \$68.92 =$ discount.

EXCHANGE.

Art. 201.

(1.) 1% of $1400 = \$14$: $\frac{1}{2}\% = \$\frac{14}{2} = \$7$: $\$1400 + \$7 = \$1407$, Ans.

(2.) $\frac{1}{2}\%$ of $2580 = \$12.90$: $\$2580 - \$12.90 = \$2567.10$, Ans.

(3.) $\$375.87 = 100\% + \frac{1}{8}\%$ of the face: $\$375.87 \div 100\frac{1}{8} = \$375.40$, Ans.

(4.) $\frac{1}{4}\%$ of $2785 = \$6.96$: $\$2785 - \$6.96 = \$2778.04$, Ans.

(5.) $100\% - 1\frac{1}{4} = 98\frac{3}{4}\% = .9875$: $\$1852.55 \div .9875 = \$1876$, Ans.

(6.) Int. of $5680. for 63 da. @ $6\% = \$59.64$; $\frac{1}{2}\%$ prem. on $5680. = \$28.40$; $\$59.64 - \$28.40 = \$31.24$; $\$5680. - \$31.24 = \$5648.76$, Ans.

(7.) Int. of $1575. for 33 da. @ $6\% = \$8.66$; $\frac{3}{4}\%$ prem. on $1575. = \$11.81$; $\$11.81 - \$8.66 = \$3.15$; $\$1575. + \$3.15 = \$1578.15$, Ans.

(8.) Int. of $2625. for 63 da. @ $6\% = \$27.56$; $1\frac{1}{2}\%$ prem. on $2625. = \$39.37$; $\$39.37 - \$27.56 = \$11.81$; $\$2625. + 11.81 = \$2636.81$, Ans.

Art. 202.

(3.) 8s. $= \frac{4}{10}$£ : £890.4 $\times$ 4.86 ($) $=$ $4327.34, *Ans.*

(4.) $2130.12 $\div$ 4.88 $=$ 436, with 244 rem.: 244 $\times$ 20s., $\div$ 4.88 $=$ 10.   *Ans.* £436 10s.

(5.) 5 fr. 15 centimes $=$ 5\frac{3}{20}$ fr.: 1290 $\div$ 5$\frac{3}{20}$ $=$ $250.49, *Ans.*

(6.) $1657.60 $\times$ 5$\frac{16}{100}$ $=$ 8553 fr. 22, *Ans.*

(7.) $12680 $\div$ 4 $=$ 3170, $\times$ .97 $=$ $3074.90, *Ans.*

(8.) If 4 marks $=$ $0.98, 1 m. $=$ $0.245 : $1470 $\div$ .245 $=$ 6000 m., *Ans.*

INSURANCE.

Art. 204.

(2.) $\frac{3}{4}$ of $5000 $=$ $3750 : $\frac{1}{2}$% of $3750 $=$ $18.75, add $1.50 $=$ $20.25, *Ans.*

(3.) $\frac{2}{3}$ of $12600 $=$ $8400, @ $\frac{3}{4}$% $=$ $63.00
$\frac{1}{2}$ of $14400 $=$ $7200, @ 2% $=$ 144.00
2 policies @ $1.25 $=$ 2.50
Ans. $209.50

(4.) $\frac{4}{7}$ of $21000 $=$ $12000, @ 1$\frac{1}{2}$% $=$ $180.00
$7200 @ $\frac{3}{4}$% $=$ 54.00
2 policies @ $1.25 $=$ 2.50
Ans. $236.50

(5.) $\frac{3}{4}$ of $5600 $=$ $4200, $\times$ .01$\frac{1}{2}$ $=$ $63, $\times$ 20 (yr.) $=$ $1260 : $4200 $-$ $1260 $=$ $2940, *Ans.*

(6.) $3600 $+$ $1600 $+$ $800 $=$ $6000 : $\frac{7}{8}$% of $6000 $=$ $52.50, $+$ $1.25 $=$ $53.75, *Ans.*

(7.) $151.25 — $1.25 = $150: $150 = $1\frac{1}{2}$% of $\frac{2}{3}$ value: $100 = 1% of $\frac{2}{3}$ value: $10000 = 100% of $\frac{2}{3}$ value: $\frac{3}{3}$, or the whole value, = $15000, *Ans.*

(8.) $\frac{4}{5}$ of $4500 = $3600: $32.75 — $1.25 = $31.50: $31.50 ÷ 3600 = .0087$\frac{1}{2}$ = $\frac{7}{8}$%, *Ans.*

(9.) $1000 + $1500 = $2500: $3.50 ÷ 2500 = .0014 = $\frac{7}{50}$%, *Ans.*

Art. 205.

(2.) $105.53 × 10 = $1055.30 = amount paid yearly: $1055.30 × 10 = $10553, *Ans.*

(3.) $47.18 × 8 × 20 = $7548.80: $60.45 × 8 × 20 = $9672.00: $9672 — $7548.80 = $2123.20, *Ans.*

(4.) $36.46 × 12 × 5 = $2187.60: $12000 — $2187.60 = $9812.40, *Ans.*

(5.) 75 yr. — 21 yr. = 54 yr.: $19.89 × 5 × 54 = $5370.30, *Ans.*

(6.) $104.58 × 10 (yr.) = $1045.80 There will be int. @ 6% on $104.58, 10 + 9 + 8 + 7 + 6 + 5 + 4 + 3 + 2 + 1, or 55, yr. = $345.11: $1045.80 + $345.11 = $1390.91, *Ans.*

(7.) $29.15 × 6 = $174.90, × 15 = $2623.50: int. @ 6% on $174.90 for 15 + 14 + 13 + 12 + 11 + 10 + 9 + 8 + 7 + 6 + 5 + 4 + 3 + 2 + 1, or 120, yr. = $1259.28, + $2623.50 = $3882.78, *Ans.*

TAXES.

Art. 208.

(2.) $2500 — $28 = $2472: 2472 ÷ 618000 = .004 *Ans.* 4 mills on $1, or $\frac{2}{5}$%.

(3.) 18409.44 ÷ 2876475 = .0064 = 6.4 mills = *Ans.*

(4.) 656491.61 ÷ 421285359 = .00156 = 1.56 mills = *Ans.*

Art. 209.

[I.] $1.25 × 57 = $71.25 : $1373.64 − $71.25 = $1302.39 :
1302.39 ÷ 748500 = .00174 = rate 1.74 mills on $1.

(2.) $2576 × .00174 = $4.48, + $1.25 (poll-tax) =
$5.73, *Ans.*

(3.) $9265 × .00174 = $16.12, + $3.75 (3 poll-taxes) =
$19.87, *Ans.*

(4.) $4759 × .00174 = $8.28, + $1.25 = $9.53, *Ans.*

(5.) $8367 × .00174 = $14.56, *Ans.*

[II.] 64375 ÷ 16869758 = .003816.   Rate 3.816 mills
on $1.

TAX TABLE.—Rate, 3.816 mills on $1.

PROP.	TAX.	PROP.	TAX.	PROP.	TAX.	PROP.	TAX.
$1	$0.004	$10	$0.038	$100	$0.382	$1000	$3.816
2	.008	20	.076	200	.763	2000	7.632
3	.011	30	.114	300	1.145	3000	11.448
4	.015	40	.153	400	1.526	4000	15.264
5	.019	50	.191	500	1.908	5000	19.080
6	.023	60	.229	600	2.290	6000	22.896
7	.027	70	.267	700	2.671	7000	26.712
8	.030	80	.305	800	3.053	8000	30.528
9	.034	90	.343	900	3.434	9000	34.344

(1.) $56875 × .003816 = $217.04, *Ans.*

(2.) $27543 × .003816 = $105.10, *Ans.*

(3.) $83612 × .003816 = $319.06, *Ans.*

(4.) $72968 × .003816 = $278.45, *Ans.*

(5.) $69547 × .003816 = $265.39, *Ans.*

Art. 211.

(1.) 36 sq. mi. contain 23040 A.: 23040 A. @ $1.25 per acre = $28800, *Ans.*

(2.) The charge will be the same as for 3 half-ounces. 3 times 3 ct. = 9 ct., *Ans.*

(3.) 1 lb. 5 oz. = 21 oz.: postage same as for 22 oz.: $22 \div 2 = 11$: 11 times 1 ct. = 11 ct., *Ans.*

(4.) 70 ct. times 40 = $28, *Ans.*

(5.) $5 = 500 ct.: $\frac{500}{1000}$ ct. = $\frac{1}{2}$ ct., *Ans.*

(6.) 30000 bl. @ $1   = $30000
    250 ret. dlrs. @ $20 ea.   =   5000
    12 wholesale dlrs. @ $50 =   600
                               $35600, *Ans.*

Art. 212.

(1.) $12\frac{1}{2}\%$ = $\frac{1}{8}$: 1760 lb. — its $\frac{1}{8}$ = 1540 lb.: 1540 times $0.01\frac{3}{4}$ = $26.95, *Ans.*

(2.) 40 bales of 400 lb. each = 16000 lb.: 5% tare = 800 lb.: 16000 − 800 = 15200: 15200 lb. @ 45 ct. = $6840: 10% ad. val. = $684: 15200 lb. @ 9 ct. duty = $1368: $684 + $1368 = $2052, *Ans.*

(3.) 365.15 fr. + 57.15 fr. = 422.30 fr., to which add 5% com. (21.1150 fr.) = 443.4150 fr.: $443.4150 \times 19\frac{3}{10}$ (ct.) = $85.58: 40% of $86 = $34.40, *Ans.*

(4.) 1317.04 mk. + 34.36 mk. = 1351.40 mk.: add 6% com. (81.084 mk.) = 1432.484 mk.: 1432.484×23.8 (ct.) = $340.93: 25% of $341 = $85.25, *Ans.*

(5.) 50 ct. per lb. duty on 1500 lb. = \$750 : £8 4s. 6d. = £8$\frac{9}{40}$ or £8.225 : £500 + £8.225 = £508.225 : add 2½% com. (£12.705+) = £520.93 : £520.93 × 4.8665 (\$) = \$2535.11 : 35% of \$2535 = \$887.25 : \$887.25 + \$750 = \$1637.25, *Ans.*

RATIO.

Art. 214.

(20.) $\frac{7}{2} \times \frac{4}{9} = \frac{14}{9} = 1\frac{5}{9}$, *Ans.*

(21.) $\frac{35}{6} \times \frac{3}{7} = \frac{5}{2} = 2\frac{1}{2}$, *Ans.*

(22.) $\frac{69}{10} \times \frac{5}{23} = \frac{3}{2} = 1\frac{1}{2}$, *Ans.*

(28.) 5 yd. 1 ft. = 192 in. : 5 ft. 4 in. = 64 in. : $\frac{192}{64}$ = 3, *Ans.*

Art. 215.

(8.) 4 lb. 8 oz. = 72 oz. : $\frac{7}{8}$ of 72 oz. = 63 oz. : 63 oz. = 3 lb. 15 oz., *Ans.*

(9.) \$4.00 × 2.6 = \$10.40, *Ans.*

Art. 216.

(3.) 42 × $\frac{10}{7}$ = 60, *Ans.*

(4.) $23\frac{3}{8} = \frac{187}{8}$: $\frac{187}{8} \times \frac{4}{11} = \frac{17}{2} = 8\frac{1}{2}$, *Ans.*

(5.) $7\frac{5}{9} = \frac{68}{9}$: \$27.20 × $\frac{9}{68}$ = \$0.40 × 9 = \$3.60, *Ans.*

Art. 217.

(2.) $\left.\begin{array}{l} 5 \times 6 = 30 \\ 10 \times 9 = 90 \end{array}\right\}$ 90 ÷ 30 = 3, *Ans.*

(3.)   2

$\begin{array}{c|c} \cancel{6\frac{1}{4}} & \cancel{12\frac{1}{2}} \\ \cancel{8\frac{1}{3}} & \cancel{33\frac{1}{3}} \end{array}$ 4 × 2 = 8, *Ans.*

4

(4.) $\frac{1}{2} \times \frac{5}{4} = \frac{5}{8}$: $\frac{2}{3} \times \frac{3}{4} = \frac{6}{12} = \frac{1}{2}$: $\frac{\frac{1}{2}}{\frac{5}{8}} = \frac{8}{10} = \frac{4}{5}$, *Ans.*

(5.) $2 \times 24 = 48$: $8 \times 12 = 96$: $96 \div 48 = 2$, *Ans.*

(6.) $2.25 \mid 6.75 \quad 3$
      $3 \mid 6 \quad\quad 2 \quad\quad 3 \times 2 = 6$, *Ans.*

(7.) $2 \mid 5$
     $3 \mid 7 \quad \frac{7 \times 3}{2} = \frac{21}{2} = 10\frac{1}{2}$, *Ans.*
     $5 \mid 9$
        3

Art. 219.

(2.) Divide by 5.   (5.) Divide by 19.

(3.) Divide by 10.   (6.) Divide by 25.

(4.) Divide by 17.   (7.) Divide by 31.

Art. 220.

(2.) $3\frac{3}{4} : 4\frac{2}{5}$ (3.) $7\frac{1}{2} : 10\frac{2}{3}$
        20 6
   $\overline{75 : 88}$, *Ans.* $\overline{45 : \;\; 64}$, *Ans.*

(4.) $\frac{5}{6} = \frac{15}{18}$: $\frac{7}{9} = \frac{14}{18}$. $15 : 14$, *Ans.*

(5.) $\frac{63}{10} = \frac{189}{30}$: $9\frac{7}{15} = \frac{142}{15} = \frac{284}{30}$. $189 : 284$, *Ans.*

PROPORTION.

Art. 223.

(3.) 4 (4.) 2
   $\dfrac{8 \times 6}{2} = 24$, *Ans.* $\dfrac{7 \times 10}{5} = 14$, *Ans.*

(5.) 3
   $\dfrac{8 \times 6}{\underset{2}{16}} = 3$, *Ans.*   (6.) 2
                         $\dfrac{5 \times 12}{6} = 10$, *Ans.*

(7.)
$$\frac{3 \times \overset{2}{\cancel{14}}}{\cancel{7}} = 6, \; Ans.$$

(8.)
$$\frac{\overset{2}{\cancel{14}} \times 9}{\cancel{7}} = 18. \; Ans.$$

(9.)
$$\frac{2 \times \overset{2}{\cancel{8}} \times \overset{5}{\cancel{45}}}{\cancel{4} \times \cancel{9}} = 20, \; Ans.$$

(10.)
$$\frac{\overset{2}{\cancel{8}} \times \overset{2}{\cancel{10}} \times 3 \times 7}{\cancel{5} \times \cancel{4} \times \underset{2}{\cancel{4}}} = 21, \; Ans.$$

(11.)
$$\frac{\overset{5}{\cancel{10}} \times \overset{2}{\cancel{14}} \times \overset{3}{\cancel{33}} \times \overset{3}{\cancel{39}}}{\underset{3}{\cancel{21}} \times \underset{2}{\cancel{22}} \times \underset{2}{\cancel{26}}} = 15, \; Ans.$$

(12.) $\dfrac{3}{\cancel{4}} \times \dfrac{\cancel{4}}{5} = \frac{3}{5} : \; \frac{3}{5} \times \frac{3}{2} = \frac{9}{10}, \; Ans.$

(13.)
$$\frac{3}{\cancel{5}} \times \frac{\cancel{5}}{4} = \frac{3}{4} : \; \frac{\overset{}{\cancel{3}}}{\underset{2}{\cancel{4}}} \times \frac{\overset{5}{\cancel{10}}}{\underset{3}{\cancel{9}}} = \frac{5}{6}, \; Ans.$$

(14.)
$$\frac{\overset{7}{\cancel{14}}}{\cancel{3}} \times \frac{\overset{5}{\cancel{15}}}{\cancel{2}} = 35 : \; \frac{\overset{5}{\cancel{35}}}{1} \times \frac{2}{\underset{3}{\cancel{21}}} = \frac{10}{3} = 3\frac{1}{3}, \; Ans.$$

(15.) $\frac{6 \times 6}{4} = 9, \; Ans.$

Art. 224.

(3.) 6 : 12 : : 3 : ?
$$\frac{\overset{2}{\cancel{12}} \times 3}{\cancel{6}} = 6, \; Ans.$$

(4.) 3 : 6 : : $8 : ?
$$\frac{\overset{2}{\cancel{6}} \times 8}{\cancel{3}} = \$16, \; Ans.$$

(5.) $5 : 3 : : \$30 : ?$ $\dfrac{3 \times \overset{6}{\cancel{30}}}{\cancel{5}} = \$18,$ *Ans.*

(6.) 3 lb. 12 oz. = 60 oz.: 11 lb. 4 oz. = 180 oz.

$60 : 180 : : \$3.50 : ?$ $\dfrac{\overset{3}{\cancel{180}} \times 3.50}{\cancel{60}} = \$10.50,$ *Ans.*

(7.) 2 lb. 8 oz. = 40 oz. $\$2 : \$5 : : 40$ oz. : ?

$\dfrac{5 \times \overset{20}{\cancel{40}}}{\cancel{2}} = 100$ oz. = 6 lb. 4 oz., *Ans.*

(8.) $4 : 10 : : \$14 : ?$ $\dfrac{\overset{5}{\cancel{10}} \times \overset{7}{\cancel{14}}}{\cancel{\underset{\cancel{2}}{4}}} = \$35,$ *Ans.*

(9.) $3 : 11 : : 69$ ct. : ? $\dfrac{11 \times \overset{23}{\cancel{69}}}{\cancel{3}} = \$2.53,$ *Ans.*

(10.) $4 : 9 : : \$7 : ?$ $\dfrac{9 \times 7}{4} = \dfrac{63}{4} = \$15.75,$ *Ans.*

(11.) $8 : 12 : : \$32 : ?$ $\dfrac{12 \times \overset{4}{\cancel{32}}}{\cancel{8}} = \$48,$ *Ans.*

(12.) $12 : 8 : : \$48 : ?$ $\dfrac{\overset{4}{\cancel{48}} \times 8}{\cancel{12}} = \$32,$ *Ans.*

(13.) $\$32 : \$48 : : 8 : ?$ $\dfrac{\overset{12}{\cancel{48}} \times 8}{\underset{\cancel{4}}{\cancel{32}}} = 12$ yd., *Ans.*

(14.) $48 : $32 : : 12 : ? $\dfrac{\overset{8}{\cancel{32} \times \cancel{12}}}{\underset{4}{\cancel{48}}} = 8$ yd., *Ans.*

(15.) 19 : 4 : : $152 : ? $\dfrac{4 \times \overset{8}{\cancel{152}}}{\cancel{19}} = \$32$, *Ans.*

(16.) 12 : 8 : : 24 : ? $\dfrac{8 \times \overset{2}{\cancel{24}}}{\cancel{12}} = 16$ da., *Ans.*

(17.) 2 : 8 : : 60 : ? $\dfrac{\overset{4}{\cancel{8}} \times 60}{\cancel{2}} = 240$ men, *Ans.*

(18.) 6 lb. = 96 oz.   15 : 96 : : 25 ct. : ?

$\dfrac{\overset{32}{\cancel{96}} \times \overset{5}{\cancel{25}}}{\underset{3}{\cancel{15}}} = \$1.60$, *Ans.*

(19.) 6 : 26 : : $2.70 : ? $\dfrac{26 \times \overset{.45}{\cancel{2.70}}}{\cancel{6}} = \$11.70$, *Ans.*

(20.) 585 lb. : 3525 lb. : : $42.12 : ?

$\dfrac{\overset{705}{\cancel{3525}} \times \overset{.36}{\cancel{42.12}}}{\underset{117}{\cancel{585}}} = \$253.80$, *Ans.*

(21.) $\frac{3}{2}$: $\frac{9}{8}$: : $2.50 : ? $\dfrac{\overset{3}{\cancel{9}} \times 2.50}{\underset{4}{\cancel{8}}} \times \dfrac{\cancel{2}}{\cancel{3}} = \$1.87\frac{1}{2}$, *Ans.*

(22.) $90 : 450 : : 6 : ?$ $\dfrac{\cancel{450} \times \cancel{6}}{\cancel{90}} = 30$ da., *Ans.*

(23.) $5 : 15 : : 6 : ?$ $\dfrac{\cancel{15} \times 6}{\cancel{5}} = 18$ men, *Ans.*

(24.) $30 : 140 : : 15 : ?$ $\dfrac{\cancel{140} \times \cancel{15}}{\cancel{30}} = 70$ bu., *Ans.*

(25.) 325 lb. $: 1625$ lb. $: : \$22.60 : ?$

$$\dfrac{\cancel{1625} \times 22.60}{\cancel{325}} = \$113.00, \text{ } Ans.$$

(26.) $4\frac{1}{2}$ ft. $: 180$ ft. $: : 3$ ft. $: ?$

$180 \times 3 = 540; \quad \dfrac{\cancel{540}}{1} \times \dfrac{2}{\cancel{9}} = 120$ ft., *Ans.*

(27.) $12 : 9 : : 60 : ?$ $\dfrac{9 \times \cancel{60}}{\cancel{12}} = 45$ da., *Ans.*

(28.) $100 : 60 : : 2200 : ?$ $\frac{2200 \times 60}{100} = \$1320,$ A's. $\Big\}$ *Ans.*
$ 100 : 60 : : 1800 : ?$ $\frac{1800 \times 60}{100} = \$1080,$ B's.

(29.) $\$800.30 + \$250 + \$375.10 + \$500 + \$115 = \$2040.40.$ $\$2040.40 : \$612.12 : : \$1.00 : ?$
$\$612.12 \div 2040.40 = \$0.30, $ *Ans.*

(30.) \$6 : \$8 : : 9 oz. : ? $\dfrac{\overset{4}{\cancel{8}} \times \overset{3}{\cancel{9}}}{\underset{2}{\cancel{6}}} = 12$ oz., *Ans.*

(31.) \$300 : \$250 : : 6 mo. : ? $\dfrac{\overset{5}{\cancel{250}} \times \cancel{6}}{\underset{6}{\cancel{300}}} = 5$ mo., *Ans.*

(32.) $27 \times 7 = 189$; $36 - 27 = 9.$
9 mi. : 189 mi. : : 1 da. : ? $\quad \frac{189}{9} = 21$ da., *Ans.*

(33.) 9 hr. : 12 hr. : : \$15$\frac{2}{3}$: ? $= $20.88\frac{8}{9}$, or 1 mo.'s
services when he works 12 hr. a day.
\$20.88$\frac{8}{9} \times 4\frac{2}{5} = $91.91\frac{1}{9}$, *Ans.*

(34.) As 5 lb. : $\frac{3}{4}$ lb. : : \$$\frac{5}{8}$: \$$\frac{3}{32}$, *Ans.*

(35.) As 6 yd. : $7\frac{3}{8}$ yd. : : \$$5\frac{3}{5}$: \$$6\frac{53}{60}$, *Ans.*

(36.) As $\frac{1}{3}$ bu. : $\frac{1}{2}$ bu. : : \$$\frac{3}{8}$: \$$\frac{9}{16}$, *Ans.* $(\frac{3}{1} \times \frac{1}{2} \times \frac{3}{8} = \frac{9}{16}.)$

(37.) As $1\frac{3}{4}$ yd. : 2 yd. : : \$$\frac{7}{24}$: \$$\frac{1}{3}$, *Ans.* $(\frac{4}{7} \times \frac{2}{1} \times \frac{7}{24} = \frac{1}{3}.)$

(38.) As \$$29\frac{3}{4}$: \$$31\frac{1}{4}$: : $59\frac{1}{2}$ yd. : ? By cancellation,
$\frac{4}{119} \times \frac{125}{4} \times \frac{119}{2} = \frac{125}{2} = 62\frac{1}{2}$ yd., *Ans.*

(39.) As .85 gal. : .25 gal. : : \$1.36 : \$0.40, *Ans.*

(40.) As 61.3 lb. : 1.08 lb. : : \$44.9942 : \$0.79, *Ans.*

(41.) As $\frac{5}{7}$ yd. : $\frac{9}{11}$ yd. : : \$$\frac{3}{5}$: \$$\frac{189}{275}$, *Ans.*

(42.) As $\frac{3}{7}$ yd. : $17\frac{3}{8}$ yd. : : \$$4\frac{2}{5}$: ?
$\frac{7}{3} \times \frac{139}{8} \times \frac{22}{5} = $178.38\frac{1}{3}$, *Ans.*

(43.) As 26 cogs : 35 cogs : : 1 rev. : $1\frac{9}{26}$ rev. Hence,
the smaller wheel gains $\frac{9}{26}$ of a revolution in each revolu-
tion of the larger wheel. Then, $\frac{9}{26}$ rev : 10 rev. : : 1
rev. of larger : $28\frac{8}{9}$ revolutions of larger, *Ans.*

(44.) 1 gal. = 32 gills; 32 — 1 = 31. As 32 : 31 : : 100 gal. : 96⅞ gal., *Ans.*

(45.) As 70 p. : 20 p. : : 60 sec. : 17⅐ sec.
1142 ft. × 17⅐ = 19577⅐ ft. = 3 mi. 226 rd. 2 yd. 2⅐ ft., *Ans.*

(46.) As 25 ft. : 25 ft. 5.25 in. : : 643 ft. 8 in. : 654 ft. 11.17 in., *Ans.*

Art. 225.

(3.) 2 da. : 10 da. $\left.\right\}$: : 24 mi. : 240 mi., *Ans.*
    4 hr. : 8 hr.

(4.) As 18 rd. : 72 rd.   The more rods, the more men.
And as 8 da. : 12 da.   The less days, the more men.
       : : 16 men : 96 men, *Ans.*

[dollars.
(5.) As 6 p.   : 15 p.   The more persons, the more
                                 [dollars.
  8 mo. : 20 mo.   The more months, the more
    : : $150 : $937.50, *Ans.*

(6.) As 7 da. : 9 da.   The more days, the more miles.
    6 hr. : 11 hr.   The more hours, the more mi.
    : : 217 mi. : 511½ mi., *Ans.*

(7.) As $100 : $75.   The less dollars, the less interest.
    12 mo. : 9 mo.   The less months, the less interest.
    : : $6 : $3.375, *Ans.*

(8.) As 10100 lb. : 100 lb.   The more lb., the less miles.
    20 ct. : $60.60   The more money, the more
    : : 20 mi. : 60 mi., *Ans.*   [miles.

(9.) As 12 cwt. 75 lb. : 10 T.   The more weight, the
                         more money.
    400 mi. : 75 mi.   The less miles, the less
                        money.
    : : $57.12 : $168, *Ans.*

(10.) As 20 men : 18 men.   The more men, the less days.

40 rd. l. : 87 rd. l.   The more length, the more days.

5 ft. h. : 8 ft. h.   The more height, the more days.

4 ft. t. : 5 ft. t.   The more thickness, the more days.

: : 15 days : $58\frac{29}{40}$ days, *Ans.*

(11.) As 100 men : 180 men.   The less men, the more days.

200 yd. l. : 180 yd. l.   The less length, the less days.

3 yd. w. :   4 yd. w.   The more width, the more days.

2 yd. d. :   3 yd. d.   The more depth, the more days.

8 hr. :   10 hr.   The less hours, the more days.

: :   6 days : 24.3 days, *Ans.*

Art. 226.

(2.) $\frac{300}{800} = \frac{3}{8}$; $\frac{3}{8}$ of $232 = $87, A's share.
$\frac{500}{800} = \frac{5}{8}$; $\frac{5}{8}$ of $232 = $145, B's share.

(3.) $70 + $150 + $80 = $300, whole stock.
$\frac{70}{300} = \frac{7}{30}$; $\frac{7}{30}$ of $120 = $28, A's share.
$\frac{150}{300} = \frac{1}{2}$; $\frac{1}{2}$ of $120 = $60, B's share.
$\frac{80}{300} = \frac{4}{15}$; $\frac{4}{15}$ of $120 = $32, C's share.

(4.) $200 + $400 + $600 = $1200, whole stock. $\frac{200}{1200} = \frac{1}{6}$, $\frac{400}{1200} = \frac{1}{3}$, $\frac{600}{1200} = \frac{1}{2}$. $\frac{1}{6}$ of $427.26 = $71.21, A's share; $\frac{1}{3}$ of $427.26 = $142.42, B's share; and $\frac{1}{2}$ of $427.26 = $213.63, C's share.

(5.) $1 + 3 + 5 = 9$. $\frac{1}{9}$ of \$90 = \$10; $\frac{3}{9} = \frac{1}{3}$ of \$90 = \$30; $\frac{5}{9}$ of \$90 = \$50, *Ans.*

(6.) $2 + 3 + 5 + 7 = 17$. $\frac{2}{17}$ of \$735.93 = \$86.58; $\frac{3}{17}$ of \$735.93 = \$129.87; $\frac{5}{17}$ of \$735.93 = \$216.45; $\frac{7}{17}$ of \$735.93 = \$303.03, *Ans.*

(7.) $3 + 6 + 9 + 11 + 13 + 17 = 59$.
$\frac{3}{59}$ of \$22361 = \$1137; $\frac{6}{59}$ of \$22361 = \$2274;
$\frac{9}{59}$ of \$22361 = \$3411; $\frac{11}{59}$ of \$22361 = \$4169;
$\frac{13}{59}$ of \$22361 = \$4927; $\frac{17}{59}$ of \$22361 = \$6443, *Ans.*

(8.) $\frac{1}{3}$, $\frac{3}{5}$, $\frac{7}{8} = \frac{40}{120}$, $\frac{72}{120}$, $\frac{105}{120}$. Since the denominators are the same, the fractions are to each other as their numerators. $40 + 72 + 105 = 217$. $\frac{40}{217}$ of \$692.23 = \$127.60; $\frac{72}{217}$ of \$692.23 = \$229.68; $\frac{105}{217}$ of \$692.23 = \$334.95, *Ans.*

Art. 227.

(1.) \$175 + \$500 + \$600 + \$210 + \$42.50 + \$20 + \$10 = \$1557.50

As \$1557.50 : \$175 : : \$934.50 : \$105.00, A's share.
As \$1557.50 : \$500 : : \$934.50 : \$300.00, B's share.
As \$1557.50 : \$600 : : \$934.50 : \$360.00, C's share.
As \$1557.50 : \$210 : : \$934.50 : \$126.00, D's share.
As \$1557.50 : \$42.50 : : \$934.50 : \$25.50, E's share.
As \$1557.50 : \$20 : : \$934.50 : \$12.00, F's share.
As \$1557.50 : \$10 : : \$934.50 : \$6.00, G's share.

(2.) \$234 + \$175 + \$326 = \$735; \$492.45 ÷ 735 = \$0.67 = sum paid on each dollar of indebtedness. \$234 × .67 = \$156.78, A; \$175 × .67 = \$117.25, B; \$326 × .67 = \$218.42, C.

(3.) \$25000 — \$4650 = \$20350.
37000 : 20350 : : \$1 : \$0.55, *Ans.*

Art. 228.

(1.) $\frac{48}{108} = \frac{4}{9}$; $\frac{36}{108} = \frac{1}{3}$; $\frac{24}{108} = \frac{2}{9}$. $\frac{4}{9}$ of $45 = 20$, A's loss: $\frac{1}{3}$ of $45 = 15$, B's loss: $\frac{2}{9}$ of $45 = 10$, C's loss.

(2.) $10000 + $15000 = 25000. $1125 \div 25000 = .04\frac{1}{2} = 4\frac{1}{2}\%$, gen. av. $2150 \times .04\frac{1}{2} = 96.75, A's loss.

Art. 229.

(3.) $23 \times 27 = 621$; $21 \times 39 = 819$; $621 + 819 = 1440$. $\frac{621}{1440} = \frac{69}{160}$; $\frac{819}{1440} = \frac{91}{160}$; $\frac{69}{160}$ of $54 = $23.28\frac{3}{4}$, A pays; $\frac{91}{160}$ of $54 = $30.71\frac{1}{4}$, B pays.

(4.) $300 \times 5 = 1500; $400 \times 8 = 3200; $500 \times 3 = 1500. $1500 + $3200 + $1500 = 6200. $\frac{1500}{6200} = \frac{15}{62}$; $\frac{3200}{6200} = \frac{16}{31}$. $\frac{15}{62}$ of $100 = $24.19\frac{11}{31}$, A's and C's loss; $\frac{16}{31}$ of $100 = $51.61\frac{9}{31}$, B's loss.

(5.) $6 \times 30 = 180$: $5 \times 40 = 200$: $8 \times 28 = 224$. $180 + 200 + 224 = 604$; $\frac{180}{604} = \frac{45}{151}$; $\frac{200}{604} = \frac{50}{151}$; $\frac{224}{604} = \frac{56}{151}$. $\frac{45}{151}$ of $18.12 = 5.40, A: $\frac{50}{151}$ of $18.12 = 6, B: $\frac{56}{151}$ of $18.12 = 6.72, C.

(6.) A, $300 \times 8 = 2400; $300 + $100 = 400;
$400 \times 8 = 3200. $2400 + $3200 = 5600

B, $600 \times 10 = 6000; $600 - $300 = 300;
$300 \times 6 = 1800. $6000 + $1800 = \overline{$7800}$
$$\overline{\$13400}$$

As $13400 : $5600 : : $442.20 : 184.80, A's.
$13400 : $7800 : : $442.20 : 257.40, B's.

(7.) $800 \times 12 = 9600; $500 \times 12 = 6000: 12 mo. $- 7$ mo. $= 5$ mo. $9600 - $6000 = 3600; $3600 \div 5 = 720, *Ans.*

Art. 230.

(2)	(3)
$2 \times 4 = 8	$8 \times 5 = 40
$6 \times 8 = \underline{48}$	$4 \times 8 = \underline{32}$
$8)\ \ \overline{\$56}$(7 mo., *Ans.*	$12)\ \ \overline{\$72}$(6 mo., *Ans.*

(4)	(5)
$250×2=$500	$100× 6=$600
500×5=2500	75× 8= 600
750×8=6000	125×12=1500
$1500) $9000(6 mo., *Ans.*	$300) $2700(9 mo., *Ans.*

(6)

$\frac{1}{5}$ of $200 = $40	$40 × 0 = 0
$\frac{2}{5}$ of $200 = $80	80 × 5 = $400
	80 × 10 = 800
	$200) $1200(6 mo., *Ans.*

Art. 231.

(2.) Counting from April 2d, it is 90 days to the first payment, and 150 days to the second.

$200 × 90 = $18000
 300 × 150 = 45000

$500) $63000(126 da. from April 2d = Aug. 6th, *Ans.*

(3.) Counting from July 6, when first bill is due,

$1250× 0 =   0
 4280× 73 = 312440
  675×168 = 113400

$6205) $425840(68.6+

Counting 69 days from July 6th, brings the time to Sept. 13, *Ans.*

Art. 232.

(2)	(3)
6 lb. at 3 ct. = 18 ct.	25 lb. at 12 ct. = $3.00
4 lb. at 8 ct. = 32 ct.	25 lb. at 18 ct. = 4.50
10 lb. cost 50 ct.	40 lb. at 25 ct. = 10.00
50 ct. ÷ 10 = 5 ct., *Ans.*	90 lb. cost $17.50
	$17.50 ÷ 90 = 0.19\frac{4}{9}$, *Ans.*

(4)

3 gal. cost	$0.00
12 gal. at 50 ct. =	6.00
15 gal. cost	$6.00

$6.00 ÷ 15 = $0.40, *Ans.*

(5)

10 at $3 =	$30.00
12 at 4 =	48.00
8 at 9 =	72.00
30 worth	$150.00

$150 ÷ 30 = $5, *Ans.*

(6)

6 to 10 =	4 hr.	63° × 4 = 252°
10 to 1 =	3 "	70° × 3 = 210°
1 to 3 =	2 "	75° × 2 = 150°
3 to 7 =	4 "	73° × 4 = 292°
7 to 6 =	11 "	55° × 11 = 605°
	24)	1509°(62$\frac{7}{8}$°, *Ans.*

INVOLUTION.

Art. 234.

(2.) $65 \times 65 = 4225$, *Ans.*

(3.) $25 \times 25 \times 25 = 15625$, *Ans.*

(4.) $12 \times 12 \times 12 \times 12 = 20736$, *Ans.*

(5.) $10 \times 10 \times 10 \times 10 \times 10 = 100000$, *Ans.*

(6.) $9 \times 9 \times 9 \times 9 \times 9 \times 9 = 531441$, *Ans.*

(7.) $2 \times 2 \times 2 \times 2 \times 2 \times 2 \times 2 \times 2 = 256$, *Ans.*

(8.) $\frac{2}{3} \times \frac{2}{3} = \frac{4}{9}$, *Ans.*   (9.) $\frac{3}{4} \times \frac{3}{4} \times \frac{3}{4} = \frac{27}{64}$, *Ans.*

(10.) $\frac{4}{5} \times \frac{4}{5} \times \frac{4}{5} \times \frac{4}{5} = \frac{256}{625}$, *Ans.*

(11.) $\frac{2}{3} \times \frac{2}{3} \times \frac{2}{3} \times \frac{2}{3} \times \frac{2}{3} = \frac{32}{243}$, *Ans.*

(12.) $16\frac{1}{2} = \frac{33}{2}$. $\frac{33}{2} \times \frac{33}{2} = \frac{1089}{4} = 272\frac{1}{4}$, *Ans.*

(13.) $12\frac{1}{2} = \frac{25}{2}$. $\frac{25}{2} \times \frac{25}{2} \times \frac{25}{2} = \frac{15625}{8} = 1953\frac{1}{8}$, *Ans.*

(14.) $.25 \times .25 \times .25 \times .25 = .00390625$, *Ans.*

(15.) $14 \times 14 \times 14 = 2744$, *Ans.*

(16.) $19 \times 19 \times 19 \times 19 = 130321$, *Ans.*

(17.) $2\frac{1}{3} = \frac{7}{3}$. $\frac{7}{3} \times \frac{7}{3} \times \frac{7}{3} \times \frac{7}{3} \times \frac{7}{3} = \frac{16807}{243} = 69\frac{40}{243}$, *Ans*

Art. 238.   **EVOLUTION**.

(5)
$$\overset{\cdot\ \cdot}{529}(20 + 3 = 23, Ans.$$

$$
\begin{array}{r}
400 \\
\hline
20\overline{)129} \\
2 \\
\hline
40 \\
3 \\
\hline
43\overline{)129}
\end{array}
$$

(6)
$$\overset{\cdot\ \cdot}{625}(25, Ans.$$

$$
\begin{array}{r}
4 \\
\hline
45)225 \\
225 \\
\hline
\end{array}
$$

(7)
$$\overset{\cdot\ \cdot}{6561}(81, Ans.$$

$$
\begin{array}{r}
64 \\
\hline
161)161 \\
161 \\
\hline
\end{array}
$$

(10)
$$\overset{\cdot\ \ \ \ \cdot}{1679616}(1296,$$
$$Ans$$

$$
\begin{array}{r}
1 \\
\hline
22)67 \\
44 \\
\hline
249)2396 \\
2241 \\
\hline
2586)15516 \\
15516 \\
\hline
\end{array}
$$

(8)
$$\overset{\cdot\ \ \cdot}{56644}(238, Ans.$$

$$
\begin{array}{r}
4 \\
\hline
43)166 \\
129 \\
\hline
468)3744 \\
3744 \\
\hline
\end{array}
$$

(9)
$$\overset{\cdot\ \ \cdot}{390625}(625, Ans.$$

$$
\begin{array}{r}
36 \\
\hline
122)306 \\
244 \\
\hline
1245)6225 \\
6225 \\
\hline
\end{array}
$$

(12)
$$\overset{\cdot\ \ \cdot\ \ \cdot}{43046721}(6561, Ans.$$

$$
\begin{array}{r}
36 \\
\hline
125)704 \\
625 \\
\hline
1306)7967 \\
7836 \\
\hline
13121)13121 \\
13121 \\
\hline
\end{array}
$$

(11)
$$\overset{\cdot\ \ \cdot\ \ \cdot}{5764801}(2401,$$
$$Ans.$$

$$
\begin{array}{r}
4 \\
\hline
44)176 \\
176 \\
\hline
4801)4801 \\
4801 \\
\hline
\end{array}
$$

(13)
$$\overset{\cdot\ \ \cdot\ \ \cdot\ \ \cdot}{987656329}(31427,$$
$$Ans.$$

$$
\begin{array}{r}
9 \\
\hline
61)87 \\
61 \\
\hline
624)2665 \\
2496 \\
\hline
6282)16963 \\
12564 \\
\hline
62847)439929 \\
439929 \\
\hline
\end{array}
$$

(14)
$\overset{\cdot\;\cdot\;\cdot}{289442169}$(17013,
1   *Ans.*
27)189
   189
3401)4421
     3401
34023)102069
      102069

(15)
$\overset{\cdot\;\cdot\;\cdot}{234.09}$(15.3,
1   *Ans.*
25)134
   125
303)909
    909

(16)
$\overset{\cdot\;\cdot}{145.2025}$(12.05,
1   *Ans.*
22)45
   44
2405)12025
     12025

(17)
$\overset{\cdot\;\cdot\;\cdot}{915.0625}$(30.25, *Ans.*
9
692)1506
    1204
6045)30225
     30225

(18)
$\overset{\cdot\;\cdot}{.0196}$(.14, *Ans.*
1
24)96
   96

(19)
$\overset{\cdot\;\cdot\;\cdot\;\cdot}{1.008016}$(1.004, *Ans.*
1
2004)008016
     8016

(20)
$\overset{\cdot\;\cdot}{.00822649}$(.0907, *Ans.*
81
1807)12649
     12649

(21.) $\sqrt{25} = 5$, $\sqrt{729} = 27$; $\sqrt{\frac{25}{729}} = \frac{5}{27}$, *Ans.*

(22.) $\frac{847}{1183} = \frac{121}{169}$; $\sqrt{121} = 11$, $\sqrt{169} = 13$; *Ans.* $= \frac{11}{13}$.

(23.) $30\frac{1}{4} = \frac{121}{4}$; $\sqrt{\frac{121}{4}} = \frac{11}{2} = 5\frac{1}{2}$, *Ans.*

	(24)
10(3.162277+,	
9	*Ans.*

```
61)100
   61
626)3900
   3756
6322)14400
   12644
63242)175600
    126484
632447)4911600
     4427129
6324547)48447100
      44271829
```

	(25)
2(1.41421+,	
1	*Ans.*

```
24)100
   96
281)400
   281
2824)11900
   11296
28282)60400
   56564
282841)383600
    282841
```

	(27)
$6\frac{2}{5} = 6.4(2.5298+,$	
4	*Ans.*

```
45)240
   225
502)1500
   1004
5049)49600
   45441
50588)415900
    404704
```

(28)

$384\frac{4}{7} = 384.5714285714(19.61049+,$ *Ans.*

```
1
29)284
   261
386)2357
   2316
3921)4114
   3921
392204)1932857
    1568816
3922089)36404114
    35298801
```

(26)

$\frac{2}{3} = .666666+(.81649+,$ *Ans.*

```
64
161)266
   161
1626)10566
   9756
16324)81066
   65296
163289)1577066
    1469601
```

Art. 239.

(2.) $16 = 2 \times 2 \times 2 \times 2:$ $\sqrt{16} = 2 \times 2 = $ 4, *Ans.*

(3.) $36 = 2 \times 2 \times 3 \times 3:$ $\sqrt{36} = 2 \times 3 = $ 6, *Ans.*

(4.) $100 = 2 \times 2 \times 5 \times 5$: $\sqrt{100} = 2 \times 5 = 10$, *Ans.*

(5.) $225 = 3 \times 3 \times 5 \times 5$: $\sqrt{225} = 3 \times 5 = 15$, *Ans.*

(6.) $\sqrt{(16 \times 25)} = 4 \times 5 = 20$, *Ans.*

(7.) $\sqrt{(36 \times 49)} = 6 \times 7 = 42$, *Ans.*

(8.) $\sqrt{(64 \times 81)} = 8 \times 9 = 72$, *Ans.*

(9.) $\sqrt{(121 \times 25)} = 11 \times 5 = 55$, *Ans.*

Art. 240.

(1)	(2)	(3)
$30^2 = 900$	$100^2 = 10000$	$45^2 = 2025$
$40^2 = 1600$	$60^2 = 3600$	$60^2 = 3600$
$\sqrt{2500} = 50$, *Ans.*	$\sqrt{6400} = 80$, *Ans.*	$\sqrt{5625} = 75$, *Ans.*

(4.) $60^2 = 3600$, $37^2 = 1369$; $3600 - 1369 = 2231$; $\sqrt{2231} = 47.2334+$ = width of street from foot of ladder on one side. $60^2 = 3600$, $23^2 = 529$; $3600 - 529 = 3071$; $\sqrt{3071} = 55.4166+$ = width of street from foot of ladder on the other side. $47.2344 + 55.4166 = 102.65$, *Ans.*

(5.) $600^2 = 360000$, $140^2 = 19600$; $360000 - 19600 = 340400$; $\sqrt{340400} = 583.43+$; $100 \div 2 = 50$; $583.43 - 50. = 533.43+$, *Ans.*

(6)

$20^2 = 400$
$16^2 = 256$
─────
656

Square of base $= 656$

The square root of 656, will give the length of the diagonal line joining opposite corners of the floor of the room: this is the base of the triangle, of which the hypotenuse is required.

$12^2 = $ perpendicular$^2 = 144$; $656 + 144 = 800$; $\sqrt{800} = 28.28+$, *Ans.*

Art. 241.

     (1)

```
    . .
  6241(79  rd., Ans.
    49
149)1341
    1341
```

     (2)

8 sq. ft. 4 sq. in. = 1156 sq. in.

```
      . .
  1156(34 in. = 2 ft. 10 in., Ans.
    9
64) 256
    256
```

(3.) $\sqrt{4096} = 64$ yd., *Ans.*

(4.) $4 \times 4 = 16$; $16 \times 9 = 144$; $\sqrt{144} = 12$, *Ans.*
    Or, $\sqrt{(16 \times 9)} = 4 \times 3 = 12$ rd., *Ans.*

(5.) There are 43560 sq. ft. in 1 acre.
    $\sqrt{43560} = 208.71+$ ft., side of acre.

Art. 244.

(3.)
```
      . .
    2197(13
      1
300|1197
 90|
  9|
399|1197

      . .
    13824(24
      8
1200| 5824
 240|
  16|
1456| 5824
```
    $\frac{13}{24}$, *Ans.*

(4.)
```
         . . .
      .800000000(.928, Ans.
       729
  24300|  71000
    540|
      4|
  24844|  49688
2539200|  21312000
  22080|
     64|
2561344|  20490752
```

(5)   (6)

$$9\dot{1}125\dot{)}(45, \textit{Ans.}$$
$$64$$
$$\overline{27125}$$

$$4\times4\times300=4800$$
$$4\times5\times30=600$$
$$5\times5=25$$
$$\overline{5425}\,\big|27125$$

$$19\dot{5}112\dot{)}(58,$$
$$125\quad \textit{Ans.}$$
$$\overline{70112}$$

$$5\times5\times300=7500$$
$$5\times8\times30=1200$$
$$8\times8=64$$
$$\overline{8764}\,\big|\,70112$$

(7)   (8)

$$9\overset{.}{1}267\overset{.}{3}(97, \textit{Ans.}$$
$$729$$
$$\overline{183673}$$

$$24300$$
$$1890$$
$$49$$
$$\overline{26239}\,\big|183673$$

$$1225043(1G7,$$
$$1\qquad \textit{Ans.}$$

$$1\times1\times300=300\,\big|\,225$$
$$10\times10\times300=30000\,\big|\,225043$$
$$10\times7\times30=2100$$
$$7\times7=49$$
$$\overline{32149}\,\big|\,225043$$

(9)

$$13\overset{.}{3}1\overset{.}{2}05\overset{.}{3}(237, \textit{Ans.}$$
$$8$$

$$2\times2\times300=1200\,\big|\,5312$$
$$2\times3\times30=180$$
$$3\times3=9$$
$$\overline{1389}\,\big|\,4167$$

$$23\times23\times300=158700\,\big|\,1145053$$
$$23\times7\times30=4830$$
$$7\times7=49$$
$$\overline{163579}\,\big|\,1145053$$

(10)
$$102503232(468, \textit{Ans.}$$

	64
$4\times4\times300=4800$	38503
$4\times6\times\ 30=\ 720$	
$6\times6\qquad=\quad 36$	
$\overline{5556}$	33336
$46\times46\times300=634800$	5167232
$46\times\ 8\times\ 30=\ 11040$	
$8\times\ 8\qquad=\qquad 64$	
$\overline{645904}$	5167232

(11)
$$529475129(809, \textit{Ans.}$$

	512
$8\times\ 8\times300=\quad 19200$	17475
$80\times80\times300=1920000$	17475129
$80\times\ 9\times\ 30=\quad 21600$	
$9\times\ 9\qquad=\qquad 81$	
$\overline{1941681}$	17475129

(12)
$$958585256(986, \textit{Ans.}$$

	729
$9\times9\times300=24300$	229585
$9\times8\times\ 30=\ 2160$	
$8\times8\qquad=\quad 64$	
$\overline{26524}$	212192
$98\times98\times300=2881200$	17393256
$98\times\ 6\times\ 30=\quad 17640$	
$6\times\ 6\qquad=\qquad 36$	
$\overline{2898876}$	17393256

(13)

$$14760213677(2453, \textit{Ans.}$$

	8
$2\times2\times300=1200$	6760
$2\times4\times\ 30=\ \ 240$	
$4\times4\ \ \ \ \ =\ \ \ \ 16$	
$\overline{\ \ \ \ \ \ \ \ \ \ \ \ \ \ \ 1456}$	5824
$24\times24\times300=172800$	936213
$24\times\ 5\times\ 30=\ \ 3600$	
$5\times\ 5\ \ \ \ \ =\ \ \ \ \ \ 25$	
$\overline{\ \ \ \ \ \ \ \ \ \ \ \ \ \ 176425}$	882125
$245\times245\times300=18007500$	54088677
$245\times\ \ 3\times\ 30=\ \ \ 22050$	
$3\times\ \ 3\ \ \ \ \ =\ \ \ \ \ \ \ \ \ 9$	
$\overline{\ \ \ \ \ \ \ \ \ \ \ \ \ \ \ 18029559}$	54088677

(14)

$$128100283921(5041, \textit{Ans.}$$

	125
$5\times\ 5\times300=\ \ \ 7500$	3100
$50\times50\times300=750000$	3100283
$50\times\ 4\times\ 30=\ \ \ 6000$	
$4\times\ 4\ \ \ \ \ =\ \ \ \ \ \ \ 16$	
$\overline{\ \ \ \ \ \ \ \ \ \ \ \ \ 756016}$	3024064
$504\times504\times300=76204800$	76219921
$504\times\ \ 1\times\ 30=\ \ \ 15120$	
$1\times\ \ 1\ \ \ \ \ =\ \ \ \ \ \ \ \ \ 1$	
$\overline{\ \ \ \ \ \ \ \ \ \ \ \ \ 76219921}$	76219921

(15)   5̇3.15̇737̇6(3.76, *Ans.*
                                27
    3×3×300=2700|26157
    3×7× 30= 630
    7×7   = 49
            ————
            3379|23653
    37×37×300=410700| 2504376
    37× 6× 30= 6660
    6× 6   =   36
            ——————
            417396| 2504376

(16)   .1̇9917̇670̇4(.584, *Ans.*
                                125
    5×5×300=7500|74176
    5×8× 30=1200
    8×8   = 64
            ————
            8764| 70112
    58×58×300=1009200| 4064704
    58× 4× 30= 6960
    4× 4   =   16
            ——————
            1016176| 4064704

(17.) ∛216=6.   (18.) ∛2744=14.
      ∛343=7. *Ans.* ⁶⁄₇.   ∛6859=19. *Ans.* 1⁴⁄₇.

(19.) $\dfrac{48778}{118638}=\dfrac{24389}{59319}$ ∛24389=29.
                                    ∛59319=39. *Ans.* ²⁹⁄₃₉.

(20.) 5¹⁰⁴⁄₁₂₅=⁷²⁹⁄₁₂₅   ∛729=9.
                         ∛125=5. *Ans.* ⁹⁄₅=1⁴⁄₅.

$$(21) \qquad 2(1.259+, \textit{Ans.}$$
$$\underline{1}$$

	1000
$300+60+4=364$	728
$12\times12\times300=43200$	272000
$12\times\ \ 5\times\ \ 30=\ \ 1800$	
$5\times\ \ 5\qquad\ \ =\qquad 25$	
$\overline{45025}$	225125
$125\times125\times300=4687500$	46875000
$125\times\quad 9\times\ \ 30=\quad 33750$	
$9\times\quad 9\qquad\ \ =\qquad\quad 81$	
$\overline{4721331}$	42491979

$$(22) \qquad 9(2.080+, \textit{Ans.}$$
$$\underline{8}$$

	1000
$2\times2\times300=1200$	1000000
$20\times20\times300=120000$	1000000
$20\times\ \ 8\times\ \ 30=\quad 4800$	
$8\times\ \ 8\qquad\ \ =\qquad 64$	
$\overline{124864}$	998912
$208\times208\times300=12979200$	1088000

$$(23) \qquad 200(5.848+, \textit{Ans.}$$
$$\underline{125}$$

	75000
$5\times5\times300=7500$	75000
$5\times8\times\ \ 30=1200$	
$8\times\ \ 8=\ \ 64$	
$\overline{8764}$	70112
$58\times58\times300=1009200$	4888000
$58\times\ \ 4\times\ \ 30=\quad 6960$	
$4\times\ \ 4=\qquad 16$	
$\overline{1016176}$	4064704
$584\times584\times300=102316800$	823296000
$584\times\ \ 8\times\ \ 30=\quad 140160$	
$8\times\ \ 8=\qquad\quad 64$	819656192

$$(24)\ .\ .\ .$$
$$9\tfrac{1}{6}=9.166666+(2.092+,\ Ans.$$

$$\begin{array}{r} 8 \\ \hline \end{array}$$

$$\begin{array}{r|l}
2\times2\times300=1200 & 1166 \\
20\times20\times300=120000 & 1166666 \\
20\times\ 9\times\ 30=\ \ 5400 & \\
9\times\ \ 9=\ \ \ \ \ 81 & \\
\hline
125481 & 1129329 \\
209\times209\times300=13104300 & 37337666 \\
209\times\ \ 2\times\ 30=\ \ \ 12540 & \\
2\times\ \ 2=\ \ \ \ \ \ \ 4 & \\
\hline
13116844 & 26233688 \\
\end{array}$$

Art. 245.

(1.) $\sqrt[3]{1953.125} = 12.5$ ft., *Ans.*

(2.) $64 \times 3 \times 3 \times 3 = 1728$ cu. in. $= 1$ cu. ft., one side of which $= 1$ ft., *Ans.*

(3.) $\sqrt[3]{512} = 8$ half in. $= 4$ in., *Ans.*

(4.) 450 cu. yd. 17 cu. ft. $= 12167$ cu. ft.; $\sqrt[3]{12167} = 23$ ft., *Ans.*

(5.) $288 \times 216 \times 48 = 2985984$, $\sqrt[3]{2985984} = 144$ ft., *Ans.*

(6.) $1728 \times 3 = 5184$, $\sqrt[3]{5184} = 17.306+$ in., *Ans.*

MENSURATION.

Art. 247.

(1.) 17 ft. $\times$ 15 ft. $= 255$ sq. ft., *Ans.*

(2.) 120 rd. $\times$ 84 rd. $= 10080$ sq. rd. $= 63$ A., *Ans.*

(3.) 65 rd. $\times$ 65 rd. $= 4225$ sq. rd. $= 26$ A. 65 sq. rd.

(4.) 35 rd. $\times$ 16 rd. $= 560$ sq. rd. $= 3$ A. 80 sq. rd., *Ans.*

(5.) 30 ft. × 30 ft. =   900 sq. ft. = 100 sq. yd.
15 ft. × 15 ft. = 225 sq. ft., × 2 = 450 sq. ft. =   50 sq. yd.
                                        Diff. =   50 sq. yd.

(7.) 5 ft. 6 in. = $5\frac{1}{2}$ ft.; 1 ft. 8 in. = $1\frac{2}{3}$ ft.; $\frac{11}{2}$ ft. × $\frac{5}{3}$ ft. = $\frac{55}{6}$ sq. ft. = $9\frac{1}{6}$ sq. ft., *Ans.*

(8.) 25 ft. 9 in. = $25\frac{3}{4}$ ft. = $\frac{103}{4}$ ft.; 21 ft. 3 in. = $21\frac{1}{4}$ ft. = $\frac{85}{4}$ ft.; $\frac{103}{4}$ × $\frac{85}{4}$ = $\frac{8755}{16}$ sq. ft. = $547\frac{3}{16}$ sq. ft. = 60 sq. yd. 7 sq. ft. 27 sq. in., *Ans.*

(9.) 80 sq. ft. ÷ 10 ft. = 8 ft., *Ans.*

(10.) 18 ft. × 15 ft. = 270 sq. ft. = 30 sq. yd.; 30 sq. yd. ÷ $1\frac{1}{2}$ yd. = 20 yd., *Ans.*

(11.) 3 yd. × $1\frac{1}{2}$ yd. = $4\frac{1}{2}$ sq. yd.; $4\frac{1}{2}$ ÷ $\frac{3}{4}$ = $\frac{9}{2}$ × $\frac{4}{3}$ = 6 yd., *Ans.*

(12.) 21 ft. 3 in. = 21.25 ft.; 13 ft. 6 in. = 13.5 ft.; 21.25 ft. × 13.5 ft. = 286.875 sq. ft.; $1\frac{1}{4}$ yd. = $3\frac{3}{4}$ = 3.75 ft.; 286.875 sq. ft. ÷ 3.75 ft. = 76.5 ft. = 25.5 yd. = $25\frac{1}{2}$ yd.

(13.) 160 sq. rd. in 1 A.   160 ÷ 15 = $10\frac{2}{3}$ rd., *Ans.*

Art. 248.

(1.) ft.   in.   61 in. ÷ 2 = $30\frac{1}{2}$ in., × 11 in. = $335\frac{1}{2}$
     2   2   sq. in.: $335\frac{1}{2}$ sq. in. ÷ 144 = 2 sq. ft. $47\frac{1}{2}$
     2   11   sq. in., *Ans.*
    ———
     5   1 = 61 in.

(2.) 25 rd. + 19 rd. = 44 rd.; 44 rd. ÷ 2 = 22 rd., × 32 rd. = 704 sq. rd., ÷ 160 = 4 A. 64 sq. rd., *Ans.*

(3.) 10 ft. 8 in. = 128 in.; 6 ft. 2 in. = 74 in.; 128 + 74 = 202 in., ÷ 2 = 101 in.; 12 ft. = 144 in.; 101 × 144 = 14544 sq. in. = 101 sq. ft. = 11 sq. yd. 2 sq. ft., *Ans.*

Art. 249.

(1.) 15 ft. × 12 ft. = 180 sq. ft., ÷ 2 = 90 sq. ft., *Ans.*

(2.) 44 rd. $\times$ 18 rd. $= 792$ sq. rd., $\div 2 = 396$ sq. rd.: 396 sq. rd. $\div 160 = 2$ A. 76 sq. rd., *Ans.*

(3.) $12\frac{1}{2}$ ft. $\times 16\frac{3}{4}$ ft. $= \frac{1675}{8}$ sq. ft. $= 209\frac{3}{8}$ sq. ft.; $209\frac{3}{8}$ $\div 2 = 104\frac{11}{16}$ sq. ft. $= 11$ sq. yd. 5 sq. ft. 99 sq. in., *Ans.*

(4.) $13 + 14 + 15 = 42, \div 2 = 21$. $21 - 13 = 8$, $21 - 14 = 7$, $21 - 15 = 6$. $21 \times 8 \times 7 \times 6 = 7056$: its square root $= 84$ sq. ft., *Ans.*

(5.) $30 + 40 + 50 = 120, \div 2 = 60$. $60 - 30 = 30$, $60 - 40 = 20$, $60 - 50 = 10$. $60 \times 30 \times 20 \times 10 = 360000$: $\sqrt{360000} = 600$ sq. ft.: 600 sq. ft. $= 66$ sq. yd. 6 sq. ft., *Ans.*

Art. 250.

(1.) 50 rd. $\times$ 30 rd. $= 1500$ sq. rd., $\div 2 = 750$ sq. rd.: 50 rd. $\times$ 20 rd. $= 1000$ sq. rd., $\div 2 = 500$ sq. rd.; 750 sq. rd. $+ 500$ sq. rd. $= 1250$ sq. rd. $= 7$ A. 130 sq. rd., *Ans.*

Art. 251.

(1.) 48 ft. $\times 3.1416 = 150.7968$ ft. $= 150$ ft. 9.56 in.

(2.) 15 ft. $\div 3.1416 = 4.7746$ ft. $= 4$ ft. 9.3 in. nearly.

(3.) $4 \times 3.1416 = 12.5664$ ft. $= 12$ ft. 6.8 in. nearly.

(4.) 12 ft. 5 in. $= 12.4166+$ ft.; 12.4166 ft. $\div 3.1416$ $= 3.952338$ ft. $= 3$ ft. 11.43 in. nearly, *Ans.*

(5.) 7912 mi. $\times 3.1416 = 24856+$ mi., *Ans.*

Art. 252.

(1.) $21 \times 21 = 441$: $3.1416 \times 441 = 1385.4456$ sq. ft. $= 153$ sq. yd. 8 sq. ft. 64 sq. in., *Ans.*

NOTE.—To find the diameter when the area is given, divide the area by .7854; the square root of the quotient will be the diameter.

(2.) 6 sq. ft. 98.115 sq. in. $= 962.115$ sq. in.; $962.115 \div .7854 = 1225$: $\sqrt{1225} = 35$ in., $= 2$ ft. 11 in. $=$ diameter. 35 in. $\times 3.1416 = 109.956$ in. $= 9$ ft. 1.9$+$ in. $=$ circum.

(3.) 160 rd. $\div$ .7854 $= 203.71785077+$; $\sqrt{203.71785077}$ $= 14.2729$; $14.2729 \div 2 = 7.1364$ rd. $= 7$ rd. 2 ft. 3 in., *Ans.*

(4.) $10 \div 2 = 5 =$ one radius; $5^2 = 25 : 16 \div 2 = 8 =$ one radius; $8^2 = 64$. $25 \times 3.1416 = 78.5400$; $64 \times 3.1416 = 201.0624 : 201.0624 - 78.5400 = 122.5224$ sq. ft.; .5224 $\times 144 = 75$ sq. in. *Ans.* 122 sq. ft. 75 sq. in.

(5.) 1 sq. ft. $= 144$ sq. in. $144 \div .7854 = 183.3460$ sq. in.: $\sqrt{183.3460} = 13.54$ in., *Ans.*

Art. 254.

(1.) $37 \times 37 \times 6 = 8214$ sq. in. $= 6$ sq. yd. 3 sq. ft. 6 sq. in., *Ans.*

(2.) $4 + 4 + 4 = 12$ ft., $\times 5$ ft. $= 60$ sq. ft. $=$ convex surface.
$$\frac{4+4+4}{2} = 6. \quad \left.\begin{array}{l} 6-4=2 \\ 6-4=2 \\ 6-4=2 \end{array}\right\} 6 \times 2 \times 2 \times 2 = 48.$$

$\sqrt{48} = 6.92+$; $6.92+. \times 2 = 13.85$ sq. ft. $=$ area of 2 bases. 60 sq. ft. $+ 13.85$ sq. ft. $= 73.85+$ sq. ft., *Ans.*

(3.) 3 ft. 6 in. $= 3\frac{1}{2}$ ft. $= \frac{7}{2}$; $\frac{7}{2} \times 2 = 7$ $\left.\begin{array}{l}\end{array}\right\} = 12\frac{1}{2}$ or $\frac{25}{2}$.
2 ft. 9 in. $= 2\frac{3}{4}$ ft. $= \frac{11}{4}$; $\frac{11}{4} \times 2 = 5\frac{1}{2}$
1 ft. 10 in. $= 1\frac{5}{6}$ ft. $= \frac{11}{6}$.

$\frac{25}{2} \times \frac{11}{6} = \frac{275}{12} =$ convex surface; $\frac{7}{2} \times \frac{11}{4} \times 2 = \frac{77}{4}$ or $\frac{231}{12} =$ areas of 2 bases: $\frac{275}{12} + \frac{231}{12} = \frac{506}{12} = 42\frac{1}{6}$ sq. ft., *Ans.*

(4.) 3.1416×4 ft. (diameter)$= 12.5664 =$ circumference.
$$12.5664 \times 5 = 62.8320 = \text{convex surface.}$$
$$2 \times 2 \times 3.1416 \times 2 = 25.1328 = \text{areas of 2 bases.}$$
$$\overline{87.96+} \text{ sq. ft., } Ans.$$

Art. 255.

(2.) 24 ft. $\times 18\frac{1}{2}$ ft. $\times 10\frac{7}{12}$ ft. $= 4699$ cu. ft. $= 174$ cu. yd. 1 cu. ft., *Ans.*

(3.) Area of base $= 1.73+$ sq. ft.; 1.73 sq. ft. $\times$ 14 ft. $= 24\frac{1}{4}$ cu. ft. nearly, *Ans.*

(4.) $2 \times 2 \times 3.1416 \times 12 = 150.8$ cu. ft., *Ans.*

(5.) $9\frac{1}{4}$ in. $= \frac{37}{4}$; $\frac{1}{2}$ of $\frac{37}{4} = \frac{37}{8}$; $(\frac{37}{8})^2 \times 3.1416 \times 8 = 537.6$ cu. in., *Ans.*

Art. 256.

(1.) 5 ft. 4 in. $= 5\frac{1}{3}$ ft.; $5\frac{1}{3}$ ft. $\times 3 = 16$ ft. $=$ perimeter of base. $7\frac{1}{2}$ ft. $\times 16 = 120$ sq. ft.; 120 sq. ft. $\div 2 = 60$ sq. ft. $=$ area of 3 sides. $5\frac{1}{3} \times 3 = 16$. $16 \div 2 = 8$; $8 - 5\frac{1}{3} = 2\frac{2}{3}$; $2\frac{2}{3} = \frac{8}{3}$; $8 \times \frac{8}{3} \times \frac{8}{3} \times \frac{8}{3} = \frac{4096}{27} = 151.70+$. $\sqrt{151.70} = 12.3+$ sq. ft. $=$ area of base. 60 sq. ft. $+ 12.3+$ sq. ft. $= 72.3+$ sq. ft., *Ans.*

(2.) $8\frac{1}{2}$ ft. $\times 3.1416 = 26.7036$ ft. $=$ circum. of base. $26.7036 \times 25 \div 2 = 333.79+$, *Ans.*

(3.) $2\frac{11}{12}$ ft. $\times 3.1416 \times 4\frac{7}{12}$ ft. $\div 2 = 21.008$ sq. ft. $=$ convex surface. $2\frac{11}{12}$ ft. $= \frac{35}{12}, \div 2 = \frac{35}{24}$; $(\frac{35}{24})^2 \times 3.1416 = 6.68$ sq. ft. $=$ area of base. $21.008 + 6.68 = 27.6+$ sq. ft., *Ans.*

Art. 257.

(1.) 5 ft. $\times$ 5 ft. $= 25$ sq. ft. $=$ area of base. 25 sq. ft. $\times 21$ ft. $\div 3 = 175$ cu. ft., *Ans.*

(2.) $(5)^2 \times 3.1416 \times 15 \div 3 = 392.7$ cu. ft., *Ans.*

(3.) 720 ft. $= 240$ yd.; 477 ft. $= 159$ yd.; $(240$ yd$)$ $\times 159$ yd. $\div 3 = 3052800$ cu. yd., *Ans.*

(4.) $37\frac{2}{3}$ ft. $= \frac{113}{3}, \div 2 = \frac{113}{6}$; $(\frac{113}{6})^2 \times 3.1416 = 1114.3+$ sq. ft. $=$ area of base. $1114.3+$ sq. ft. $\times 79\frac{3}{4}$ ft., $\div 3 = 29622+$ cu. ft., *Ans.*

Art. 258.

(2.) $(4\frac{1}{2}$ ft.$)^2 \times 3.1416 = 63.6+$ sq. ft., *Ans.*

(3.) $(7912)^2 \times 3.1416 = 196663355.75$ sq. mi., *Ans.*

Art. 259.

(1.) $13 \times 13 \times 13 \times .5236 = 1150.3+$ cu. ft., *Ans.*

(2.) $2\frac{1}{2}$ ft. $= \frac{5}{2}$: $\frac{5}{2} \times \frac{5}{2} \times \frac{5}{2} \times .5236 = 8.18+$ cu. ft., *Ans.*

(3.) 1 cu. ft. $= 1728$ cu. in.; $1728 \div .5236 = 3300.229$; $\sqrt[3]{3300.229} = 14.9$ in. nearly, *Ans.*

Art. 260.

(1.) $20\frac{1}{2} \times 16\frac{1}{4} =$ area of ceiling; $20\frac{1}{2} \times 10\frac{1}{12} \times 2 =$ area of 2 sides; $16\frac{1}{4} \times 10\frac{1}{12} \times 2 =$ area of other 2 sides. Add these amounts together, and deduct $6\frac{1}{4} \times 4\frac{1}{6}$, fire-place; $7 \times 4\frac{1}{6}$, door; $6 \times 3\frac{1}{4} \times 2$, two windows.

(2.) $20 \times 10\frac{1}{3} \times 2 =$ area of two sides; $14\frac{1}{2} \times 10\frac{1}{3} \times 2 =$ area of other 2 sides. Deduct $4 \times 4\frac{1}{3}$, fire-place; $6 \times 3\frac{1}{6} \times 2$, two windows. The remainder is in sq. ft. Divide by 9, and multiply by 27 ct. $= \$19.73+$, *Ans.*

(3.)   21 yd. $\times$ 15 yd. $= 315$ sq. yd.
     5 ft. $= 1\frac{2}{3}$ yd.   21 yd. $\times$ $1\frac{2}{3}$ yd. $= \underline{\ 35}$ sq. yd.
                                       280 sq. yd.

$35 \times .36 = \$12.60$; $280 \times .24 = \$67.20$; $\$12.60 + \$67.20 = \$79.80$, *Ans.*

(4.) $15\frac{1}{2}$ ft. $\times$ $12\frac{1}{2}$ ft. $\times 2 = 387.5$ sq. ft. $= 43.06$ sq. yd.; 43.06 sq. yd. @ 10 ct. $= \$4.31$, *Ans.*

(5.) 6 ft. 11 in. $+ 5$ ft. 4 in. $+ 4$ ft. 3 in., $\times 7 = 115\frac{1}{2}$ ft., $\times 3\frac{1}{2}$ ft. $= 404\frac{1}{4}$ sq. ft., $\times 16$ ct. $= \$64.68$, *Ans.*

(6.) $36\frac{1}{4}$ ft. $\times$ $16\frac{1}{2}$ ft. $= 598$ sq. ft. $= 5.98$ squares; $5.98 \times \$3.00 = \$17.94$, *Ans.*

(7.) 40 ft. $\times$ $18\frac{1}{2}$ ft. $\times 2 = 1480$ sq. ft. $= 14.80$ squares; $14.80 \times \$3.50 = \$51.80$, *Ans.*

Art. 261.

(1.) $16 \times 1\frac{1}{4} = 20$ ft., *Ans.*

(2.) $12\frac{1}{2} \times 2\frac{1}{4} \times 2 = 56\frac{1}{4}$ ft., *Ans.*

(3.) $15 \times \frac{1}{3} \times 3 = 15$ ft., *Ans.*

(4.) $12 \times 2 \times 24 = 576$ ft., *Ans.*

(5.) 1 ft. 3 in. $+$ 11 in. $= 2\frac{1}{6}$ ft., $\div 2 = 1\frac{1}{12}$ ft. $=$ **average** width. $12\frac{1}{2} \times 1\frac{1}{12} = 13\frac{13}{24}$ ft., *Ans.*

Art. 262.

(1.) 97 ft. 5 in. $= 97.416+$ ft.; 18 ft. 3 in. $= 18.25$ ft.; 2 ft. 3 in. $= 2.25$ ft.: 97.416 ft. $\times$ 18.25 ft. $\times$ 2.25 ft. $=$ 4000.1445 cu. ft. 4000.1445 $\div$ 24.75 $= 161.6+$ P., *Ans.*

(2.) 53 ft. 6 in. $= 53.5$ ft.; 12 ft. 6 in. $= 12.5$ ft.; 53.5 $\times$ 12.5 $\times$ 2 $= 1337.5$ cu. ft. $= 54.0404+$ P. 54.0404 $\times$ $2.25 = \$121.59+$, *Ans.*

(3.) $48\frac{1}{3} \times 16\frac{1}{2} \times 1\frac{1}{2} = \frac{145}{3} \times \frac{33}{2} \times \frac{3}{2} = \frac{14355}{12} = 1196\frac{1}{4}$ cu. ft.; $1196\frac{1}{4} \times 20 = 23925$ bricks, *Ans.*

(4.) $120 \times 8 \times 1\frac{1}{2} = 1440$ cu. ft. $= 2488320$ cu. in. in wall; $8 \times 4 \times 2.25 = 72$ cu. in. in each brick; 2488320 $\div 72 = 34560$ bricks, *Ans.*

(5.) $240 \times 6 \times 3 = 4320$ cu. ft. $= 7464960$ cu. in. in wall; $9 \times 4 \times 2 = 72$ cu. in. in brick; 7464960 $\div 72 =$ 103680 bricks; 103680 $\div 1000 = 103.68$; 3.25×103.68 $= \$336.96$, *Ans.*

Art. 263.

(1.) 15 ft. $\times$ 5 ft. $\times$ 4 ft. $= 300$ cu. ft. $= 518400$ cu. in.; 518400 $\div 2150.4 = 241+$ bu., *Ans.*

(2.) 10 ft. $= 120$ in.; 5 ft. $= 60$ in.; 4 ft. $= 48$ in.; $120 \times 60 \times 48 = 345600$ cu. in.; 345600 $\div 231 = 1496+$ gal., *Ans.*

(3.) $(6)^2 \times .7854 = 28.2744 =$ area of end; $28.2744 \times 8 = 226.1952$ cu. ft. $= 390865.3056$ cu. in. This divided by 2150.4 $= 181.76+$ bu., *Ans.*

(4.) 4 ft. = 48 in.; 6 ft. = 72 in.; $(48)^2 = 2304$; 2304 × .7854 × 72 = 130288.4352 cu. in.; 130288.4352 ÷ 231 = 564.019+ gal.; 564.019+ ÷ 31½ = 17.9+ bl., *Ans.*

PROGRESSIONS.

ARITHMETICAL PROGRESSION.

CASE I.

Art. 265.

(3.) 50 − 1 = 49; 49 × 3 + 2 = 149, *Ans.*

(4.) 54 − 1 = 53; 53 × 2 = 106; 140 − 106 = 34, *Ans.*

(5.) 99 − 1 = 98; 98 × $\frac{7}{8}$ = 85$\frac{3}{4}$; 329 − 85$\frac{3}{4}$ = 243$\frac{1}{4}$, *Ans.*

CASE II.

Art. 266.

(2.) 300 − 3 = 297; 10 − 1 = 9; 297 ÷ 9 = 33, *Ans.*

(3.) 50 − 5 = 45; 10 − 1 = 9; 45 ÷ 9 = 5 miles, *Ans.*

CASE III.

Art. 267.

(2.) 50 + 2 = 52; 52 × 24 = 1248; 1248 ÷ 2 = 624, *Ans.*

(3.) 1 + 12 = 13; 13 × 12 = 156; 156 ÷ 2 = 78 strokes, *Ans.*

(4.) The number of terms is evidently 100. The boy travels 6 yards to put the first apple in the basket, 12 the second, and so on; hence, the first term is 6, and the common difference 6. 100 − 1 = 99; 99 × 6 + 6 = 600, last term. 6 + 600 = 606; 606 × 100 = 60600; 60600 ÷ 2 = 30300 yd.; 30300 yd. = 17 mi. 69 rd. ½ yd., *Ans.*

(5.) Common difference $= 193 \times 2 = 386$ in. $60 - 1 = 59$; $386 \times 59 + 193 = 22967$ in., distance fallen in the last second. 193 in. $+ 22967$ in. $= 23160$ in.; $23160 \times 60 = 1389600$: 1389600 in. $\div 2 = 694800$ in. $= 57900$ ft., *Ans.*

GEOMETRICAL PROGRESSION.

CASE I.

Art. 269.

(3.) $2^{12} = 4096$; $4096 \times 2 = 8192$, *Ans.*

(4.) $4^8 = 65536$; $262144 \div 65536 = 4$, *Ans.*

(5.) Ratio $= 3$; $3^9 = 19683$; $19683 \times 10 = 196830$, *Ans.*

CASE II.

Art. 270.

(2.) $3^6 = 729$; $729 \times 10 = 7290$, last term. $7290 \times 3 = 21870$; $21870 - 10 = 21860$: $21860 \div 2 = 10930$, *Ans.*

(3.) $2^{11} = 2048$; $2048 \times 1 = 2048$, last term. $2048 \times 2 = 4096$; $4096 - 1 = 4095$, and $4095 \div 1 = 4095$, *Ans.*

(4.) $4^{11} \times 4194304$; $4194304 \times 1 = 4194304$, last term. $4194304 \times 4 = 16777216$; $16777216 - 1 = 16777215$; $4 - 1 = 3$; $16777215 \div 3 = 5592405$ ct. $= \$55924.05$, *Ans.*

(5.) $.3 \times 10 = 3$; $10 - 1 = 9$; $3 \div 9 = \frac{1}{3}$, *Ans.*

(6.) Ratio $= 3$; $\frac{1}{3} \times 3 = 1$; $3 - 1 = 2$; $1 \div 2 = \frac{1}{2}$, *Ans.*

(7.) Ratio $= 2$; $\frac{1}{2} \times 2 = 1$; $2 - 1 = 1$; $1 \div 1 = 1$, *Ans.*